PERILS OF THE PEACEFUL ATOM

It is a generally accepted belief that atomic energy for peaceful purposes is safe, clean, reliable, and economical. *But the shocking fact is that this is a myth,* and our atomic energy program involves nothing less than tampering with elemental fire.

"Far and away the most comprehensive and sensible statement ever made about the hazards and limitations of atomic power. Once a bright hope shared by all mankind, myself included, the rash proliferation of atomic power plants has become one of the ugliest clouds overhanging America. . . This book will have to be answered, soberly and persuasively, by those responsible for this proliferation."

—David Lilienthal,
    Former Chairman of the Atomic Energy Commission

More Ballantine Books
You Will Enjoy

PERILS
OF THE
PEACEFUL
ATOM

The Myth
of Safe
Nuclear Power Plants

Richard Curtis
and
Elizabeth Hogan

BALLANTINE BOOKS • NEW YORK

An Intext Publisher

Grateful acknowledgment is made to the following for permission to reprint their material:

Rolla D. Campbell for letter printed in the record of hearings before the Joint Committee on Atomic Energy of the U. S. Congress; *Her Majesty's Stationery Office* for excerpt from *The Hazard to Man of Nuclear and Allied Radiations,* Cmd. 9780; *United States Atomic Energy Commission* for excerpts from a booklet distributed by Division of Technical Information, *Nuclear Reactors,* by John F. Hogerton. Quote from a speech delivered by Hal Stroube entitled "Public Acceptance of Nuclear Power," published in *Nuclear Power Reactor Siting,* CONF 65201; Quote from the introduction to Thompson and Beckerley's *The Technology of Nuclear Reactor Safety,* copyright © 1964 by The M. I. T. Press; *University of Chicago Press* for excerpts from *Living with the Atom,* by Ritchie Calder; *Pergamon Press, Inc.* for quote from Report CRR-836, by W. B. Lewis, and from Report GPI-14, by Hurst; *The Viking Press, Inc.* for excerpts from *Radiation: What It Is and How It Affects You,* by Jack Schubert and Ralph E. Lapp; *The World Publishing Company* for excerpts from *Nuclear Policy for War and Peace,* by T. E. Murray, copyright © 1960 by Thomas E. Murray.

This edition published by arrangement with Doubleday & Company, Inc.

First Printing: March, 1970

Cover photograph by Wide World Photos, Inc.

Printed in the United States of America

BALLANTINE BOOKS, INC.
101 Fifth Avenue, New York, N.Y. 10003

This book is dedicated
to tomorrow's children

Nuclear Power Plants in the United States

	Site	Capacity (Kilowatts)	Utility	Startup
Alabama	Browns Ferry	1,064,500	Tennessee Valley Authority	1970
	Browns Ferry	1,064,500	Tennessee Valley Authority	1971
	Browns Ferry	1,064,500	Tennessee Valley Authority	1972
Arkansas	Dardanelle Lake	850,000	Arkansas Power & Light Co.	1972
California	Humboldt Bay	68,500	Pacific Gas & Electric Co.	1963
	San Clemente	430,000	Southern Calif. Edison and San Diego Gas & Electric Co.	1967
	Corral Canyon	462,000	L.A. Dept. of Water & Power	1973
	Diablo Canyon	1,060,000	Pacific Gas & Electric Co.	1971
	Sacramento County	800,000	Sacramento Municipal District	1973
Colorado	Platteville	330,000	Public Service Co. of Colorado	1971
Connecticut	Haddam Neck	462,000	Conn. Yankee Atomic Power Co.	1967
	Waterford No. 1	652,100	Northeast Utilities	1969
	Waterford No. 2	828,000	Northeast Utilities	1974
Florida	Turkey Point No. 3	651,500	Florida Power & Light Co.	1970
	Turkey Point No. 4	651,500	Florida Power & Light Co.	1971
	Red Level	825,000	Florida Power Corp.	1972
	Hutchinson Island	800,000	Florida Power and Light Co.	1973
Georgia	Baxley	786,000	Georgia Power Co.	1973
Illinois	Morris No. 1	200,000	Commonwealth Edison Co.	1959
	Morris No. 2	715,000	Commonwealth Edison Co.	1968
	Morris No. 3	715,000	Commonwealth Edison Co.	1969
	Zion No. 1	1,050,000	Commonwealth Edison Co.	1972
	Zion No. 2	1,050,000	Commonwealth Edison Co.	1973
	Quad Cities No. 1	715,000	Comm. Ed. Co.—Ia.—Ill. Gas & Elec. Co.	1970
	Quad Cities No. 2	715,000	Comm. Ed. Co.—Ia.—Ill. Gas & Elec. Co.	1971
Indiana	Burns Harbor	515,000	Northern Indiana Public Service Co.	1970's
Iowa	Cedar Rapids	537,600	Iowa Electric Light and Power Co.	1973
Maine	Wiscasset	790,000	Maine Yankee Atomic Power Co.	1972
Maryland	Lusby	800,000	Baltimore Gas and Electric Co.	1973
	Lusby	800,000	Baltimore Gas and Electric Co.	1974
Massachusetts	Rowe	175,000	Yankee Atomic Electric Co.	1960
	Plymouth	625,000	Boston Edison Co.	1971
Michigan	Big Rock Point	70,300	Consumers Power Co.	1962
	South Haven	700,000	Consumers Power Co.	1969
	Lagoona Beach	60,900	Power Reactor Development Co.	1963
	Bridgman	1,060,000	Indiana & Michigan Electric Co.	1972
	Bridgman	1,054,000	Indiana & Michigan Electric Co.	1973
	Midland	650,000	Consumers Power Co.	1974
	Midland	650,000	Consumers Power Co.	1975
Minnesota	Elk River	22,000	Rural Cooperative Power Assoc.	1962
	Monticello	471,700	Northern States Power Co.	1970
	Red Wing No. 1	550,000	Northern States Power Co.	1972
	Red Wing No. 2	550,000	Northern States Power Co.	1974

*Site not selected. †State not selected.

	Site	Capacity (Kilowatts)	Utility	Startup
Nebraska	Fort Calhoun	457,400	Omaha Public Power District	1971
	Brownville	778,000	Consumers Public Power District and Iowa Power and Light Co.	1972
New Jersey	Toms River	515,000	Jersey Central Power & Light Co.	1968
	Toms River	810,000	Jersey Central Power & Light Co.	1973
	Artificial Island	1,050,000	Public Service Gas and Electric Co. of New Jersey	1971
	Artificial Island	1,050,000	Public Service Gas and Electric Co. of New Jersey	1973
New York	Indian Point No. 1	265,000	Consolidated Edison Co.	1962
	Indian Point No. 2	873,000	Consolidated Edison Co.	1969
	Indian Point No. 3	965,300	Consolidated Edison Co.	1971
	Scriba	500,000	Niagara Mohawk Power Co.	1968
	Easton	765,800	Niagara Mohawk Power Co.	1971
	Rochester	420,000	Rochester Gas & Electric Co.	1969
	Shoreham	523,000	Long Island Lighting Co.	1973
	Lansing	829,200	New York State Electric & Gas Co.	1973
	•	1,115,000	Consolidated Edison Co.–Orange and Rockland Utilities, Inc.	1973
North Carolina	•	800,000	Carolina Power and Light Co.	1973
	•	800,000	Carolina Power and Light Co.	1974
	•	800,000	Carolina Power and Light Co.	—
Pennsylvania	Peach Bottom No. 1	40,000	Philadelphia Electric Co.	1966
	Peach Bottom No. 2	1,065,000	Philadelphia Electric Co.	1971
	Peach Bottom No. 3	1,065,000	Philadelphia Electric Co.	1973
	•	1,065,000	Philadelphia Electric Co.	1975
	•	1,065,000	Philadelphia Electric Co.	1977
	Shippingport No. 1	90,000	Duquesne Light Co.	1957
	Shippingport No. 2	783,000	Duquesne Light Co.–Ohio Edison Co.	1973
	Three Mile Island	831,000	Metropolitan Edison Co.	1971
	•	1,100,000	Pennsylvania Power and Light	1975
	•	1,100,000	Pennsylvania Power and Light	1977
Puerto Rico	Punta Higuera	16,500	Puerto Rico Water Resources Authority	1964
South Carolina	Hartsville	663,000	Carolina Power & Light Co.	1970
	Lake Keowee No. 1	841,100	Duke Power Co.	1971
	Lake Keowee No. 2	841,100	Duke Power Co.	1972
	Lake Keowee No. 3	841,100	Duke Power Co.	1973
South Dakota	Sioux Falls	58,500	Northern States Power Co.	1964
Vermont	Vernon	513,900	Vermont Yankee Nuclear Power Corp.–Green Mt. Power Corp.	1970
Virginia	Hog Island	783,000	Virginia Electric & Power Co.	1971
	Hog Island	783,000	Virginia Electric & Power Co.	1972
	Louisa County	800,000	Virginia Electric & Power Co.	1974
Washington	Richland	790,000	Washington Public Power Supply System	1966
Wisconsin	Genoa	50,000	Dairyland Power Cooperative	1967
	Two Creeks No. 1	454,600	Wisconsin Michigan Power Co.	1970
	Two Creeks No. 2	454,600	Wisconsin Michigan Power Co.	1971
	Carlton	527,000	Wisconsin Public Service Co.	1972
†	•	1,125,000	Tennessee Valley Authority	1973
†	•	1,125,000	Tennessee Valley Authority	1974

Nuclear Power Plants in the United States

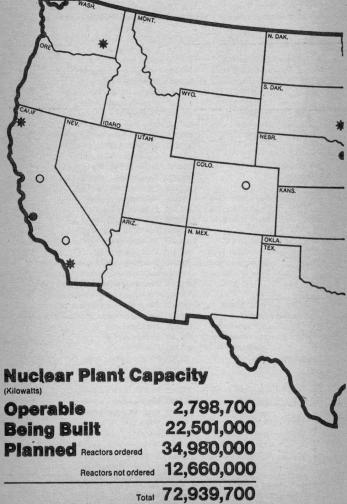

Nuclear Plant Capacity
(Kilowatts)

Operable		2,798,700
Being Built		22,501,000
Planned	Reactors ordered	34,980,000
	Reactors not ordered	12,660,000
	Total	72,939,700

The nuclear power plants included in this map are ones whose power is being transmitted or is scheduled to be transmitted over utility electric power grids and for which reactor suppliers have been selected

Legend

Operable	✳	15
Being Built	●	31
*Planned Reactors ordered	○	42

*14 more reactors with over 12,660,000 kilowatts have been announced for which reactors have not yet been ordered.

U.S. Atomic Energy Commission map, as of June 30, 1968

Contents

Acknowledgments

We are deeply indebted to many people for help and encouragement in writing this book.

Our lasting gratitude is extended to Dr. LaMont C. Cole, Professor of Ecology and Systematics, Cornell University, who read the manuscript and contributed enormously helpful suggestions which we have incorporated into the book.

We have also received invaluable guidance from Leo Goodman, Consultant for the United Auto Workers in Washington, D.C., who, having followed the development of nuclear power plants from their earliest days, has accumulated vast knowledge of the field which he has shared most generously with many writers over the years—but never, we feel sure, more generously or helpfully than to the authors of this book.

Special thanks are also due to Larry Bogart, Director of the Anti-Pollution League and co-founder of the Citizens' Committee for the Protection of the Environment, who has graciously shared his knowledge and experience with us, and who, like Mr. Goodman, has made untiring efforts to bring the hazards of nuclear power plants to public attention.

We wish to express special appreciation to Edward A. Friedman, Assistant Professor of Physics of the Stevens Institute of Technology, for many valuable conversations in which he clarified certain technical points about nuclear technology.

We are grateful, too, to Harold Grabau of Doubleday & Company, Inc., to Larry Grow and David

Curtis, for their skillful editorial assistance; and to our agents, Scott Meredith and John Schaffner, for their efforts on our behalf. Finally, our deepest appreciation to Doubleday & Company, Inc., particularly its Vice-President and Editor-in-Chief, Ken McCormick, for recognizing the importance of wider public understanding of the hazards inherent in the civilian nuclear power program, and for making these hazards known through publication of this book.

To the many other courageous individuals, too many to list individually, who have persisted in opposing nuclear power plants and publicizing their risks in the face of formidable obstacles and frequent frustrations, we are indebted not only as writers, but as private citizens.

Finally, it is impossible to express adequately our gratitude to Joanne Curtis and Margaret Hogan for their faith, patience, and many more tangible contributions to a book which would not have been possible without them.

RICHARD CURTIS
ELIZABETH HOGAN

In Defense of Fear

This book deals with the peaceful uses of nuclear power, a power widely believed to hold the answer to man's future energy problems, but one which has also been described by Supreme Court Justices William Douglas and Hugo Black as "the most deadly, the most dangerous process that man has ever conceived."

As this is being written, 102 commercial nuclear power plants are operable, under construction, or planned, and most are scheduled to begin generating electricity in the coming decade. Each will be fueled with a great many times the amount of uranium required to destroy Hiroshima. Under certain circumstances a portion of the intensely radioactive contents of such a reactor can be released into our environment in the form of gas or finely divided particles. This material has been characterized as a million to a billion times more toxic than any known industrial agent, and under not unusual weather conditions could fall out over a large area. Under less common but still conceivable conditions it could blanket a territory as large as one twentieth of the continental United States.

Despite the fact that atomic power and reactor technologies are still saturated with unknowns, these reactors are going up in close proximity to heavy population concentrations. Some have even been proposed for location in the heart of a city. Most will be of a size never before attempted by scientists and engineers; they are, in effect, experiments. Indeed, because atomic power plants have not to date proved to be of practical economic value, they are still officially licensed by our Government under the research and development rather than the commercial clause of the Atomic Energy Act.

We are deeply concerned that this program represents a peril to every living American, and to America's unborn.

We are by no means alone in this concern. Congress too has begun to show growing uneasiness with the haste and hazard of the atomic power program. No fewer than twenty-six Joint Resolutions were before the legislature of the United States when it adjourned in 1968, urging investigation and re-evaluation of our atomic power program. ". . . the damage we may already have done to future generations cannot be rescinded," said Senator Thruston B. Morton of Kentucky on February 29, 1968, "but we cannot shirk the compelling responsibility to determine if the course we are following is the one we should be following." Morton then introduced a resolution calling for a comprehensive review of the Federal Government's participation in the atomic energy electric power program, saying ". . . I have begun to look more deeply into our present energy resources and nuclear power safety situation. I am dismayed at some of the things I have found—warnings and facts from highly qualified people who firmly believe that we have moved too fast and without proper safeguards into an atomic power age."

Representatives John P. Saylor, a Pennsylvania Republican, and Arnold Olsen, a Montana Democrat, urging their House colleagues to support a Resolution creating a Federal Committee on Nuclear Power, pointed out that Resources for the Future, a prestigious research and advisory organization in the field of energy which had been commissioned by the President's Office of Science and Technology, had raised serious questions about the true costs of nuclear power, about thermal pollution, and about Federal expenditures on atomic energy. This group and others have indicated not only that atomic power is proving an economic disappointment, but that it may prove an economic catastrophe because of unwise fuel policies and failure of fuel production technology. Indeed, the fuel which was supposed to provide cheap energy for centuries to come may be exhausted before the twenty-first century arrives.

The Resolutions put forward by Senator Morton and Representatives Olsen and Saylor were by no means the most extensive. Senator Edward Kennedy of Massachusetts proposed a bill which would virtually declare a moratorium on construction of new plants until the Federal Power Commission had made a study of such matters as siting, environmental hazards, seismological and meteorological problems, and disposal of atomic wastes.

In addition to the misgivings of legislators are those felt by many highly trained, skilled, experienced men intimately associated with nuclear power: physicists, biologists, engineers, public health officials, business executives, and technicians. Many of these individuals have indicated that the proliferation of atomic power plants and related facilities represents a threat to human welfare meriting comparison with that of nuclear war. Some believe it even more insidious, because the idea that nuclear energy can serve as a force for peace has led the public to minimize the attendant radiation hazards. Yet, as the evidence will show, these are just as great as—indeed, quantitatively they are greater than—those of nuclear war.

Because this faulty reasoning has led to complacency and relaxed vigilance, it may be among the most unfortunate errors men have ever made. Yet it is the foundation for a stupendous and violently expanding industrial effort, with some seven to ten billion dollars of non-Federal capital already committed, and twenty-two billion estimated by 1980.

Examining the contentions of experts, we have been moved to conclude that such a foundation cannot bear its burden, and that unless the warnings are heeded soon, the momentum of the atomic power effort will carry it beyond the reach of effective control. Not a few authorities feel that it may already be too late.

These persons point to visible and widening cracks in the structure of the nationwide atomic power edifice. They mention ill-defined and -maintained codes and criteria, for instance—citing the fact that of the 2800 to 5000 standards necessary for a typical reactor power plant, only about 100 have been approved; they mention poor design of reactors and reactor components, loose supervision and quality control, ignorance of vital physical and chemical processes, irresponsible handling of critical materials, hazardous location of plants, insufficiently developed means of containing, storing, and disposing of extremely lethal radioactive waste, inadequate safeguards, reckless transportation of nuclear material, unacceptable workmanship, faulty construction material and techniques, human error, unthought-out effects on the environment, and neglect of questions of evacuation, first aid, decontamination, or compensation in the event of a serious or disastrous accident.

They also point out the tendency of nuclear power advocates to minimize the possibility of a major nuclear plant accident, the unknown effects on reactors of natural catastrophes such as earthquakes and severe storms, and the ever present possibility of sabotage. And some of these experts have been forced to admit that *we can destroy ourselves without a war,* simply by mismanaging peaceful nuclear power. They are distressed, and if experts are distressed, the public is obliged to give these matters its weightiest attention.

Unfortunately, public consciousness of such conditions appears to be dim, and even some utility executives have confessed to being inadequately informed about them. Because the facts have been published in a wide variety of reports, statements, and hearings, many of which do not reach the general public, and because those facts have been published over a long period of time, the significance of the total picture they create has been obscured, even to those who are experts in particular areas of this complex science. Even taken individually, many of these facts are sufficiently disturbing to persuade any thoughtful reader that a more cautious approach is urgently needed, yet somehow even such unnerving glimpses seem to have been veiled from public consideration or have failed to make a deep impression.

The purpose of this book, then, is to piece together these facts and present them comprehensively in order to alert our nation to the risks, problems, and errors which may otherwise remain buried in the mass of literature that has accumulated on the subject.

While we have put this book together as laymen, we have drawn, as the reader will see, upon authorities in many fields, and have garnered much information from official reports of the Atomic Energy Commission itself. Despite our lack of scientific expertise, then, we are confident that the documentation offered in these pages will gain the respect of those whose technical backgrounds would ordinarily make them leery of allegations framed by lay persons. Here will be found the considered views of scientists, engineers, lawyers, science writers, insurance specialists, businessmen, and public health officials, as well as members of the Atomic Energy Commission, the Congressional Joint Committee on Atomic Energy, and others concerned with atomic power. Each sees our nuclear policies and programs from the special viewpoint of his own discipline and contributes interpretations of specific aspects which may not have occurred to, or been disseminated among, experts working in other specialized fields.

In essence, it is our hope that, presented in this way, stripped of technical jargon and "officialese," confusing charts and bewildering statistics, and organized to provide a clearer, broader view of the facts which Congress and the public need to form a valid judgment about the perilous direction in which we are heading, a more cogent understanding will emerge.

For the most part we have allowed the facts and conclusions brought forth by these experts to speak for themselves, keeping our own reactions and interpretations as laymen to a minimum. At the same time, we recognize that a body of informed laymen constitutes, in a democracy, the most important agency for determining the course our country will take in this matter. Thus in the last chapter we have assumed the citizen's responsibility of pointing out the changes we believe are essential in national policies and programs related to peacetime nuclear power.

In urging Congress to re-evaluate the nuclear power projects now burgeoning all over our country, we do not believe ourselves against progress. We believe progress can and should be achieved, but not at such high risk. We believe, with the deepest conviction, that unless this re-evaluation is made soon and greater caution exercised at once, we will be inviting unprecedented national calamity. For if, as we believe this book demonstrates, the familiar concept of nuclear plants as clean, safe, reliable "good neighbors" is a myth, then a single major accident may cost the lives of tens and perhaps hundreds of thousands of Americans, affect the health of millions more, and cause property damage and loss in the billions of dollars. Even if such an event is forestalled, the gradual accumulation of immense stores of radioactive material and the inevitable release of a measure of its radiation represent a long-term threat not merely to the population of our country, but to life everywhere on this planet.

This book presents hard facts, and because the facts are frightening, our work may be assailed as a "scare" book. To a certain extent this is unavoidable. We cannot help being alarmed by some of the facts gathered here, and if some of our distress is communicated to the reader, it will only convince him of the depth of our anxiety. It is a tendency of our times to be ashamed of fear of the scientific unknown, and to believe that no technological hazard is a match for human ingenuity. But we believe that in the case of atomically generated electrical power, human ingenuity has created technological hazards far beyond mortal competence to control. Are these not valid grounds for fear?

Although this book is necessarily critical of the unprecedented power which has been vested in the Atomic Energy Commission, and of many of the Commission's policies and programs, it is not intended to reflect on the integrity of its members and staff, nor to castigate it for the unprecedented dangers to which we are exposed.

Created in a whirlwind of national and international enthusiasm for the peaceful industrial uses of nuclear power, burdened by Herculean responsibilities, and hampered further by a self-contradictory mandate both to promote and to regulate atomic power, the Commission has done as well, by and large, as any other agency or group of men could be expected to do.

But as we shall point out time and again in the following pages, regulatory performance which would be acceptable in less hazardous industries is simply nowhere near good enough in dealing with nuclear power. Our concern about the policies and practices of the Atomic Energy Commission is predicated on this most demonstrable truth. Expert and conscientious though the personnel of the Commission may be, they are still mortal and hence subject to many forces and conditions beyond their control. The mere fact that they are part of one of the most complex governments on earth is sufficient testimony on that score. That the Joint Committee on Atomic Energy, which is charged with reviewing the Commission's activities, and that the nuclear industry and utilities are all subject to the same human limitations and potential errors, goes without saying. But although in that respect their errors are understandable, in a matter as delicate yet frightfully harmful as atomic processes their errors are nevertheless intolerable. We are convinced that those who favor our present commercial nuclear power program do not recognize how far we are in actual practice from the high standards and ideal conditions which even the most enthusiastic proponents acknowledge to be essential to public health and safety.

It is our hope, then, that this book will not be viewed as an irresponsible attack on the atomic energy establishment or the nuclear industry, but will rather be looked upon as an urgent plea to our nation and its leaders, to those directly connected with the industry and those—meaning every citizen—who stand to be affected by it, to re-examine our peaceful nuclear program in the perspective we have tried to achieve in these pages.

Perils of the Peaceful Atom

"Our technology has outpaced our understanding, our cleverness has grown faster than our wisdom."

> DR. ROGER REVELLE, Chairman of the U. S. National Committee for the International Biological Program

"Ours is a world of nuclear giants, and ethical infants."

> GENERAL OMAR BRADLEY

"The men who create power make an indispensable contribution to the nation's greatness. But the men who question power make a contribution just as indispensable—for they determine whether we use power or power uses us."

> PRESIDENT JOHN F. KENNEDY

"Some say the world will end in fire . . ."

> ROBERT FROST

CHAPTER I

The Goose That Laid the Radioactive Egg

Lagoona Beach, Michigan, is not to be confused with Laguna Beach, California. The one in Michigan is located on the western shore of Lake Erie, near the city of Monroe, population 20,000. The farmland around there, irrigated by the Raisin River, is rich, the scenery agreeable, and the beach resorts attractive. It's no more than an hour by car from there to downtown Detroit; a radioactive cloud takes a little longer, unless there's a strong wind.

What a radioactive cloud would be doing drifting from Lagoona Beach to Detroit is an interesting question. No such event has taken place, but for thirty days in the autumn of 1966, you might have been hard put to find a reliable nuclear physicist prepared to wager it could not happen by the time he got his wallet out of his trousers. For something immeasurably frightening had happened at the Enrico Fermi Power Plant on October 5, and during the four-week period that followed, scientists, engineers, utility executives, and members of the Atomic Energy Commission held their breath while viewing a situation raising the possibility that Detroit with its more than 1.5 million inhabitants might have to be evacuated.

On some eight hundred acres in Lagoona Beach the plant stood, dedicated to the memory of the Italian physicist whose prodigious intellect had largely been responsible for the first controlled release of atomic energy. By invoking Fermi's name the plant's promoters had undoubtedly hoped his spirit would smile on

1

their project, which promised consequences as significant to world peace as those the atomic bomb had had to world war. Yet the history of the enterprise seemed to suggest that the late Nobel Prize winner was having difficulty complying with their petitions.

At the heart of Fermi was an atomic reactor, fashioned to generate enormous heat through controlled fission of the uranium fuel in its core. The heat would convert water into steam, which would in turn operate electricity-producing turbines.

The plant had a number of features that had never been tested conclusively in the commercial field. While all atomic reactors produce plutonium as a by-product of normal operation, it was hoped that the Fermi would produce large surpluses, which could be used either to produce atomic weapons or to fuel other reactors—hence the name "breeder" for this kind of reactor.

Fermi, then, was in many ways an experiment, yet here it was making its public debut only thirty miles from Detroit, stoked with about half a ton of uranium, enough to make an arsenal of atom bombs of Hiroshima potency.

One might have rested easier had earlier test reactors employing these principles and features proved reliable, but experiences with them had proved little more inspiring than those with other kinds of reactors. Furthermore, trial runs at Fermi had given no one reason to hope that this machine would give a better accounting of itself than any other. The plant had been plagued by mishaps since completion, the latest of which revolved around the system by which molten sodium is circulated through the tubes containing uranium fuel, cooling them and carrying off heat to the boilers. Liquid sodium is at best a tricky substance, and at worst a violent one, and it had been misbehaving in Fermi's core. Finally, complications in the steam generator, where the sodium system heats the water, had caused a prolonged shutdown.

By the fall of 1966, however, the apparatus seemed

to be back in working order, and on the evening of October 4 clearance was given to start up the reactor. With the utmost delicacy, technicians in the control room activated machinery for withdrawing control rods from the reactor's core. These rods absorb radioactivity; when withdrawn, they increase the fuel's rate of chain reaction and thus its heat. Withdrawal of the rods raised the temperature of the reactor to a little beyond 550°, at which point the engineers leveled off operation for the night.

On the following morning, after discovery and repair of a faulty valve, they set about boosting the power. Slowly, slowly, withdrawal of the rods resumed. Around two in the afternoon a pump malfunctioned, but by 3 P.M. a replacement was activated and they brought the power up to 20,000 kilowatts of heat energy.

At this time one of the instruments in the control room registered erratic fluctuations. Though not necessarily ominous, they led the technician to conclude it might be a good idea to switch from automatic control of the rods to manual for better handling if trouble should develop. When the signal steadied off, he went back to automatic, pushing the power up to 34,000 kilowatts, or 17 per cent of maximum capacity. The fluctuations reappeared on his instrument. In addition, a couple of temperature recorders showed excessive heat in certain spots in the core. And an observer noticed that the control rods appeared to be withdrawn farther than they should be for the desired heat level.

While they were wondering what to do next, the bells went off.

Both inside the reactor and in some adjoining buildings, sensors were picking up high radiation readings, setting off alarms throughout the complex. Automatic devices sealed off every area where high radiation was manifest. Luckily, no one was in those areas. But there *were* people outside—about two million of them within a radius in which fatalities could conceivably occur.

And some radioactive gas, it was later determined, was released during the accident.

An agonizing length of time seemed to pass before the word went out to "scram" the reactor. Accordingly, six safety rods were thrust into its bowels to absorb radiation and kill a potential runaway chain reaction. Then everybody breathed slowly, waiting for the thing to go one way or the other.

Undoubtedly, in the agonizing moments that followed, many present at Fermi wondered about matters they had never really wondered about until that moment, particularly what it was like to die from radiation poisoning. Some may have been thinking of those poor souls at SL-I, the experimental reactor out in Idaho Falls, Idaho. In 1961 the plug had blown off its fuel core, sending three men to a particularly gruesome death. The first was dragged out by a heroic rescue team who suffered a three or four years' dose of radiation from the few moments in which they were in the contaminated chamber and in contact with the victim, who died a few minutes later, apparently of a head injury. But the test-house had been filled with so much radioactive poison it took more than five days before rescuers could recover the last of the bodies. If the explosion itself didn't kill the fellows, they must have been roasted alive by fission products. It was reported that highly radioactive portions of their bodies were removed and buried in the hot-waste dump at the site, the rest put in small lead boxes and placed in caskets for burial.

But quick death like that was a blessing compared to the hideous torture of slow radiation poisoning. It would start with nausea and vomiting; the bowels would turn to water, then to blood. Fever, prostration, a gamut of mental symptoms ranging from stupor to hysteria. Then the burns would appear. Reduction of white blood cells would cancel bodily defense against infection, initiating internal and external bleeding. The hair would come off in obscene patches. Delirium, then death. If not death, something worse: life. Permanent emaciation, crippling, recurring symptoms, unthinkable pain, vulnerability to further disease and infection, cancer or leukemia, shortening of life expectancy, sterility or damage to reproductive organs leading to genetic defects in offspring.

Others at Fermi, perhaps, were able to turn their thoughts away from themselves and reflect on broader consequences. *Would* they have to evacuate Detroit? What plans had been drawn up by the city and state governments to effect the orderly withdrawal of up to two million people from their homes? Where would they go? Who would remain behind to protect their property? What would happen to their businesses? What would happen to *the* business of Detroit, the automobile industry? How long would they have to remain in exile? What radiological procedures and facilities existed to handle victims? The questions begot more questions until the prospects took on the proportions of a stupendous nightmare. Their only contact with sane reality lay in the radiation gauges and badges in their control room: So far, these did not register contamination.

A cautious investigation indicated that a runaway had been averted by "scramming," the emergency insertion of the control rods. But the crisis was far from over. On the contrary, the initial diagnosis was that some of the reactor fuel had melted, a matter of profoundest gravity. When a critical mass of uranium 235 is collected in one place, it undergoes a violently spontaneous chain reaction. At a hasty meeting the fear was expressed that enough uranium had recongealed so that a disturbance of the core—by an attempt to remove the damaged fuel, for example—would jar it into a critical mass too great to be controlled by the control rods, which were already at their maximum. The stuff could explode, not with the force of an A-bomb, but still with sufficient impact to breach the steel and concrete containment structures of the building and hurl clouds of lethal gas into the sky. Then, depending on which way the wind blew, and how strongly, and how much material escaped . . .

Walter J. McCarthy, Jr., assistant general manager for the company that had developed Fermi, attended that meeting. He was later to say that the possibility of such a secondary accident was "a terrifying thought."

For the next month technicians and experts tiptoed around Fermi and spoke if its ailment in whispers, like aborigines camped on the slopes of the volcano, fearful of provoking the earth god's wrath. And though they were to proceed with excruciating deliberateness, they had no way of knowing whether their next probe might not bring the god raging to his feet.

In one sense the Fermi was a special reactor. Its potential for "breeding" more fuel than it consumed was seen as answering many of the world's fuel-energy problems for centuries to come. Indeed, because the entire future of atomically produced electricity depended on the success of breeders—if they failed, low-cost uranium supplies would be exhausted before the end of this century—Fermi represented some of the highest expectations of government, industry, and tomorrow's electricity consumer.

In another sense, though, Fermi shared almost all of the problems and treacherous hazards confronting every other reactor designed before and since. The Fermi story is especially representative, however, because almost all of the issues raised in the pages that follow were raised, futilely, in a battle over that power plant that proceeded to the highest court in the land—where they were shockingly resolved in favor of atomic power's proponents. That the menaces of which the public was then warned are today growing to monstrous proportions makes it imperative that the lessons inherent in the Fermi episode not be lost on us.

Early in the 1950s, some thirty-five utilities and equipment manufacturers formed a company to design the Fermi plant, and the following year these firms were assembled into the Power Reactor Development Co.—known as PRDC—for the purpose of constructing, owning, and operating it. Late in 1955 PRDC filed its application for a construction permit with the AEC, and humbly lowered its head in anticipation of applause from a public grateful to be getting atomically produced, low-cost electricity in the near future, and delighted at having a pace-setting scientific facility for a neighbor.

But although PRDC was certain everyone would find the proposition irresistible, no applause was forthcoming. Murmurs in the Detroit area indicated that a lot of people found the idea of Fermi considerably less than compelling. In fact, some were so little taken with it that they talked of going to court to stop it.

It seems that these people were anxious about the safety features of the proposed reactor; or rather, the lack of them. They just weren't convinced that the scientists and engineers constructing the plant knew enough about the behavior of atomic materials in reactors to predict how they would behave under power.

Of course, many persons who know little about reactor physics think of only one thing when someone mentions nuclear energy, and it is likely that some of those who objected to Fermi labored under the mistaken notion that an accident there could set the reactor off like an atomic bomb. Promoters of the project therefore took pains to assure the worried that such an event was, by every known law of physics, out of the question.

And yet few took much comfort in these reassurances. All they knew was that the building would house enough nuclear material to flatten dozens of Hiroshimas. That much lethal material sitting in a neat little pile thirty miles southwest of one of the world's industrial capitals simply wasn't calculated to inspire ease of mind, even if it *couldn't* go up in a mushroom cloud.

Some of them had read John Hersey's book on Hiroshima, and whether it was morbid of them or not, they just couldn't stop dwelling on his images of the leveled city and the mutilated souls "lucky" enough to have escaped instantaneous vaporization in the fireball. These Detroiters knew it was irrational, that we had tamed the atom and all that. Still . . .

Since these fears had no technical basis in reality, the proponents of the plant dismissed them as invalid. A good public relations campaign, it was viewed, would dispel most of the anxiety. Once people understood the thing couldn't go off like an A-bomb they'd buy the idea without a qualm. And if not—well, you can't please everyone.

What was more disturbing to PRDC, however, was the body of *enlightened* men and women who did not want the reactor built. *They* knew very well that Fermi couldn't go up in a mushroom cloud—but that wasn't what they were complaining about. They were talking about a conventional-sized explosion, the kind that could happen if too much melted nuclear fuel came together inside the reactor core. They talked about unperfected cooling systems. They talked about potential failures of safety devices, of power failures, of unthought-out emergency procedures, of untested materials, of untried construction techniques, of unplanned radioactive waste disposal systems, of human error. They talked in facts and figures, and they talked with authority.

And what was disturbing above everything else was that *a body of extremely knowledgeable technical authorities designated by the Atomic Energy Commission itself had deep misgivings.*

The Advisory Committee on Reactor Safeguards is an august panel of experts established by Congress for the purpose of advising the parent AEC on the safety of proposed reactors. The AEC is required to submit all data on those reactors to the ACRS for evaluation. Although the ACRS is not empowered to implement its findings or impose sanctions on applicants, its opinions should, by virtue of its members' integrity and prestige, be tantamount to law. One would think, certainly, that if the ACRS had serious reservations about the safety of a reactor, all forward progress on it would be stopped until all objections were totally satisfied.

When AEC Chairman Lewis Strauss opened the Advisory Committee's report on Fermi, dated June 6, 1956, it read:

> Although there are no facts or calculations available to the Committee that clearly indicate that the proposed reactor is not safe for this site, the Committee believes there is insufficient information available at this time to give assurance that the PRDC reactor can be operated at this site without public hazard.

It can be imagined that the AEC reaction would have been to hold up all further progress on Fermi until the information void mentioned by the Committee had been filled. It must be understood, however, that in 1956 the Atomic Energy Commission's role as promoter of nuclear power was just beginning to show signs of forward movement. American industry and investment capitalists were scrutinizing the reactor program for signs of vigor, and the breeder reactor was looked to with special hope because it would mean the difference between unlimited fuel and a fuel supply largely exhausted before atomic power really got under way. But although the AEC must have recoiled sharply from the humiliating prospect of having to confess that Fermi might be a gross and dangerous mistake, it is almost impossible to understand what motivated it to do what it next did.

What the Commission did, according to Representative Chet Holifield of California, was to suppress the Advisory Committee's negative report.

Had not another member, Thomas E. Murray, courageously stepped forward to disclose the AEC's action, it might never have come to light. When Murray did, the "fallout" hit the fan. The AEC's excuse, brought out later, was that its Commission was under no obligation to follow the Committee's advice—that it was only one of the factors to be considered along with others in reaching a decision as to whether it was proper to issue a permit. This explanation put things in an even worse light, raising questions as it did about the independence of this all-important safety advisory body, and about the AEC's apparently self-contradictory dual role as both promoter of atomic energy and regulator.

Representative Holifield, by no means backward in advocacy of commercial nuclear power, termed the AEC's action "reckless and arrogant." And the indignation expressed by Senator Clinton Anderson of New Mexico, Holifield's chairman on Congress's Joint Committee on Atomic Energy, was nothing less than Olympian. He called the AEC's proceedings a "star chamber" and strongly suggested the Commission had yielded to expediency in overruling the ACRS report:

> . . . From a practical standpoint, AEC might feel obligated to go through with a bad deal with respect to public safety because they will have permitted the expenditure of huge sums under the construction permit. It is my belief that decisions on safety should be made without any examination of dollars involved, but only from the standpoint of human lives.

When the AEC, even after admitting that "this fast breeder was the most hazardous of all the reactors," determined to go ahead with Fermi anyway, Senator Anderson began sketching battle plans. And when the AEC, on August 4, 1956, issued its approval of the construction permit just in time for the groundbreaking ceremony at Lagoona Beach, Anderson picked up the phone.

Among the most important persons he reached were G. Mennen Williams, then Governor of Michigan, and

President Walter Reuther of the United Auto Workers. He told them how the AEC's blue-ribbon panel had urged postponement of Fermi, and how the AEC had so cavalierly put the report in a drawer. He told them all he knew about the hazards of reactors, and much of what science *didn't* know about them. And although he may not exactly have told them in so many words to sue, he left them in no doubt that merely a few picket signs and baby carriages weren't going to stop this powerful government agency from triumphing.

The State of Michigan, caught in the squeeze, was to hold to a non-partisan course in the ensuing events. But the unions dug in for a fight. At the end of August, three big labor organizations petitioned to intervene in the Atomic Energy Commission's procedures. They alleged that the construction permit "will result in the construction of a reactor which has not been found to be safe, and whose operation will create a hazard which would place Petitioners, their members and their families in danger of an explosion or other nuclear accident which would imperil their lives, health and property." Citing the reservations raised by the AEC's own Advisory Committee, the attorney for the Petitioners stated:

> The greatest potential hazard presented lies in the possibility that the tremendous accumulation of radioactive fission products imprisoned in the fuel might somehow be released into the atmosphere and be distributed by wind, and contaminate inhabited areas. . . . *These fission products are more toxic per unit weight than any other industrially known materials by a factor of a million to a billion.* [Emphasis his.]

The AEC came back with the argument that it was merely issuing to the development syndicate a permit to *build* the reactor. AEC would never issue a license to *operate* it until satisfied that all safety conditions and standards had been met. And certainly, AEC added, between commencement and conclusion of Fermi's construction the serious kinks and information gaps in the reactor's plans would be resolved.

This view was greeted with some skepticism by the unions, who reasoned that if you invest forty million dollars in construction of a plant, you darned well expect clearance to operate it when it's finished. Was the AEC prepared for the kind of pressure it would meet if it decided against issuance of an operating license after a utility had poured so much money into the project? Could rugged businessmen be expected to selflessly write off their titanic outlay in the interests of public safety if the reactor didn't pan out? The labor unions did not think so; and who knew more about rugged businessmen than labor unions?

Attention focused early in 1957 on the soon-to-be-published findings of a study team appointed by the AEC to determine what the chances of nuclear plant accidents were, and what the consequences might be. The team had been directed to think in the most pessimistic terms possible, the idea being to get some notion of the worst we could expect, or what nuclear scientists call the "maximum credible accident." But while the credentials of the group were faultless, the objectivity and pessimism with which they'd been charged somehow got subverted in preparation of the study. For when *Theoretical Possibilities and Consequences of Major Accidents in Large Nuclear Plants,* known also as the "Brookhaven Report," was issued that March, its primary conclusion was that a major accident was almost beyond possibility.

The team heavily stressed that "the likelihood of accidents which would release major amounts of fission products outside the containment . . . ranged from one chance in 100,000 to one in a billion per year for each reactor." Rearranging its figures, the committee estimated that "there would be one chance in 50 million per year that a person would be killed by reactor accidents." This the AEC favorably weighed against the chance a man faces of being killed in an auto accident in the United States annually: about one in a mere five thousand.

While the desired response to these statistics may have been for Americans to abandon their autos and crowd close to the walls of the nation's nuclear plants, the effect was quite the opposite. The reason is that the AEC's study team also surmised that in the extremely unlikely event of a major reactor accident, people could be killed at distances up to fifteen miles, and injured up to forty-five miles. As many as 3400 could be killed and 43,000 injured. Property damage, due mainly to radioactive contamination of land, could range as high as seven *billion* dollars, the area affected being as great as 150,000 square miles.

However much the AEC might have hoped to use *Theoretical Possibilities* to pacify opposition to Fermi and other potentially controversial nuclear projects, the report backfired. The odds against a major accident were largely overlooked by the report's audiences. All people could think about was 3400 killed, 43,000 injured, seven billion dollars in property damage. And instead of having their questions answered, they were asking a host of others, for the report had raised a threat beyond anything Americans had ever had to contemplate short of atomic war.

The builders of Fermi, PRDC, had meanwhile turned the problem over to the Engineering Research Institute of the University of Michigan, hoping perhaps to get better odds. But this one blew back in their faces too. The Institute replied in July that the number killed by escape of radioactive material from Fermi could run as high as 133,000. The report went on to scoff at the possibility of that kind of accident: "An incredible event!" it declared. But what people remembered was the death toll.

The AEC emphasized that the question of harm was largely irrelevant because of the low probabilities. Indeed, when the intervening unions sought to expand the issues in the Fermi case to include many of these crucial matters, the AEC denied their motion, interpreting the Commission's rules of practice as allowing no such privilege.

Although these wranglings over potential damage and harm, and over the AEC's autocratic control over quasi-judicial proceedings, were anything but irrelevant, they were definitely at this stage academic. There had never been a reactor accident so severe that radioactive material escaped in appreciable doses from the site.

And so, as if to oblige the litigants in the Fermi action, the Number One Pile at the Windscale Works in England, a breeder reactor, suffered a serious accident on October 10, 1957, spewing fission products over so much territory that authorities had to seize all milk and growing foodstuffs in a four-hundred-square-mile area around the plant. According to Sir John Cockcroft, a leading British nuclear scientist, considerably more radioactivity was released at Windscale than is released during an explosion of a Hiroshima-type atom bomb. Command Paper 302, a British report on the disaster, stated that all of the reactor's containment features had failed.

The Windscale reactor and the Fermi reactor were by no means identical, and Fermi's apologists hastened to point out that their facility possessed features that ruled out a Windscale-type accident. But their antagonists hastened right back to point out that Fermi was, after all, as much a one-of-a-kind proposition as Windscale had been. Could not Fermi be prone to its own unique kind of disaster? The U. S. Naval Ordnance Laboratory, in its containment study of Fermi was to state: "Many of the containment problems that are peculiar to this reactor have never been solved experimentally or theoretically."

Leo Goodman, speaking for the United Auto Workers, put it in graphic terms that people in the Motor City could appreciate: "To locate this experimental plant that has never been brought to full power so near population centers is as reasonable as trying to control a ten-ton truck with untested brakes in a congested city street," he said.

Of course, it *was* reasonable in one respect. Because it is expensive to transmit electricity over long distances, utilities find it expedient to build power plants as close to population centers as possible.

Goodman's simile, and everything else the unions threw at PRDC-AEC, was to no avail. On December 10, 1958, the Commission, with a few modifications, reaffirmed its orignal permit to PRDC, and on May 26, 1959, issued its "Opinion and Final Decision" dismissing all exceptions taken by the Petitioners on the grounds that there was enough assurance, for the purpose of the provisional permit, that Fermi could be built and operated without risk to the health and safety of the public.

But the unions were not to be put down so easily, and they went to court. There their assertions were upheld. Two of the three Circuit Judges hearing the case in the U. S. Court of Appeals, in a decision rendered June 10, 1960, felt the AEC's permit should be set aside. The AEC's "predictions," the decision stated, did not satisfy the requirements of the Atomic Energy Act of 1954 *that safety be established before, not during or after,* construction gets under way. "The possibilities of harm," Judge Edgerton said for the majority, "are so enormous that any doubt as to what the Act requires, and any doubt as to whether the Commission made such findings, should be resolved on the side of safety."

The AEC and the Fermi people did not accept this line of reasoning, however, especially as construction of the plant was already far along. So they carried their case to the Supreme Court, on the grounds that the lower court's decision would have a "seriously disturbing effect on the development of the peaceful uses of atomic energy"—a thoroughly irrelevant argument.

It was while the highest court in the land was considering the merits of the case that the lid blew off the SL-I reactor in Idaho Falls, killing the three men tending it.

Unfortunately, the implications failed to register on judicial geiger counters. The majority of justices on the Supreme Court upheld the PRDC permit, and Justice Brennan, delivering the opinion on June 12, 1961, affirmed his faith in the AEC to stand up against business pressures when the time came to issue an operator's license. At the same time, he affirmed faith in PRDC to turn its back on tens of millions invested if, when the time came for an operator's license to be issued, the AEC should find the plant faulty:

> PRDC has been on notice long since that it proceeds with construction at its own risk, and that all its funds may go for naught. With its eyes open, PRDC has willingly accepted that risk, however great.

Justice Douglas, with Justice Black concurring, took the most strenuous issue with the verdict, declaring: "The construction given the [Atomic Energy] Act by the Commission is, with all deference, a lighthearted approach to the most awesome, the most deadly, the most dangerous process that man has ever conceived."

But that, as the Court had found, was not relevant.

The legal issues resolved at last, PRDC finished construction and began testing Fermi's systems. But what the laws of man had put together, the laws of nature now conspired to tear asunder. From the outset the plant seemed jinxed. According to Saul Friedman, a *Detroit Free Press* staff writer reviewing the reactor's history up to July 1966, nothing worked the way it was supposed to. The thirty-inch-long pins containing uranium fuel were designed to last until 3 per cent of each pin's fuel had been consumed. But after a short time they swelled, making it difficult for the liquid sodium coolant to flow between them. So the engineers had to replace the fuel core after only four tenths of 1 per cent of the fuel had been consumed.

You don't replace fuel cores the way you change tires. The process is so delicate and complicated that it took a year to make the switch—the bill coming to four million dollars. Then, when they finally got the new core in, they found that liquid sodium had clogged a number of key components. It had also eroded some graphite, a radiation absorber used to "moderate" or control the fuel's activity. That meant more graphite.

Then, in Friedman's words:

> The steel dome over the reactor vessel had to be redesigned to prevent the giant plug that bottled up the reactor from shooting through the roof in the event of explosion.
>
> The mechanism to move the fuel elements in the reactor failed. . . . The giant cask car, which transports radioactive elements, failed. . . . The giant sodium steam generators constantly caused trouble, and one nearly exploded. They leaked sodium. . . .

Some of the technicians wondered if the reactor was trying to tell them something.

By summer of 1966 it was estimated that Fermi, originally financed for between $40 and $45 million, had cost about $120 million. It had produced no more than $303,000 worth of electricity and bred nary a gram of fuel. The reactor hadn't been brought to anything like its maximum capacity, and the way things were going it would be a long time before it even approached it—to say nothing of sustaining it.

In spite of all these setbacks, the reactor still bumbled along, trying to work out the eighty million dollars worth of bugs it had developed during its ten-year sojourn. But although a lot of observers were beginning to call this golden goose a white elephant, it still had one more egg to lay.

And that brings us up to October 5, 1966.

A year after the accident, it was announced that the eight-inch piece of metal in Fermi's core, pinpointed as the immediate cause of the accident—and it was *not* a beer can, as had been suggested half facetiously by some—had been identified. According to *Scientist and Citizen,* it was one of six identical sheathing elements in the cooling system, elements not even called for in the original plans for the reactor, nor officially recorded after installation. They'd been kind of thrown in, you might say, as last-moment safety measures during construction. Unfortunately, a workman had failed to secure one properly, and it had been swept up by the sodium rushing through the cooling system and cast against coolant nozzles, blocking them. This caused several fuel subassemblies to overheat, warp, melt, and shove a couple more out of kilter, making the meltdown, in the words of Sheldon Novick, reporting in *Scientist and Citizen,* "a bit worse than the 'maximum credible accident.' "

No one involved with Fermi was injured by radiation; yet all got fingers burned. There was a lesson in the experience, and AEC, taking a cautious stance toward the future of the breeder program, seemed to be willing to learn it. Not so with the business community. The Fermi reactor was cool but a few months when, at a panel discussion of the Atomic Industrial Forum's winter convention, Chauncey Starr of Atomics International complained: "The national fast-breeder program is too small, too slow, and too timid."

Plans have just been announced for starting the Fermi reactor up in June 1969, two years and eight months after an event as close to Armageddon as this country has ever known.

CHAPTER II

Those Who Favor Fire

President Truman, reeling from the horrors he had authorized to be unleashed on Japan, described atomic energy as "a force too revolutionary to consider in the framework of old ideas." It stood to reason, then, as Congress took up the burden of postwar legislation of atomic energy, that if the energies involved were nothing less than cosmic, and the human prospects and national destinies nothing short of fundamental, then the responsibilities to be fixed on those designated to regulate atomic energy would be close to Herculean. After all, *someone*—a man or a group of men—had to be entrusted with control over forces directly bearing on human survival. The leverage inherent in that trust was practically infinite; the wisdom and restraint involved would demand the best that men were capable of giving.

Many Americans were overwhelmed with remorse and fear over the awful destructive energy we had liberated. Sentiment ran high in many quarters for the total abandonment of *any* kind of atomic power, for good or for evil. Humanity had gone too far, they were saying, and must turn back at once before it was propelled on a mad, irrecoverable course.

Tragically, it was out of the question. Russia's dismaying belligerence, and the ominous fact that it had captured some German nuclear scientists, ruled out any possibility of dropping our guard, let alone our ultimate punch. But even if Russia had not so behaved, it was naïve to think our Government would dump its atomic bombs and all pertinent information into the sea. Sooner or later, someone else would learn how to make A-bombs; we were obliged to maintain our advantage.

One fact, therefore, was inescapable: This nation was committed to continuation of research and development of atomic energy, particularly for the purpose of defense.

It was a fact that many must have found unbearably bitter. Indeed, it would not be hyperbole to suggest that immediate rearmament, and rearmament with atomic weapons following the most savage war of all time, was a fact the American nation, as a psychological entity, literally could not face. The traumatic cruelty of it demanded some sanity-saving rationale, some desperate hope to which we could cling while we stockpiled atomic bombs. The hope took the form of a belief in the atom's capability for peaceful service. Many psychologists and social scientists have advanced this theory, stating that the American people as a whole, in order to assuage their guilt feelings over the destruction of Hiroshima and Nagasaki—and, more importantly, over the godlike (or demonlike) powers their science had created—embraced atomic energy as an important contributor to the peacetime needs of the world's people.

This conviction was given great impetus by many scientists who—perhaps for the very same reason of compensation for guilt—sincerely believed that the atom could be turned from mankind's foe to one of its closest allies, that it could be clean, safe, reliable, and economical. Psychology aside, a great deal of scientific optimism about the future of atomic power was founded on a gross misjudgment of the problems and dangers inherent in the young technology. In the mid-forties, and indeed well into the 1950s, many of the most serious reactor safety problems were unknown. Most reactor malfunctions were completely unexpected, since, as Dr. James McDonald has pointed out, they would have been engineered out had they been anticipated. Barry Commoner in an article in *Scientist and*

Citizen has described how the biological and genetic effects of different radioisotopes were a very long time in being recognized; it was not until weapons-testing had already introduced quantities of these poisons into the environment that short- and long-term consequences could be described with reasonable scientific accuracy.

These then were the factors that accounted for America's embarkation on the journey into peacetime nuclear power. The need to continue development of atomic weaponry provided the technological impetus; the dream of the atom's commercial and humanitarian usefulness—a dream fostered by what later proved unjustified optimism on the part of many influential nuclear scientists—provided the rationale; and pervasive guilt about stealing divine fire supplied the psychological climate in which the whole mammoth venture could thrive.

Congress and the President, no less than the American people—and perhaps more so, in view of their direct role in the development and employment of the atomic bomb—were subject to these psychological fluxes, and found the vision of a future energized by the peaceful atom difficult to resist. These were the circumstances in which the Atomic Energy Act of 1946, setting up the program and providing for the establishment of the civilian-run Atomic Energy Commission, was passed.

But Congress, an institution that was supposed to know something about political power, still could not or would not cope with the fact that unprecedented responsibilities demand unprecedented prerogatives. Perhaps no legislation could have been framed so as to curtail the AEC's potential privileges. Whether that is so or not, the Act created opportunities for the assumption and exertion of prodigious, if not unlimited, power.

Two major faults were built into the 1946 Act, either of which would have been grave enough by itself in a matter of such overriding importance, but which together constituted a truly formidable governmental force. The first of these was the conferment of unprecedented power on the Atomic Energy Commission; the second was the granting to the Commission of unprecedented independence and privileges of self-regulation.

As to the first, the Act stipulated that the AEC would have exclusive control over production, ownership, and use of fissionable material. Furthermore, the control extended totally or largely into such areas as mining and refining of ore, research and development, information dissemination, radiological health and safety programs, licenses and agreements, bomb production and other military applications, patents and inventions, security matters, administration of international arrangements on atomic energy, the right of eminent domain over lands containing radioactive resources or lands on which atomic facilities were to be built, and of course ownership of the facilities themselves.

The establishment of a Government monopoly shattered what Truman had called "the framework of old ideas," and the Act of 1946 made the AEC exclusive steward of the new framework. It was reasoned by some that such a monopoly was necessary then in view of the delicacy and secrecy involved. That may have been so at the outset, but time was soon to alter the conditions in which atomic energy operated, making the AEC's immense power a dangerous archaism. Senator Thruston B. Morton, in the 1968 speech quoted earlier in this book, reminded his colleagues of "the oft repeated statement in those days that electrical power from atomic reactors would be so cheap that it would not even be worthwhile to meter it," and of the now ironic words of General Leslie Groves when he turned over nuclear responsibility for the Manhattan Project to the Atomic Energy Commission: " 'You of the Army's Manhattan Project . . . have raised the curtain on vistas of a new world.' "

"No one," continued Morton, "questions that the development of the ability to create electrical energy through atomic fission is a tremendous accomplishment, or that someday in the distant future we may be forced to depend on it after our other bountiful sources of electrical energy are exhausted or become too scarce and costly to utilize. But we also know that atomic energy is not the panacea of all our energy problems it was once expected to be, and we are becoming more aware every day of the costs in terms of potential danger to humanity which this proliferating atomic energy program may entail."

The second major weakness in the original Atomic Energy Act was the extraordinary independence it afforded the Commission. Part of the problem stemmed from the fact that the Commission was *a* commission, because commissions in our Government are by nature free of much of the restraint that characterizes other governmental bodies. These regulatory bodies "drift along," in the words of former AEC member Thomas E. Murray, "somewhere in a 'twilight zone' among the three branches of the Government—President, Congress, and the courts. Subject to all three branches in specific respects, the commissions nevertheless evade complete and continuing control by any one of them. That is why they have sometimes been called the 'headless fourth branch' of the Government."

Thus commissions of *any* sort, being neither fish nor fowl, can with any degree of power create for themselves a most advantageous niche from which to dictate without being dictated to. But what is one to say about a commission endowed with *unprecedented* powers *and* "drifting along somewhere in a 'twilight zone' " among the three branches of the Government? Was this not a unique combination? Would the Commission, as time went by, be able to resist taking advantage of its dizzyingly special status?

It was not simply that there were too many loose threads; it was that the threads trailed from a mantle that few men in the history of government had ever worn.

On paper the AEC appeared anything but independent, for its activities came under the jurisdiction of all three branches of government. The President of the United States had the power of hiring, with the advice and consent of the Senate, the five members of the Commission, and he could remove them before expiration of their terms for "inefficiency, neglect of duty, or malfeasance in office." The President also exercised general executive power over all independent AEC commissions, had considerable control over the budget, over classified information, over weapons quotas, and over settlement of disputes involving the AEC; and the President had to approve all agreements for international co-operation in atomic energy. Furthermore, the Act called for establishment of a Joint Congressional Committee on Atomic Energy to review all proposed legislation pertinent to atomic energy, to hold hearings and make recommendations to Congress. Finally, judicial review of the Commission's actions was provided for by the Act.

A number of factors, however, balanced and eventually outweighed these Government controls. The first was the scientific complexity, indeed the sheer opacity, of atomic energy as far as the layman was concerned. The nature of the work was far beyond the technical comprehension of men in other branches of the Government. Only scientific experts understood it, or said they did, and everyone else from the President—whose scientific advisers were largely pro-atom—on down had to take it on faith. Second was the top priority of maintaining a big lead over the Russians in atomic research. National survival was at stake, and our government had to give the atomic energy establishment the widest latitude in the interests of national security. Third was the rapid proliferation of a bureaucracy, replete with Advisory Committees on This, Divisions of That, Offices of the Other Thing, panels, boards, and what have you, making it harder and harder for Government overseers to keep track of what the Commission was doing, and therefore harder and harder to maintain control.

꠵ Here then were all the ingredients for a virtually independent government within the Government, a scientocracy invested with nearly complete powers of policy-making and self-regulation. Furthermore, the Atomic Energy Commission found itself the repository of a dual and conflicting role: It had to *promote* an atomic energy program on the one hand, and *regulate* it on the other. The position was not unlike that of the family that not only owns the sole grocery store in town, but serves as mayor, sheriff, judge, and town council as well. Getting one's way becomes a simple matter of donning the right hat.

Many years afterward the Commission's first chairman and later a harsh critic of atomic policy, David E. Lilienthal, was to score the AEC's best-of-both-possible-worlds position, and the danger it posed to the public:

> It is unfortunate that the AEC is not only the overall protagonist of a nationwide atomic-power program; it is also the body that must sit as judge of the safety to the public of the design, mode of construction, and site of particular atomic power plants. In short, the AEC, as a general promoter of atomic power, must also decide the quasi-judicial issue of whether a license is issued. With a world of goodwill and integrity and technical competence on the part of the AEC, how well is the public protected by this dual and conflicting role?

The mischief inherent in the situation did not become apparent until the early 1950s. Certainly, the original members of the Commission conducted themselves with the highest probity—and it should be emphasized here that the integrity of the AEC is nowhere in this book called into question: only, to use David Lilienthal's distinction, its infallibility. The Commission of the late 1940s sincerely believed that in promoting this new discovery for man's good, it would be rendering an invaluable service to the country. Furthermore, during that period the Commission did not, any more than anyone else, fully appreciate the complications and dangers residing in a commercial reactor program, nor did it completely recognize the extent of the responsibility that had been placed on its members' all-too-human shoulders. Undoubtedly, it *was* conscious of the duality of that responsibility, however, and the conflict between promotional and regulatory must have caused many sleepless nights for the conscientious personnel of the AEC.

During this period, roughly to 1953, the foundations of power reactor technology were laid. Basic research into properties of various fuels, coolants, and moderators was undertaken, designs and materials were tested, experimental reactors were built. While electricity generation was an important goal, most of the allocations, labor, and practical knowledge went into development of reactors for propelling submarines and aircraft. As long as military priorities prevailed, the AEC could not make its debut in the market place.

But military priorities could not prevail forever. The airplane reactor technology flopped, and naval reactor technology did not promise to absorb anywhere near our total nuclear effort. Neither did nuclear armament. Even though the Russians had the atomic bomb, and though nuclear fusion, the principle on which the hydrogen bomb is based, had given the Cold War a new boost, the arms race did not strain the capacity of the atomic energy program. And of course, the public was growing eager to see the atom put to uses other than belligerent ones, to see it fulfill the promise envisioned in the days right after the war. Russia was building a nuclear power plant that would be ready before we got our own power program going; *that* was incentive enough right there.

Looking back in the early 1950s, our Government

must have realized it had an enormous investment to protect, not the least part of which was prestige in the world community. Looking ahead, it could foresee its titanic atomic industrial effort bogging down unless it broadened its base and went commercial. The Atomic Energy Commission therefore, cautiously at first, began to remove the hat of self-restraint and raise that of promoter to its head.

Though nuclear information was still highly classified, some non-priority data was cleared and a number of qualified industrial teams were invited in 1952-53 to study it with a view to evaluating the economic outlook. A number of them came away smiling. For one thing, the AEC itself was buoyant about prospects, the threat of major technological headaches being at that time a cloud no bigger than a man's hand. For another, the visiting teams may have glimpsed stimulating incentives. It is generally acknowledged that the Government gave assurances to the effect that the plutonium produced as a by-product of the fission process would be bought back by the Government for good prices—plutonium being essential to atomic weapons, of course. Saul Friedman, a *Detroit Free Press* staff writer, suggested, in an article about the group that pursued the breeder reactor franchise, that the AEC had encouraged them to believe the Government would pay them ninety dollars a gram for their plutonium—almost three times as much as the Government was then paying for high-grade, weapons-type plutonium.

It is also possible that the industrialists who peeked into the AEC's cupped palms saw something rather distressing, in the form of a hint that if private capital didn't develop a nuclear power industry, Uncle Sam would extend his atomic monopoly to include the generation of electric power—in direct competition with the utilities. The smiles on their faces must have frozen when they saw that.

In any event, the consensus of the industry observer

teams was that nuclear plants could produce electricity at a cost roughly competitive with conventionally fueled plants.

Heartened by industry's optimistic if totally predictable response, the AEC now set the hat marked "promotion" at a more rakish angle, preparing a breathtakingly ambitious blueprint for the advent of commercial nuclear power. Some officials were talking about half of America's electricity being generated by the atom by the end of the century.

Of course, the Atomic Energy Act of 1946 prohibited private initiative in the nuclear power field, and it was therefore necessary to effect a change in the law. Since that change had the official approval of the President, the support of the Joint Congressional Committee on Atomic Energy, and the apparent approval of the electorate, the conclusion was forgone. Congressional opponents, armed only with their nameless dread, were pushed aside easily. In 1954 the Atomic Energy Act was rewritten to permit private organizations to build and own atomic energy facilities and operate them under AEC license and regulation.

The rationale for this effort was termed "Atoms for Peace," a truly inspiring motto, and it had been enunciated by President Eisenhower before the United Nations on December 8, 1953: ". . . the United States pledges before you—and, therefore, before the world—its determination to help solve the fearful atomic dilemma—to devote its entire heart and mind to find the way by which the miraculous inventiveness of man shall not be dedicated to his death, but consecrated to his life."

These words were not insincere. They were, however, dangerously simple. But their austere beauty appealed to a jingle-conscious age; and the nobility of the concept, contrasted against the terrors of the arms race then in full swing, was a blessed relief. The mellifluous phrase "Atoms for Peace" set a classic pattern for the glib promotional slogans for atomic energy that were soon to follow, in which the atom became a good friend and neighbor, a plowshare beaten from swords. And into these hollow catch phrases crept the notion that radioactivity consecrated to the benefit of mankind was somehow less poisonous than that dedicated to man's destruction. Battening on mankind's profoundest yearnings, the notion quickly swelled into a widely held assumption, and was eventually adorned by promoters with the trappings of gospel.

Not everyone was carried away by these tantalizing vistas. Representative John P. Saylor of Pennsylvania, speaking before Congress some time later, was to recall the deep misgivings he and many other colleagues felt about the Great Leap Forward into commercial nuclear power:

It was not too many years ago, Mr. Speaker, that the general public was excited at the prospect of the development of an atomic reactor which purportedly would bring vast cost savings to consumers of electric power. It is true that a number of Members of Congress had serious doubts about the practicability of using millions upon millions of dollars of U. S. Treasury funds merely to utilize a new source of energy for power generation. I recall that many of us stood on the floor of this House time and again as far back as 1956 to question the wisdom of such tremendous expenditures, particularly when the U. S. Geological Survey has established without qualification the existence of sufficient coal reserves to satisfy the power requirements of the entire nation for at least a century to come. Congress also was reminded of warnings by distinguished scientists who believed that the safety issues entwined in the fission process should be resolved before the wholesale construction of nuclear facilities.

But caution and economy could not prevail in a climate of optimism and enthusiasm generated by wanton promises of miracle and magic through applications of a glamorous rare element whose material value had previously been confined exclusively to its destructibility factor.

Such profound reservations, however, carried no weight against an extremely determined Government policy reinforced by the clamor of a utility lobby eager to get in on the ground floor of what might turn out to be one of the most prodigally subsidized undertakings in American peacetime history. The Atomic Energy Commission, of course, was to be the instrument of that policy, and it was around this time that the complexion of the Commission began to change visibly. The Commission started emerging from its relatively passive role to become a most aggressive instrument indeed. It started picking up the loose threads that the Atomic Energy Act of 1946, and to an even greater extent that of 1954, had left hanging, and began to feel at ease in the mantle from which they were suspended.

Unfortunately, at the very same time—from 1954 onward—serious problems began cropping up in reactor technology, and bomb tests disclosed somatic, genetic, and environmental dangers far worse than anyone had anticipated. So now the AEC had a double problem; it not only had to promote atomic power against ordinary resistance to anything new—it also had to promote it against concrete evidence that it might not be safe, might not be clean, might not be reliable, might not be economical. The Commission probably could not see it clearly, for it all happened gradually and subtly, but the only way out of the bind—aside from admitting that we had all made a gigantic mistake—was to begin erecting an elaborate structure of psychological defenses.

Although a large number of companies came into the AEC's camp directly after passage of the Act of 1954, it would be wrong to assume that private industry, uniformly, was deliriously happy about the new status of atomic energy. Naturally, component manufacturers, utility operators, and other industrialists and businessmen followed these developments with keen interest, but when it came to a deeper commitment many dragged their heels. It was not that they doubted that

American know-how could lick the technical problems in due time. But from an investor's point of view, nuclear technology was still very much in the gestation state, and the economic challenge was far less surmountable than was being generally and generously proclaimed. The hazards were still a giant question mark, and questions of liability had scarcely been thrashed out. Why not wait and see how these questions were resolved, and how the experimental and demonstration projects worked out before casting one's lot with Atoms for Peace?

For six months following the Act of 1954, therefore, the AEC found itself in the position of a puzzled hostess on the night of her party who, hours having passed without a guest showing up, suddenly wonders if she put the correct message on the invitations. It is true that planning nuclear power projects takes time, especially when much data is classified, as was the case in 1954. Nevertheless, industry seemed to be shuffling its feet, waiting to see how the Government's own pioneer reactor, the 60,000-kilowatt plant going up at Shippingport, Pennsylvania, would do. Not a single application for a construction license came in. ". . . There is little question but that industry's initial response was disappointing to a Joint Committee and an AEC bent on accelerating the national nuclear power effort," says John F. Hogerton in a *Scientific American* review of the growth of atomic power.

By winter the AEC realized there was need to prime the pump, and accordingly, in January 1955, the Commission announced a "Power Demonstration" program designed to stimulate plant construction. Liberal aid was offered to any utility prepared to put up a plant, in the form of research and development assistance and waiver of fuel inventory charges for the first five years of plant operation. At last, that March, the first application came in, and by year's end there were two more takers. In addition, two other projects, privately financed rather than plugged into the Power Demonstration program, were launched.

Despite this forward motion, industry as a whole continued to hesitate, and it steadily grew apparent that the real reason why many businessmen had supported the Act of 1954 was to ward off a Federal Government threat to go into the electricity business if private industry declined to take the nuclear initiative. James W. Kuhn, in a recently published book, *Scientific and Managerial Manpower in Nuclear Industry,* confirms this view:

> Under the threat of public power, several utility companies did come forth with plans for large-scale nuclear power plants. Officers of the companies expected no profit from the plants. The incentive was largely negative—to keep civilian nuclear power private. As the president of one of the companies remarked, "We acted because we needed to guarantee the position of private industry. The money spent was a gamble to preserve the private sector." The president of another of the companies explained why his management pushed into nuclear power: "We made a proposal on what became Shippingport and we breathed a good deal easier when we didn't get the contract. We weren't anxious to get into nuclear power, and I don't think any other company in its right mind wanted to get into it either. But you see, we had to bid—we had to act—whether we wanted to or not. We had been pushing the private development of nuclear power and we couldn't refuse to get into it after pushing so hard."

The lobby had managed to get a clause written into the 1954 Act specifically forbidding the Government to engage in the sale or distribution of electricity for commercial use. Now that the threat was averted, and the lobby had it in writing, private industry could take its time going nuclear. That clause had a big loophole, however: It permitted Uncle Sam to sell electricity "incident to the operation of research and development facilities of the Commission. . . ." What was to prevent the Government from building scores of "research and development" facilities and selling the "incident" electricity all over the country? This was one of the AEC's bigger whips, and the Commission applied it adroitly.

But as all mule skinners know, a carrot ahead is worth a whip behind. When the power industry in 1955 continued hedging, taking just enough initiative to keep the Government happy, and minimizing risks by forming large joint-venture investor groups, the AEC announced the "second round" of its Power Demonstration program—more subsidies. Three more reactors went up as a result, but *still* the industry balked.

Late in 1956 the Argonne National Laboratory's experimental boiling water reactor, designed specifically for electricity generation, went into operation, and the next year Shippingport was completed. Industry nodded appreciatively, but its attention was really fixed on the units being erected by the utilities, not those by the Government. The former were proving more expensive to build than expected, and it looked as if they might prove more expensive to run as well; and the fossil-fuel industry was preparing a counterattack that would make it much tougher for the Government to produce nuclear-generated electricity at competitive prices.

Furthermore, anxiety about safety was really begining to percolate. There had been talk at the 1955 Geneva conferences on atomic energy about the probabilities and consequences of a major accident, and a number of actual accidents in Government reactors had made a lot of people stop and ponder. The issue reached a boil with publication of the Brookhaven Report early in 1957, with its estimates of as many as 3400 fatalities, 43,000 injuries, and $7 billion in property damage.

Would the public stand for the idea of nuclear powerhouses virtually in its back yard? Would the costs of building safe reactors make nuclear power financially unfeasible? Wouldn't the cost of insurance alone price reactors out of the market? If not, who was going to be liable for damage claims?

Apparently, until the investor's mind was set at ease on the big question of safety and liability, investment capital was never going to flow freely. Accordingly, our Government held out the biggest carrot yet.

Perhaps "plum" describes it better, for through passage of the Price-Anderson Act, it was guaranteed that private industry would not be held liable for more than a token of damage costs in case a major nuclear plant accident happened. This Act, passed in 1957, set a limit of $560 million worth of indemnity on any radiological accident—but only $60 million of that amount would be put up by private operators. *There was no fiscal responsibility beyond $560 million, even though damages could run as high as $7 billion!* Total coverage amounted to only 8 per cent of potential claims— and private industry's liability came to less than 1 per cent.

While this was going on, the AEC was applying the whip with a will. In the words of James W. Kuhn, "The chairman of the AEC, Lewis L. Strauss, made explicit the choices before industry in 1957. 'It is the Commission's policy,' he said, 'to give industry the first opportunity to undertake the construction of power reactors. However, if industry does not, within a reasonable period of time, undertake to build types of reactors which are considered promising, the Commission will take steps to build the reactors on its own initiative.' "

Meanwhile, in the Fermi action the AEC had overruled the plea of its Advisory Committee on Reactor Safeguards for caution, initiating a policy of approving reactor applications before safeguard plans and technology supported such an action. Its handling of the Fermi hearings indicated a dangerous tendency to manipulate procedures in order to minimize opposition. The Atomic Energy Commission was flexing its muscles—muscles that Congress had molded in 1946 and 1954—at every sector involved in atomic energy: the public, Congress, the judiciary, the President, private industry, and the Commission's own advisory bodies.

The Fermi case was not to be resolved for some years, though when it finally did come to a decision the AEC would prevail.

Despite the foregoing, however, all the plans and programs, ultimatums, and incentives could not bring into the world a technology whose limbs and vital organs were still largely unformed. With one exception, the plants built during the first and second rounds of the Power Demonstration program had weighed in at higher cost than anticipated, and one cost nearly double the estimate. The generating costs achieved in these plants at the outset were 50 per cent higher than predicted. Conventionally fueled power was effecting savings in a variety of ways, and the price of coal was dropping. The insurance issue was by no means resolved, for utilities knew that even if they were only nominally liable on paper, a major accident would nevertheless be ruinous. The Fermi case, on which so much was riding, began making its way up the chain of courts.

In the late 1950s, therefore, the Commission initiated a Ten Year Program, establishing short- and long-term goals in atomic energy—and *still* industry stayed away: Only four more plants went up as a result of the "third round" of the Power demonstration program. The AEC may have been demonstrating power, but it was not demonstrating might. A crisis began to loom, and after President Kennedy took office he requested a thorough assessment of the past, present, and future of atomic energy from the AEC.

The Commission responded with its 1962 Report to the President on Civilian Nuclear Power, a major policy statement. Because the chips were down, this document had to be carefully worded—and it was. How, for instance, was the Commission to explain its failures? In one key passage, that question is answered:

Nuclear electric power had been shown to be *tech-*

nically feasible, indeed, readily achieved. Power reactors can be reliably and safely operated. However, contrary to earlier optimism, the economic requirements have led to many problems—combining low capital cost with long life and assured reliability; lowering costs by improved efficiency; developing long-lived and, therefore, economic fuels. Attempts to optimize the economics by working on the outer fringes of technical experience, together with the difficulties always experienced in a new and rapidly advancing technology, have led to many disappointments and frustrations. Experiments have not always worked as planned. Many construction projects have experienced delays and financial overruns. Such difficulties led to considerable diminution of the earlier optimism regarding the early utilization of nuclear power, which in turn contributed to the withdrawal of some equipment and component manufacturers from the field.

However cleverly the AEC phrased it, the meaning of this admission was certain: that power reactors could not at that stage be made both technically feasible *and* economical. If we wanted safe, reliable reactors under present technology, we would have to build and operate them at a loss; if we wanted economically competitive reactors, we would have to compromise safeguards. Phrased another way: Nuclear power works in theory, and in limited experiments, but as for commercial viability it has proved a great big—dud.

But that is not the kind of admission one makes to one's Congress and President after spending more than a billion dollars in Treasury funds. "To have second thoughts in the pursuit of a will-of-the-wisp in public programs or in private enterprise takes moral courage and aroused taxpayers or stockholders," David Lilienthal was to say the following year. And again: "The initial goal that was the justification both for the unique status given the Peaceful Atom and the gargantuan scale of public expenditure has long since proved to be a mirage. That myth of a revolution continues to be fed by the American taxpayer. Private firms repeat this fiction at this late day, as part of institutional promotion of the sale of their atomic reactors."

But the AEC was not so objective. The habit of "denial," of constantly belittling hazards and problems while emphasizing progress and promise, apparently had become second nature to proponents of atomic power.

And *that* was the most treacherous fact of all.

Under that circumstance, what course was there but to plunge even more deeply into the morass? In the very same Report to President Kennedy that stated ". . . for safety reasons, prudence now dictates placing large reactors fairly far away from population centers," the Commission announced its decision to encourage the launching of huge commercial reactors, far bigger than anything tried thus far:

> To encourage construction of full-scale power installations by utilities, the support of research and development and the temporary waiver of fuel charges have recently been augmented by the offer of reimbursement of design costs for fuel installations of 400 megawatts [400,000 kilowatts] or more. Both public and investor-owned utilities are eligible. It is hoped that these forms of assistance will suffice to bring about a marked increase in the number of full-scale installations.

Presumably the AEC was hoping that by the time the big installations went up technology would have caught up and discovered a way to make them work. This topsy-turvy philosophy was sanctioned now by the highest court in the land, for in June 1961 the Supreme Court had upheld the developers of the Fermi project.

Thus without ever having proved that power reactor technology was technically reliable, commercially viable, or safe, the AEC was encouraging industry to build reactors of untested size and immeasurable danger on sites close to major population centers.

But this encouragement apparently did the trick. The power brokers' defenses began crumbling, slowly at first, but as the mid-sixties dawned, with greater and greater speed. Private industry began tooling up in a big way. Connecticut Yankee Atomic Power Co. put in for a $13,195,000 subsidy for a 490,000-kilowatt reactor at Haddam Neck on the Connecticut River; Southern California Edison and San Diego Gas & Electric asked for $13,022,000 to build a 395,000-kilowatt reactor near San Diego; the City of Los Angeles requested $16,200,000 for help in putting up a 490,-000-kilowatt reactor in the Rancho-Malibu area; Niagara-Mohawk Power filed for a reactor on Lake Ontario, graciously declining a subsidy—all it wanted was free nuclear fuel for its first five years of operation. Jersey Central proposed a 500,000-kilowatt reactor near Toms River, New Jersey: the Oyster Creek Plant. With financial assistance under the AEC's Power Demonstration program, announced Jersey Central, its plant could be made competitive with a fossil-fueled plant. ("By the same token," said Representative John Saylor in an excoriating speech in the House, "Jersey Central may have pointed out that old newspapers or imported Swedish timber would be competitive with coal if Government subsidies were sufficient to absorb the cost differences.")

Another passage from Saylor's speech sums things up splendidly:

In other words, Mr. Speaker, although at least 1.3 billion dollars has been poured into the civilian reactor program by the AEC in the past nine years, the imbalance of costs between electricity generated by the atom and that generated by conventional fuels is still of such magnitude that even the current multi-million-dollar bestowals by the Federal Government to the investor-owned utilities may have to be increased in order to get the program moving at the rate desired by the AEC. Meanwhile, irrespective of the expensive research carried out since 1954, the degree of danger hovering over a nuclear powerplant remains a mystery.

By 1966, industry's resistance to nuclear power had effectively collapsed. The AEC's Annual Report to Congress for that year declared that "The year 1966 saw atomic energy become a major factor in the planning for meeting the Nation's future electric power needs as 55 percent of the new steam-electric generating capacity announced by U.S. utilities was for nuclear plants." Applications for sixteen reactors were filed that year. In 1967, the AEC's Annual Report blared that "utility planning announcements doubled the previous pace-setting growth of 1966," with twenty-nine permit applications in hand.

But the upshot of this story is a monumental irony.

For by 1967 the Atomic Energy Commission, deluged by applications, pressured maddeningly by utilities to clear licenses, besieged by industry for guidance in standards and criteria, critically hampered by manpower shortages, and inundated by innumerable problems never anticipated when it put its promotion into high gear—the Atomic Energy Commission began to grow conscious that the harvest it had so assiduously cultivated was threatening to overwhelm it.

CHAPTER III

Thresholds of Agony

Because much of what follows in this book deals with the perils of radioactivity, it is important to review some of the things known about the way radioactivity kills and injures. Most readers are probably familiar with many of these facts, but are accustomed to thinking about them only in relation to nuclear war. It is imperative, however, that we be fully aware that mismanagement of the peaceful uses of atomic energy will subject humans to many of the same gruesome afflictions and agonizing deaths as those suffered by survivors of Hiroshima's fireball. It will also create profound environmental disorders, as will be demonstrated later in these pages.

One of the best works on the subject is *Radiation: What It Is and How It Affects You* by Professors Jack Schubert and Ralph E. Lapp. This book, though published in 1957, is still considered authoritative in its fundamental aspects, and sheds much light on the hazards inherent in radioactive processes. With the help of Professors Schubert and Lapp, a brief review can be attempted.

Radiation damage may be inflicted in a number of ways: in large doses or small, all at once or by stages, externally or internally. Irradiation may be of the whole body, of specific organs or tissues, or of only a few cells.

A number of basics should be understood at the outset.

First, there is and always has been an external and

internal "background" of natural radiation. Until the Atomic Age, that background was constant. One source is the earth's crust. Although some areas, such as those where granite predominates, may exhibit more radioactivity than others, such as limestone formations, the earth's surface is estimated to contain an average of about three tons of uranium, six tons of thorium, and one gram of radium per square mile to a depth of one foot. Also, every person bears a small but detectable amount of radium and other radioactive emitters inside his body, owing to infinitesimal amounts of those substances absorbed and retained by eating, drinking, and breathing. Cosmic rays also contribute a share of radiation. Experts calculate that the sum of internal and external natural background radiation is about five roentgens over the first thirty years of one's life.* That 5 r is the base on which all discussion of radiation in this book will be built.

Second, it must be understood that any kind of radiation—alpha rays, beta rays, gamma rays, neutrons, cosmic rays, X rays, etc.—produces *some* effects on cells and organs. The essential difference between one ray and another, from the viewpoint of biological effects, is one of dosage. Some kinds of rays must be more intense than others to do the same amount of harm. The important point to bear in mind is that some types of radiation produced in reactor fission processes are extremely vicious even in minutest quantities.

Third, radioactivity is undetectable by human senses, and ineradicable except through natural decay, which for some elements take hundreds and even thousands of years.

Fourth, the design of all atomic power plants projected for the next decade in the United States is such that they must unavoidably produce large quantities of radi-

---

*Roentgens are a measure of the actual energy absorbed in tissue. For comparison's sake, a single dental X ray will run about 1 roentgen (expressed as "1 r"), and a full mouth X ray series may involve between 14 and 18 r.

ation and radioactive waste known as "fission products."

Fifth, experts state that these fission products are a million to a billion times more toxic than any industrial pollutant known heretofore.

Finally, scientists have produced convincing evidence pointing to the conclusion that no cell ever fully recovers from a dose of radiation. It may *appear* to recover, these authorities point out, but a certain degree of damage is irreversible and may show up a considerable time after exposure.

Consider first the consequences of an intense single dose of radiation suffered by the whole body, since in its simple graphic horror it is easiest to comprehend.

In the event of a major reactor accident in which radioactive gas and fission products were dispersed into the atmosphere, a large number of people would be exposed directly to massive doses of radiation. What would happen to them?

While the amount of radiation necessary to produce various effects might vary according to a variety of conditions, the following thresholds expressed in roentgens can be taken as fairly universal:

A dose of 600 r or more would probably kill nearly everyone exposed within a month.

A dose of 400-450 r would be deadly in half the cases.

A dose of 300 r would kill one quarter of those exposed, and induce serious injury in 90 per cent of the remaining number.

A dose of 200 r would kill about 2 per cent, and induce serious illness in half of the remaining cases.

From 200 r down to zero the effects diminish proportionately, and between 0 and 25 r no *observable* effects are produced directly. But this statement must not be misinterpreted to mean that such low doses are harmless.

What happens when a dose of 600 r, the amount guaranteed to be fatal in almost 100 per cent of all cases, is received all at once by the whole body, is vividly described by the British Medical Research Council:

> The first effect . . . is a sensation of nausea developing suddenly and soon followed by vomiting and sometimes by diarrhea. In some people, these symptoms develop within half an hour of exposure; in others, they may not appear for several hours. Usually, they disappear after two or three days. In a small proportion of cases, however, the symptoms persist; vomiting and diarrhea increase in intensity; exhaustion, fever, and perhaps delirium follow; and death may occur a week or so after exposure.

> Those who recover from the phase of sickness and diarrhea may feel fairly well, although examination of the blood will reveal a fall in the number of white cells. Between the second and fourth weeks, however, a new series of ailments, preceded by gradually increasing malaise, will appear in some of those exposed. The first sign of these developments is likely to be partial or complete loss of hair. Then, from about the third week onwards, small hemorrhages will be noticed in the skin and in the mucous membranes of the mouth, which will be associated with a tendency to bruise easily and to bleed from the gums. At the same time, ulcerations will develop in the mouth and throat, and similar ulceration occurring in the bowels will cause a renewal of the diarrhea. Soon the patient will be gravely ill, with complete loss of appetite, loss of weight, and sustained high fever. Feeding by mouth will become impossible, and healing wounds will break down and become infected.

> At this stage the number of red cells in the blood is below normal, and this anemia will increase progressively until the fourth or fifth week after exposure. The fall in the number of white blood cells, noted during the first two days after exposure, will have progressed during the intervening symptomless period, and will by now be reaching its full extent. The changes in the blood count seriously impair the ability to combat infection, and evidence from Nagasaki and Hiroshima shows that infections of all kinds were rife among the victims of the bomb. Many of those affected die at this stage and, in

those who survive, recovery may be slow and convalescence prolonged; even when recovery appears to be established, death may occur suddenly from an infection which in a healthy person would have only trivial results.

The above pattern, known as "marrow death," is the result of the failure of the cells in the bone marrow to produce blood. It appears that if a few healthy marrow cells survive, or if the victim receives injections of marrow from healthy donors, this form of death can be averted. But the victim is actually only buying time, for the chances are high that cancer, leukemia, acute anemia, or some other ailment will strike in due course.

What about higher doses than the minimum lethal dose of 600 r? If the victim receives a dose of 1000 r or more, it would appear that nothing can help him, and he is doomed to live no longer than a week. The symptoms leading to his demise are characterized as "intestinal death."

At considerably higher doses, say 3000 r and up, the nerve tissue functions break down and a "central nervous system death" follows quite rapidly. There is a case on record of an AEC employee who succumbed to the latter a day and a half after taking a whole-body dose estimated at 12,000 r. Plutonium was being recovered from the Los Alamos reactor, and through an error three batches in different stages of purification were put in a large tank together. When an electric stirrer was activated, the plutonium reached critical dimensions and exploded.

The workman operating the stirring device was thrown from a low ladder, got to his feet, and ran outside crying that he was burning up. His skin was indeed glowing cherry red. Within minutes he began vomiting and discharging a profuse, watery diarrhea. By the time he got to the hospital he was in shock. Thirty-six hours after the accident he was, mercifully, dead. Autopsy revealed symptoms of all three kinds of radiation death—marrow, intestinal, and central nervous system—plus considerable damage to the heart muscle.

We have been talking about so-called "whole body" doses. In the event of a nuclear accident, however, it is likely that many people will suffer damage not to their whole bodies, but to specific organs only. What are some of the effects of high doses on those organs and tissues?*

Female Sex Organs:

The National Research Council reports that single doses to the ovaries of 125 to 150 r may produce cessation of menstruation in 50 per cent of women. A single dose of 170 r can produce temporary sterility for one to three years, and a dose of 500 r will mean permanent sterility for most women.

It should be borne in mind that the female child is born with all the ova she will ever produce. Exposure of her ovaries will thus affect eggs which are to be fertilized when she matures, leading either to defective offspring or to hereditary defects which will manifest themselves in future generations.

Male Sex Organs:

Very small doses of radiation, 50 r or less, can lead to inhibition of sperm production. A 250 r dose may produce sterility for a year or more, and 500-600 r will bring about permanent sterility. Even if sterility is temporary, the sperm that does return will bear defective genes that will eventually appear as mutations in future generations.

---

*In a "whole body" exposure, the amount of tissue absorbing the dose is much greater than in a localized exposure such as a dental X ray. Therefore, a high dose of radiation applied to a local area of the body might not necessarily prove as harmful to the entire human system as the same dose distributed over the whole body.

Blood and Blood-Related Organs:

No more than 50 r applied to the whole body will cause the number of lymphocytes, a variety of white blood cell, to drop by 50 per cent, and it will take about a week before the number returns to normal. Higher doses, or repeated or prolonged exposure, will lead to precipitous drops in blood cell count from which recovery is much slower.

Destruction or disturbance of red and white blood cells will injure the body's ability to protect against infection, repair damaged tissue, and promote clotting. Many organs in the body responsible for blood cell production, removal of dead cells, blood storage, and other functions can also be hurt. Among these organs are the lymph nodes, spleen, and bone marrow.

Skin:

Thousands of cases of skin cancer have been produced by overdoses of radiation, usually high doses in the thousands of roentgens. Smaller doses may not produce immediate damage, but latent periods of twenty years or more may pass before ulcerations or malignancies appear. In 1955 two British doctors reported a case of skin cancer in a seventy-year-old woman. She had received about 1500 r from a fluoroscope trained on her abdomen to detect kidney stones. A burn had appeared shortly after the exposure, then healed. In 1947, however, a skin cancer, which ultimately proved fatal, developed in precisely that spot. How long had it taken? Forty-nine years. The original fluoroscope irradiation had occurred in 1898!

Radiation of the skin at 300-400 r and up can also cause temporary or permanent loss of hair, graying of hair, destruction of sweat glands, and loss of the skin's natural suppleness and glossy texture.

Eyes:

Cataracts, characterized by opacity of the lens, have been produced thousands of times as a result of deliberate irradiation of patients for cancer and other conditions. The latent period, observed in studies made by Dr. G. R. Merriam, Jr., of the Institute of Ophthalmology of New York, averaged almost four years, but one case took as long as thirteen years to appear.

Bones and Teeth:

Bone cancer has often appeared years after exposure to heavy doses of radiation, 1500 r and more. The bones are particularly susceptible to radiation from certain isotopes, such as strontium 90, absorbed as a result of ingestion of radioactively contaminated food, such as fallout-tainted milk.

Radiation of children's bones has caused retardation of growth: About 150 r will do it, and heavier doses have resulted in limb shortening. Local irradiation of the jaws has slowed tooth growth, and large doses may be followed by infection about the teeth, loss of teeth, and destruction of the jawbone.

Brain:

Relatively small doses of radiation to localized regions of the brain have produced a variety of symptoms, depending on what functions those regions control. In one experiment, a couple of volunteers who had been given 100 r in the diencephalon, or middle brain, experienced a number of symptoms ranging from ringing in the ears to apathy to hyperactivity. Single doses on the order of 500 r and more have produced brain damage in children. X-radiation for scalp conditions has produced such effects as blindness, paraplegia, epilepsy, delirium, twitches, and ulcerations.

Lung:

Heavy doses of radiation, such as those received for treatment of breast cancer (2,000-3,000 r) have produced swelling and scarring of lung tissue, and possibly tumors. Breathing of radioactive material, such as radon (the gas found in uranium mines), has produced numerous lung cancers, with a latent period as long as seventeen years.

Thus far we have been discussing acute effects of large doses of radiation taken on the whole body or on specific organs and tissues, the kind of doses likely to be received by people in the immediate and intermediate vicinity of a serious reactor accident. Suppose it could be vouchsafed that no such calamity would ever happen: Would you then be able to rest easily?

The answer is most emphatically *No.* As we shall see, the merely commonplace activities of the nuclear industry, the mining, milling, and processing of fuel, the day-to-day operations of nuclear electric plants, the reprocessing of fuel, and the transportation, storage, and disposal of waste fission products, are already contaminating our air and water with radioactivity. If the atomic power program is permitted to proliferate in the coming decade, the presence of these poisons in our environment will reach alarming proportions.

Just how much does our level of "background radiation" have to be raised to be considered alarming? The accretion of evidence garnered in the last twenty years or so by a large number of responsible scientists demonstrates that *there is no radiation threshold below which genetic damage, cancer, or shortening of life is impossible.* Any dose, however small, will take some toll of vital cell material, and may initiate far-reaching, harmful processes.

Cancer:

While there is no argument that radiation causes many forms of cancer, including leukemia ("blood cancer"), there has been debate over the threshold dose. Research findings have been clouded because scientists still haven't recognized precisely what it is that makes a cell cancerous, nor have they been able to sort out the many factors besides radiation that might, over a period of years, cause or nourish the disease.

In spite of this confusion, two indisputable certainties have now emerged. The first is that *cancer can begin when a single cell is altered* in such a way that its normal self-reproductive powers are affected. Such a cell begins multiplying rapidly, undeterred by influences which customarily inhibit cell growth. The second certainty is that *the nucleus of a cell,* in which are contained the cell's reproductive mechanisms, *can be damaged by a single particle of radiation.* Although Hermann J. Muller, as long ago as 1927, demonstrated the effects of radiation on reproductive processes—for which he won a Nobel Prize—it has more recently been shown by Robert C. Von Borstel of Oak Ridge National Laboratory that just one alpha particle irradiating the nucleus of an insect egg will kill that egg.

The only question remaining is how long it takes before a malignancy manifests itself. The answer is, it may take generations of the given cell type. The "turnover" in some skin cells, for instance, is about four months, but it may take years or even decades before the "descendants" of a radiation-damaged skin cell form cancerous ulcerations.

The direct relations between cancer and infinitesimal amounts of radiation has been particularly well illustrated in leukemia. Studies of Japanese cases show a straight-line relation between dosage and leukemia-induction down to nearly zero. Even as early as 1948, Dr. N. P. Knowlton at Los Alamos had shown that no more than .2 r—one fifth of one roentgen—per week of gamma radiation was sufficient to depress white cell numbers, and even smaller radiation doses produced detectable abnormalities in the lymphocytes as demonstrated by Dr. M. Ingraham II in 1952. Though such abnormalities did not produce immediate ill effects, it was thought that they could well be the forerunners of anemia, leukemia, and other serious or fatal blood diseases. Analyses of leukemia incidence in bomb victims, radiologists, and persons irradiated as treatment for various ailments, made in 1957 by E. B. Lewis of the California Institute of Technology, pointed to a possible threshold *lower* than the amount of radiation we will be exposed to as a result of growing radiation in our environment from the normal operations of nuclear plants and related facilities.

Thus, in the words of Schubert and Lapp:

In the light of recent data provided by the careful examination of patients who have less than the present-day maximum permissible levels of radium in their bones but who nonetheless exhibit bone lesions, we feel that the concept of a threshold for radiation injury is probably wrong. Any radiation produces some biological effect, which would be demonstrated if our methods of assay were sensitive enough to detect it.

One of the most highly regarded experts on environmental cancer is Dr. W. C. Hueper of the National Cancer Institute. In an exhaustive study Dr. Hueper listed the report of carcinomas and sarcomas attributable to radiation of one kind or another, natural and man-made. His concluding sentence is worthy of quotation:

The sum total of the numerous observations on occupational, medicinal and environmental radiation cancers cited, indicates that civilized and industrial mankind has entered an artificial carcinogenic environment, in which exposures to ionizing radiations of various types and numerous sources will play an increasingly important role in the production of cancers.

The connection between radiation and cancer has been brought officially to the attention of the American people and its Government through The President's Commission on Heart Disease, Cancer and Stroke. In Volume II of its Report to the President, February 1965, the Commission stated that "The prevention of cancer at present involves avoidance or removal of known environmental causes of cancer. This includes (1) avoidance of unnecessary and avoidable exposure to ionizing radiation and excessive exposure to ultra-violet radiation. . . ."

Unfortunately, because such visible and palpable agents as cigarette smoke, industrial smoke, chemical insecticides, and the like are more likely to stimulate associations in the public mind with cancer, radiation has largely been overlooked as a key carcinogenic factor. The late Rachel Carson's book *Silent Spring* is widely remembered (though, sadly, also widely ignored) as a study of *chemical* poisons in our environment. A closer reading, however, reveals her equally deep concern with radioactivity. The conclusion of her chapter on environmentally caused cancer deserves citation here:

Today we find our world filled with cancer-producing agents. An attack on cancer that is concentrated wholly or even largely on therapeutic measures (even assuming a "cure" could be found) in Dr. Hueper's opinion will fail because it leaves untouched the great reservoirs of carcinogenic agents which would continue to claim new victims faster than the as yet elusive "cure" could allay the disease. . . .

In one important respect the outlook is more encouraging than the situation regarding infectious disease at the turn of the century. The world was then full of disease germs, as today it is full of carcinogens. But man did not put the germs into the environment and his role in spreading them was involuntary. In contrast, man *has* put the vast majority of carcinogens into the environment, and he can, if he wishes, eliminate many of them. . . .

Shortening of Life:

To what extent radiation shortens human life—and in this context we mean simply premature aging rather than curtailment of life due to some specific radiation effect like cancer—it is difficult to say. Statistical measurement is impossible, both because of the time factor and the innumerable variables involved. But scientists believe that radiation of any amount definitely ages the population so that it dies off from all causes at earlier ages than it otherwise would. They have managed to extrapolate to human values observations made of mice and other experimental subjects, a process which, though subject to some error, can still give us a rough idea of what we can expect for the human condition. Robert S. Stone, in a paper entitled "Maximum Permissible Exposure Standards," stated the following:

> . . . It has been shown with certainty insofar as mice are concerned that exposure to daily doses of X rays of slightly greater than 1 r causes a reduction in lifespan. Boche has shown that the lifespan of the rat is definitely shortened by daily exposures of 0.5 r and probably 0.1 r, the exposures starting at the time of maturity. On the basis of such figures it was felt that for whole-body exposure the permissible dose should not exceed 0.05 r per day. Even this provides a factor of safety of only 2.

Walter R. Guild, assistant professor of biophysics at Yale University, in an essay on "Biological Effects of Radiation," also extrapolated results of life-shortening experiments on mice and surmised that intense single doses of 300-400 r will shorten human life by between four and nine days per roentgen of exposure. What about lesser doses?

"There seems," he concluded, "to be no dose threshold for the life-shortening effect."

Genetic:

Ordinarily a gene, the fundamental unit of heredity located in the chromosomes of cells, is stable. It copies itself unerringly generation after generation. Occasionally, however, it undergoes a spontaneous change, presumably chemical, called a mutation. Then a gene that had hitherto been producing, say, blue eyes suddenly starts producing brown eyes. From then on, all future generations derived from that gene are brown-eyed. Such gross alterations of hereditary characteristics can also result from breakage of chromosomes, the bodies containing genes, and rearrangement of the broken chromosome parts.

Under natural conditions, mutations are exceedingly rare, on the order of one in 100,000 generations. But Muller, in the 1920s, exposing fruit flies to radiation managed to increase the number of hereditary abnormalities in their descendants. Subsequent studies in a wide range of plants and animals have confirmed Muller's discoveries: In every organism examined, it has been observed that high-energy radiation reaching the chromosomes will produce mutations.

The number of mutations has been shown to be directly proportional to the amount of radiation, right down to low levels. The important question is, how low does the level go before we can declare unequivocally that no genetic damage will occur? In 1960 James F. Crow, professor of genetics at the University of Wisconsin School of Medicine and president of the Genetics Society of America, provided the chilling answer:

Geneticists are convinced that there is no threshold for radiation-induced mutations: that is, there is no dose so low that it produces no mutations at all. Each dose, however small, that reaches the germ cells between conception and reproduction carries a risk to future generations proportional to the dose.

What could this mean for the future of mankind? Professor Crow, calculating the possibilities in an article entitled "Radiation and Future Generations," suggested that for every roentgen of slow radiation, the kind of radiation we can expect to receive in increasing doses from peacetime nuclear activity, about five mutations per hundred million genes exposed will manifest themselves, meaning that "after a number of generations of exposure to one roentgen per generation, about one in 8000 of the population in each generation would have severe genetic defects attributable to the radiation."

What are some of the more harmful defects geneticists fear? A few examples are hemophilia, erythroblastosis fetalis (a blood disease of the fetus or newborn child), familial periodic paralysis, nervous and mental diseases, metabolic and allergic disorders, and certain congenital diseases.

A variety of anomalies, many verging on the monstrous, are possible as a result of radioactive damage to the genes. Gigantism, dwarfism, albinism, clubfoot, harelip, cleft palate, Siamese twins, Janus monsters (two faces on a single head and body), phocomelia (rudimentary limbs), sirenomelus (legs fused with no separate feet), hydrocephalus (grotesquely distended head), hermaphroditism (physical bisexuality) may be induced by radioactive bombardment of reproductive cells.

Of course, in the evolutionary process, harmful mutations—and most mutations are decidedly harmful— tend to eliminate the hereditary lines that carry them, because of sterility, disease, and feebleness. But even if this process of natural selection does erase harmful strains, the elimination process itself entails suffering of every imaginable sort, whole heritages of suffering perpetuated from parent to child to grandchild until the last tormented descendant is laid to rest.

That henceforth man must live in constant dread of a

major nuclear accident which will wreak death and harm on a level potentially surpassing Hiroshima and Nagasaki, is unnerving enough, certainly. But we must realize that even if such accidents are averted, the slow, silent saturation of our environment with radioactive poisons will be raising the odds that you or your heirs will fall victim to any one of the horrors depicted here, and possibly to some unexperienced in human history.

CHAPTER IV

Nuclear Roulette

The members of the International Conference on the Peaceful Uses of Atomic Energy, meeting in Geneva in the fall of 1955, found it appropriate to devote four sessions to the subject of reactor safety. One paper in particular gave estimates of the theoretical magnitude of damage resulting from a reactor accident, and out of these conjectures emerged a more formal study of the possible extent of harm and damage should a mishap occur. That study, published by the Atomic Energy Commission in March 1957, was entitled *Theoretical Possibilities and Consequences of Major Accidents in Large Nuclear Plants*.

The study, undertaken by more than forty leading experts in the sciences and engineering specialties— many from Brookhaven National Laboratory, hence the document's familiar name the Brookhaven Report— attempted to answer five vital questions:

1. How likely is a major reactor accident?
2. If one occurs, what are the chances that radioactive material will be released into the environment?
3. What factors and conditions would affect the distribution of that material over public areas?
4. What levels of exposure or contamination would cause injury to people or damage to property?
5. If releases of fission products should occur, what would be the scale of death and injury and the costs to property?

To understand the answers, the meaning of the term

"major reactor accident" should be made clear. Although nuclear reactors use essentially the same fissionable material as atomic bombs, there is nothing in reactor technology comparable to the mechanisms necessary for triggering an atomic explosion. Thus it is technically impossible for a reactor to explode with the force of an atomic warhead.

That fact does not, however, rule out the possibility of an explosion of conventional size. Loss of coolant or failure of various safeguards could cause the melting or vaporization of fuel. The melted or vaporized fuel could react violently with water or air, or could produce sufficient steam to rupture the reactor container. Under certain conditions, sodium, used in liquid form to cool certain reactors, can react violently with air. And as we've seen in the Fermi accident, melted fuel can recongeal to form an explosive "critical mass" in one type of reactor.

The force of such an explosion could not only destroy the reactor and breach the containment structures housing it, but cause failure of secondary or emergency safeguards as well. This combination of failures would make it possible for gaseous or finely pulverized fission products to be released into the atmosphere, where an unfortunate combination of weather conditions could disperse them over surrounding property and population. People and livestock would be killed and injured, crops and real estate rendered temporarily or permanently useless.

In trying to determine what the chances were of such a disaster happening, and what the specific damage would be, the AEC team was faced with an awesome number of factors—variations in design, construction, capacity, location, local conditions, etc. Were we talking about a boiling water reactor of 100,000-kilowatt capacity, located twenty-five miles from a small city, that has a minor accident on a rainy night in a ten-mile wind blowing toward the population center? Or a fast breeder reactor of 500,000-kilowatt capacity, located forty miles from a large city, that has a severe break-down in a hurricane moving away from the population center? And so on.

The combinations were endless, and the experts of the AEC realized that unless they were prepared to issue a report that was all qualifying footnotes, they would have to make some general assumptions.

They therefore hypothesized a typical reactor in a typical location breaking down under typical atmospheric conditions. They presupposed a thermal reactor of 100,000-200,000-kilowatts capacity—that is, one capable of generating a maximum of 100,000-200,000 kilowatts of electricity. This reactor was located near a body of water, probably a river, about thirty miles from a major city of 1,000,000 population.

It was further presupposed that this reactor was nearing the end of its 180-day fuel cycle when the accident occurred. The fuel cycle is the time it takes for radioactive waste products in the reactor core to build up to the point where they interfere with the reactor's efficiency and the fuel load must be replaced. The AEC team estimated that at the end of the 180-day cycle an inventory of 400,000,000 curies* of poisonous material, measured twenty-four hours after the accident, would exist in the reactor core. For comparison's sake it can be pointed out that the amount of only one of the many radioactive isotopes contained in the reactor at that time, strontium 90, would be equal to that produced in the explosion of a 3.8-megaton bomb—a bomb 190 times more powerful than the one dropped on Hiroshima. And, to illustrate the potency of radioactivity, it might be mentioned that one *trillionth* of a

---

*A curie is a standard unit of radioactivity describing the number of atomic fissions taking place per second. One gram (1/28th ounce) of radium transforms thirty-seven billion atoms per second; and that, or its equivalent in some other radioactive element, is a curie. A simple distinction to bear in mind is that curies describe the number of emissions from a radioactive source, while roentgens describe the amount of radiation energy an object *absorbs*.

curie of radon, a gas found in uranium mines, per cubic meter of air is ten times higher than the official maximum permissible dose for miners.

Weather conditions and other factors that might influence the rate and pattern of contaminant distribution were then postulated. It might be dry, for instance, or a gentle rain might be falling. The atmospheric stability might be a typical daytime lapse (meaning the temperature decreases with elevation) with a wind speed of twelve miles per hour; or a typical nighttime "inversion" with a wind speed of seven miles per hour up to fifty meters of height and thirty-five mph above that altitude. In an inversion, the temperature *rises* with elevation, meaning it is colder at ground level than it is above. Heat naturally rises, but in an inversion, gases and particles that would ordinarily rise into the atmosphere are trapped at or near ground level. Inversions are thus a very dangerous form of weather condition in this context, for a cloud of radioactive stuff, instead of soaring high into the sky and dispersing over a large part of the atmosphere, will be held down and spread over sizable portions of land—a smog, in other words, consisting of radioactive rather than conventional pollutants.

The ground rules thus laid out, the team was solicited for estimates of the odds against three types of accident: (1) one which destroyed or seriously damaged the reactor core, but released no fission products outside the reactor vessel; (2) one which released fission products outside the vessel but not outside the building; and (3) one which released them outside the building and the general environment. For our purposes only the third type is pertinent.

Not all of the AEC team members were willing to assign numerical values to the probabilities of such an accident, but the odds given by those who *were* willing were so reassuring that the authors of the Report could state flatly: "The probability of occurrence of publicly hazardous accidents in nuclear power reactor plants is exceedingly low." The odds ranged from one chance in 100,000 to one in a billion per year for each reactor.

Supposing this "incredible" long shot materialized, the team was asked to estimate the worst consequences that could be expected.

The statistics were no less stupefying for being couched in the typically bland language of governmental reports. *As many as 3400 people might be killed, 43,000 injured, and as much as $7 billion of property damage done. People could be killed at distances up to 15 miles and injured as far away as 45. Land contamination could extend for greater distances— indeed, agricultural restrictions might prevail over an area of 150,000 square miles.*

The significance of these figures may be difficult to comprehend even for those who have experienced the ravages of flood or fire, earthquake or war. Certainly, nothing remotely comparable can be cited by way of industrial disasters. The worst one of modern American times was the Texas City catastrophe of April 16, 1947, when a ship loaded with ammonium nitrate fertilizer exploded, virtually leveling the city, killing 468, and causing an estimated $67 million worth of damage. Another major accident occurred in October of the following year, when a five-day smog at Donora, Pennsylvania, resulted in the deaths of twenty persons and the illness of nearly six thousand, some 43 per cent of its population. Yet, awesome though these figures seem, they don't begin to approach the dimensions of death, disability, and damage rendered by a nuclear smog cast over a territory possibly as large as 5 per cent of the continental United States.

The potential for havoc in our hypothetical reactor, then, clearly has no precedent in peacetime commercial enterprise, and indeed few parallels in wartime. It is therefore tranquilizing to remember that the whole thing is merely hypothetical; that the odds against catastrophe are at least 100,000 to 1; and that the experts, in the words of Harold S. Vance, Acting AEC Chairman at the time the Brookhaven Report was submitted to Congress's Joint Committee on Atomic Energy, had to "stretch possibility far out towards its extreme limits" in calculating the chances of a major accident.

Suppose, however, that it could be demonstrated that the chances of mishap were nowhere near as remote as the Brookhaven experts claimed?

Testimony of a number of experts suggests just that.

The Brookhaven team predicated its odds on the increasing difficulty for an accident to progress from rupture of the reactor core to that of the surrounding vessel and then to breaching of the building's containment structure. This approach implies that each of those units functions in virtual independence from the other two. That assumption is not warranted.

The men who design and build reactors have tried to ensure against the kind of interrelationships among components that would create a "house of cards" type of failure. A completely foolproof arrangement of independent systems, however, is exceedingly difficult to construct. We have it on the authority of numerous experts that this notion really has very little substance. Theos J. Thompson, a former chairman of the AEC's Advisory Committee on Reactor Safeguards, and J. G. Beckerley stated in the introduction to Volume I of their book *The Technology of Nuclear Reactor Safety* that chains of dependency among components may be extremely subtle. "In fact," they said, "reactor designers and operators should beware of the label 'independent.' A structure as complex as a reactor and involving as many phenomena is likely to have relatively few completely independent components."

Even granting that it *is* possible to design totally independent components and systems, though, the possibility that several *independent* failures can occur successively within an appreciable period is not negligible. Thompson and Beckerley state in their book that at least three independent causes were involved in almost every reactor accident they had studied to date: a design flaw, a human error, and an instrumentation problem. These and other causes may be operative at the same time in independent areas of the reactor, so that breakdown in one area for one reason and breakdown in another area for another reason might occur coincidentally or as an unexpected result of a third breakdown somewhere else. Thompson and Beckerley have in fact pinpointed thirteen different contributing causes in at least three accidents.

What is more, such successive independent failures can occur within moments, too fast for even automatic equipment to be of any help—so fast, in fact, as to be considered spontaneous. "A typical nuclear runaway accident may start and be over in times appreciably less than a second," stated three highly regarded experts, C. R. McCullough, N. M. Mills, and Edward Teller, in one paper on reactor safety.

A description of some of the problems that beset just one reactor can give a good idea of the numerous and diverse areas in which failure may lurk. Volume I of *Small Nuclear Power Plants,* an AEC publication, describes ten plants, their design, construction, and operating history. One, the Big Rock Nuclear Plant, about three miles northeast of Charlevoix, Michigan, is a relatively small (75,000 kilowatts) reactor ordered by Consumers Power Company in 1959. It generated electricity for the first time late in 1962, but suffered a number of "outages," or interruptions of operation, because of technical problems. Investigations found the following defects in the reactor: (1) vibrations had jostled a number of screws out of their holes, and these had lodged in key moving parts, jamming them; (2) six out of twelve studs holding down an important piece of shielding had failed, and a seventh was severely cracked; (3) control rods were sticking in position; (4) a valve was malfunctioning for no fewer than twelve reasons (and those were just "some of the known causes"); (5) foreign material was lodged in the rods controlling critical chain reactions; and (6) welds on every one of sixteen screws holding two vital components in place were cracked.

Although none of these defects caused an accident, it is not difficult to imagine how failure of one component might lead to failure of some or all of the others.

A profile of a real reactor accident will show how independent difficulties produced a cascading effect which almost ended in catastrophe. As mentioned earlier, on January 3, 1961, three men working inside the containment building of the SL-1, an experimental reactor near Idaho Falls, Idaho, were killed by a blast characterized as a "divergence." According to a reconstruction of the accident published in *Nuclear Engineering* a few months later, the accident was believed to have happened while the men were reconnecting a control rod, which regulates the reactivity of the uranium fuel in the core, to the rod's drive mechanism. Subsequent investigation disclosed that numerous causes had been at work independently or semi-independently.

One was a design flaw: The control rods were designed in such a way that they had to be attached manually to the upper mechanism. In attempting to raise a rod the necessary few inches excessive force had to be applied to overcome stickiness, so that when it finally did become unstuck it jumped. A second design flaw vested excessive reactivity control in the individual rods, so that if only a single one were withdrawn too far the reactor would "go critical."

Another cause was human error, and on a number of levels. The obvious error was that of the operators in pulling the rod out too far, but the supervisory personnel might also be faulted for proceeding with operation knowing that a number of things weren't working properly.

Inadequate instrumentation was another factor. No instrumentation, except for one floor monitor, was in operation at the time of the accident.

A fourth cause was defective equipment: the sticky control rods, for one thing. For another, aluminum casings on cadmium devices used for increasing the margin for shutting down the reactor safely were found to be poorly suited to the heat and corrosiveness of the reactor.

A fifth cause: poor inspection techniques. During the shutdown prior to the accident, the bottom of the reactor vessel should have been inspected for boron, a material which adds substantially to reactivity in the core. It had not been, however.

Acts of God or plain dumb luck can also be independent causative factors in reactor accidents, and could have brought about calamity in the SL-1 far worse than the deaths of three workers. According to an article in the London *Daily Telegraph* of January 6, 1961, at the time of the incident there was an opening in the plant's outer shell for the accommodation of a crane. This opening should have been large enough for a high level of radiation to escape in the event of such a mishap. "It is remarkable," an AEC official told the reporter, "that radiation did not escape in sufficient quantity to form a cloud which could have caused a disaster." "I can only say we were amazed!" the relieved AEC official remarked.

And had the cloud been released during a squall or atmospheric inversion or some other Act of God, that might have been *it* for Idaho Falls and environs.

It should be stressed that not only can *components* be damaged by a violent accident, but *the very safeguards designed to protect those components can be damaged as well*. In the SL-1 accident, emergency cooling systems designed to prevent core meltdown, and the emergency system for injecting material that inhibits reactivity, were themselves rendered completely useless by the violent movement of the reactor, which sheared all connecting lines

Perhaps, theoretically, "redundant" safeguards can be designed and built to plug all loopholes and create truly foolproof independent systems. In reality, however, the complexity and expense of those measures are so high as to threaten defeating the purposes both of people concerned with safety and of people concerned with economics. Representative Craig Hosmer of California, speaking at a congressional hearing, suggested that if designers continue drawing "everything but the kitchen sink on there in order not to have an argument about whether their reactor is safe or not, . . . we are going to accumulate large, unwieldy, and very expensive reactors in which some of the safety features may cancel out twice as many of the other ones and we will have a less safe reactor than we would want to begin with." And in the spring of 1967, an Atomic Industrial Forum task force sent a letter to the AEC expressing similar concern with proliferation of safeguards. *Nucleonics Week* reported the group as taking the position that "carrying engineered safeguards to an extreme is not always in the best interests of safety." The task force went on to bemoan current emphasis on "studying the cause and course of accidents which have only a remote probability of occurrence."

Ironically, then, too many safeguards may be as dangerous as too few. Even if they weren't they'd still be too costly. The paradox seems to indicate that the public may be damned if the industry does proceed with utmost caution, and damned if it does not.

Actually, the whole question of whether reactor components are independent or not becomes irrelevant when matters are examined from another viewpoint. An analogy might help to get the point across.

Suppose we wanted to calculate the odds against a convict escaping from prison. We could first determine how hard it was for him to get out of his cell; then the difficulty of getting out of the cell block; then the difficulty of getting out of the building; then the difficulty of going over the wall. This presumes a sequence of escapes through independent systems, and the odds against a successful series of escapes would be high.

But suppose the prison's boiler exploded, leaving gaping holes in his cell wall, the building wall, and the wall around the prison itself, injuring guards, damaging floodlight and siren systems, and liberating enough prisoners to overcome whatever remaining obstacles confronted them. Under ordinary circumstances, each wall in the escape sequence is independent of the other walls. But *all* of the walls are dependent on the integrity of the boiler. The odds against our convict breaching all walls may be 100,000 to one, but the boiler blast renders the odds meaningless.

To carry the analogy home, utility engineers might design three "independent" systems in such a way that although they all rely on a single electrical power source, they will automatically switch to their own individual generators should that main power source be knocked out of commission by a storm. It sounds good on paper, but could not a flood—brought on, perhaps, by the very storm that knocked out the main power source—swamp the reactor and disable all three auxiliary generators?

The Brookhaven Report pays scant attention to such "incredible" possibilities, yet examples of disasters that successfully bucked all odds come readily to everyone's mind: the sinking of the "unsinkable" *Titanic,* the burning of the "fireproof" Iroquois Theater, the collison of two big airliners over the Grand Canyon. In each instance the odds against the event were fantastically high, and subsequent investigations revealed chains of circumstances so complex and unlikely that one would dismiss them as contrived if they appeared in a work of fiction.

The utility industry itself can point to a prime example: the power failure of November 9, 1965, that blacked out a major portion of the United States' eastern regions. Here was a chain of electric utilities designed to establish independent operation should failure occur in any sector—yet, through a chain of events so incredible that the odds defy calculation, the lights went out anyway. Another example: the New York *Times* recently reported that with all the world beneath it to crash into, an American military jet plunging into the city of Fukuoka, Japan, narrowly missed a nuclear research center.

We know that nature is no respecter of enormously adverse odds. Everyone lives within range of at least one of nature's destructive forces—earthquake, volcano, tidal wave, flood, heat wave, drought, cold wave, hurricane, tornado, electric storm—and every reactor projected for the future will be within range of one as well. But while experience with these phenomena has enabled utility designers to anticipate them in certain areas of the country, and to anticipate their intensity, nature continues to display perverse reluctance to behave in accordance with man's expectations. Scarcely a day passes without a meteorological or geological anomaly: a hottest day here, a coldest month there, a severest hurricane here, an inordinate number of tornadoes there, lakes drying up for the first time in human memory, snow falling where snow has never before been seen, age-old faults in the earth's crust collapsing inexplicably under seismic strain, long-dormant volcanoes relenting without notice to the pressure of magma seething beneath them. Each of these natural disasters can have fatal effects on nuclear reactors.

Consider tornadoes. They are capable of incredible violence; their rotary winds, achieving speeds of three hundred miles per hour or better, can make a deadly missile out of a piece of straw, uproot trees and hurl automobiles effortlessly. The partial vacuum created inside its deadly funnel can make buildings explode, sucking their contents into its vortex and raining debris around the countryside. In 1931 a twister in Minnesota carried an eighty-three-ton railroad coach and its 117 passengers eighty feet through the air.

How well will tomorrow's reactors be constructed to withstand tornadoes? In the wake of disastrous damage done to utilities by twisters in April 1965, Philip

Sporn, one of the electric industry's leading engineer-executives (now retired), was dumfounded. Though known for his farsightedness in all phases of system design, he had to admit that "nothing within a tenth of this severity ever happened before." "The devastation happened because we didn't dream it could ever be that bad," he explained.

The following November—one of the lowest tornado-frequency months of the year—a tornado felled a number of transmission lines a half mile from the Dresden power plant in Illinois. The Dresden is nuclear-powered, and it was probably to this plant that Dr. David Okrent, another former chairman of the Advisory Committee on Reactor Safeguards, was referring when he told a congressional hearing: "We do have on record cases where, for example, an applicant, appearing before an atomic safety and licensing board, stated that a mathematical impossibility had occurred; namely, one tornado took out five separate powerlines to a reactor. If one calculated strictly on the basis of probability, and multiplied the probability for one line five times, you get a very small number indeed, but it happened."

Though usually thought of as indigenous to the western and mid-western United States, tornadoes have occurred on the average of twice a year in New York State, six times in Pennsylvania, four in Maine, five in Massachusetts, and once a year each in Connecticut, New Jersey, and Delaware, between 1953 and 1965. Has the possibility of tornado damage in these areas been given serious consideration?

Around the same time that a tornado was shearing the Dresden reactor's lines, operating and maintenance crews in Minnesota were frantically sandbagging the area around the Black Dog power station, threatened by the rising Mississippi River. While a flood is devastating enough to conventional utility plants like Black Dog, necessitating the dismantling and drying out of just about every component that gets wet, the damage to a nuclear station could be incalculably worse, not only in the harm done to the delicate components, but in the potential harm resulting from contamination of flood waters with radioactivity. All power plants are going up on one body of water or another; are they designed to withstand floods? Appearing on television after the great power blackout of 1965, Otto Manz, executive vice-president of New York's Con Edison, told of a harrowing experience:

> I mentioned earlier to you gentlemen, . . . I worked in Oak Ridge for Carbide and Carbon Chemicals Corporation and I ran the electrical system down there, and one of the things I was told was don't ever let that plant stop because you might collect a critical mass of uranium hexafluoride in the cascade. . . . And one day the bottom of the Clinch River came up and cut off all our cooling water, and the plant shut down, and that's the only other time my heart was in my mouth 'cause I kept expecting to hear a big atomic explosion. But thank God it never happened.

One of the most serious concerns of critics of atomic power is earthquakes, and thereby hangs one of the most incredible tales in the annals of the nuclear industry.

In 1961 Pacific Gas and Electric Company announced plans to build a nuclear power plant fifty miles north of San Francisco on Bodega Head, the first of five reactors on the 225 acres it had purchased for the purpose. A group of about a dozen citizens banded together to oppose it, at first simply on the grounds that land use and conservation would not be well served by the destruction of scenic Bodega Head. PG&E went ahead with its excavations anyway, in anticipation of the AEC construction license.

Because many conservation groups are simply no financial match for powerful utility companies, PG&E didn't anticipate much resistance from the Northern California Association to Preserve Bodega Head and Harbor. But the group wouldn't quit, appearing at

County Commission hearings, before the State Utilities Commission, and finally before the State Supreme Court. As it progressed, the movement attracted some well-informed consultants and prominent legal talents, so that by the time AEC hearings were scheduled, a formidable party of two thousand indignant, knowledgeable individuals had rolled up its sleeves and dug in for a fight. More importantly, by that time the original conservation arguments had given way to a far more serious allegation: that Bodega Head #1 was going up smack-dab on top of one of the largest and most unpredictable earthquake zones on earth, the San Andreas Fault.

This famous fault extends from north of Bodega Bay almost to the Mexican border, and is part of a larger system of instabilities known as the Circum-Pacific earthquake belt, on which the western coast of South America, the eastern coast of Asia, and the islands of the Pacific including Japan are located. Smaller faults parallel to the San Andreas pass through Bodega Head as well. Large earthquakes occurred in the fault area and San Francisco region in 1838, 1857, and 1906, the last being *the* San Francisco earthquake. That quake affected Point Reyes, some fifty miles north of San Francisco, and only a few miles from Bodega Head. With each quake the fault has moved between thirteen and twenty-six feet.

The AEC's Reactor Siting Criteria stated explicitly that "No facility should be located closer than one-fourth mile from the surface location of a known active earthquake fault." Yet the reactor was going up 1000 feet from the edge of the San Andreas, about 320 feet shy of a quarter of a mile.

According to a report by Lindsay Mattison and Richard Daly in the April 1964 issue of *Nuclear Information,* the citizens called in Dr. Pierre Saint-Armand, a professional seismologist from the Naval Ordnance Test Station at China Lake, California. After studying the excavation he reported two crucial findings.

First, the reactor site lay in an area where great strain accumulates in the geologic formations. Here exceptionally high earthquake intensities develop when the material finally breaks, producing the quake movement or "fling." He even suggested that a great earthquake could be expected within the lifetime of the reactor, a view which has since been confirmed by a number of authorities. In such an event the site would "probably undergo some three or four meters permanent horizontal displacement."

Second, Saint-Armand found that the reactor was being built, in effect, on sand. After describing the ways in which the foundation material of crushed rock and alluvium would shift or transmit shock waves, resulting in serious damage to the reactor, its cooling system and supporting structures, Saint-Armand concluded: "A worse foundation situation would be difficult to envision."

Interestingly, the consultants hired by PG&E itself differed little with Saint-Armand. "It is surprising," the latter said, "in view of the expert advice given by [the utility's advisers] that another site was not chosen and that construction has gone ahead." It becomes less surprising, however, when one realizes that PG&E had already sunk some four million dollars into the morass under the future Bodega Head #1.

Borings taken by the company's consultants showed almost sixty feet of silt, clay, and sand, and one of these experts, Dr. Don Tocher, recommended that if further studies supported this conclusion, "then serious consideration should be given to resiting the reactor in a location where the quartz-diorite bedrock lies at a depth shallow enough that there can be no possibility of wall failure from seismic forces acting on the sands and clay."

PG&E declared it had designed the Bodega Head structure to resist the severest shocks recorded or estimated in California. However, resistance to shock is not the same thing as resistance to lateral or vertical movement of the ground as a result of slippage in the fault. PG&E stated that its multiple safeguards satisfied the condition that a reactor be designed to withstand the "maximum credible operating accident." Yet in its hazards report, no consideration was given to the possibility that the huge shear forces generated in an earthquake could breach *all* containment structures. The company justified this exclusion by claiming that no slippage in that part of the fault had occurred for thousands of years, at least according to their evidence.

The AEC decided to bring in a couple of members of the U. S. Geological Survey, who said (a) the rock in that area could have slipped in recent geologic time, but left no evidence of the shear; and (b) whatever had happened in the past had no bearing on what could be surmised to happen in the future: "If in some future earthquake surface rupture comparable in severity to that produced in 1906 occurs on the San Andreas Fault, the near surface granitic rock of Bodega Head would be expected to rupture," and "displacement on the order of a few feet, either horizontally or vertically, should be anticipated."

If the AEC was praying for guidance in determining the validity of PG&E's application, its prayers were heeded on Good Friday, March 27, 1964, when a severe earthquake ripped Alaska, killing 114 and casting tidal waves into the Pacific. The Alaskan fault was part of the same system as the one on which Bodega Head #1 was to rest.

Four days later, PG&E filed an amendment to its hazards report which proposed a building structure surrounded by a layer of compressible material, allowing for movements up to two feet without critical damage, "even though the possibility of such movement occurring is not considered to be credible." Seven months later, when the excavation turned up a secondary earthquake fault, the Bodega Head plans were dropped.

The AEC has since seen fit to take a firmer hand with schemes for reactors in fault zones. Recently it sent the plans for the Malibu, California, Plant #1 back to the drawing board for supplementary provision for ground displacements due to earthquake activity: Malibu #1 was also found to be situated squarely over faulted rock. On the other hand, the AEC did decide to leave in operation the Humboldt Bay reactor, a 68,-500-kilowatt nuclear plant started up in 1963. Humboldt Bay is a little up the coast from San Francisco, but since the reactor doesn't sit *squarely* on any earthquake fault—at least not on any we know of—that one has been permitted to go on.

Only *since* the Alaska quake has the AEC promoted the sort of formal geological study necessary to develop conclusive criteria for building reactors on or near sites of known seismological activity. In its *Fundamental Nuclear Energy Research 1967* the AEC asserted: "A *prior* knowledge of areas in which geologic-seismologic problems exist *will* facilitate the selection of safe reactor sites. Experience has shown that knowledge of the regional geologic environment is particularly important in areas of high seismicity, such as California, because the earthquake potential of faults and other zones of earth deformation cannot always be determined from investigations in small areas." (Emphasis ours.)

This view was strongly reinforced by a report issued at the end of 1968 by the Federal Council for Science and Technology. On December 30 a special group from the council, headed by William T. Pecora, director of the United States Geological Survey, stated that only 18 per cent of the country had sufficiently detailed geological mapping to give more than the most rudimentary idea of local earthquake hazards. Asserting that experience in this country had given a misleadingly mild picture of earthquake potency, the group recommended a ten-year research program to assess earthquake hazards and set up guidelines for construction policies so that those hazards would be minimized where quakes were likeliest. Referring to the San Francisco earthquake, the report said: "If such an earthquake were to occur in or near a densely populated modern urban area today, the total losses would be measured in many billions of dollars and hundreds, perhaps thousands of lives." The newspaper article describing the council's report does not mention the additional toll that might result from complications following radioactive releases from a quake-damaged reactor.

Warnings such as the foregoing only emphasize the tremulous foundation of seismological knowledge on which tomorrow's reactors are being sited, but other reactor-related sciences rest on equally shaky ground. Indeed, one may read, mingled among the Brookhaven Report's projections of death and destruction, the following admissions—and these are direct quotes:

> The cumulative effect of radiation on physical and chemical properties of materials, after long periods of time, is largely unknown.
> Various metals used in reactors such as uranium, aluminum, zirconium, sodium and beryllium, under certain conditions not at present clearly understood, may react explosively with water, also present in many reactors.

> Much remains to be learned about the characteristics and behavior of nuclear systems.

> The criteria used in establishing [ranges of potential loss due to land contamination and evacuation of personnel] are based on meager data.

> It seems reasonable to assume that the gaseous elements, halogens and the noble gases, would also escape quantitatively although no determination was made [in a certain experiment]. Unfortunately, such data are not available for the corrosion of more typical reactor fuels such as uranium-zirconium alloy at more realistic temperatures. . . .

> It will be clear that the conclusions reached can be little more than educated guesses, since the direct effects

on humans of exposures of this character are largely unknown. Similarly, setting definite limits on acceptable
contamination levels for land to be used in agriculture is
risky because of the incomplete state of present knowledge of the soil-plant-animal-human relationships involved.

Comparatively little is known about the problems involved in living in an environment heavily contaminated
by radioactive material.

Exceedingly little is known about the details of atmospheric distribution. . . .

It is important to recognize that the magnitudes of
many of the crucial factors in this study are not quantitatively established, either by theoretical and experimental data or adequate experience.

While it can be argued that these disclaimers were
written in 1957, a glance at any current report by the
AEC on fundamental research will disabuse skeptics of
illusions that all the problems of 1957 have been
solved, or that many new ones have not cropped up
since. Furthermore, it must be remembered that solutions found in the next four or five years will come too
late to serve reactors built during this period, or will be
inapplicable without extensive dismantling. The utility
industry is already complaining volubly about the high
cost of "backfitting" new components and safeguards to
bring reactors up to date and in line with constantly
shifting standards.

One need not be an expert to realize that the whole
premise on which the AEC based its findings is essentially meaningless—namely, that generalized conditions
or an "average reactor" or a "typical accident" can be
formulated. Every reactor has inherent nuclear, chemical, metallurgical, physical, and mechanical characteristics that do not precisely correspond to any other. Each
is located at a different distance from a population

center, and each population center differs in layout and density from every other. Each stands on a site possessing distinctive hydrological, meteorological, and seismological traits. Each plant is governed by regulations unique to its own situation, and these are administered and executed by men whose capabilities differ.

The AEC, in short, had to construct the Report on a foundation of assumptions having very little correlation with the billions upon billions of specific realities of reactor operations. But while such a statement could be made of any industrial report, such a technique in the evaluation of hazards as great as those of the atomic industry leads to extremely dangerous oversimplifications. The impression one gets from the Brookhaven Report is that a high degree of standardization exists throughout the nuclear utility industry, which in turn suggests strict uniformity of operation, codification of regulations, and intensive quality control. If the AEC can assert that the chances of a major accident in its hypothetical reactor are on the order of 100,000 to 1, the public might complacently be led to believe that the same odds hold true of the reactor being built up the river.

The oversimplification of the Report constitutes the primary fiction from which many myths about safe nuclear power plants have sprung, and the point which cries out for explicit statement in the Brookhaven Report is that every reactor constructed tomorrow will be in some sense an experiment—not a stereotype but a prototype. The soundness of individual processes and techniques going into it may have been established in experiments or in other commercial reactors, or presumed from mathematical calculations. How sound they will be in a new combination can only be determined by putting them together in a commercial power plant and trying it out on the public. Such experience is usually gained at the cost of many mistakes, however, and the public must decide whether the magnitude of potential consequences is worth the knowledge acquired. "Every reactor that has been operated to date, unless it has had at least one almost exact prototype, ... has demonstrated some small differences from expected behavior," Dr. Theos Thompson told a congressional group. "Almost always these have not been important, but they seem to indicate that one should be very careful in locating a first of its kind (or size) reactor in a place where engineered safety is used exclusively."

That man does not understand many principles and forces in nature is not to his discredit. That he has built empires in the teeth of his incomplete understanding is to his glory. But that he is gambling with this ignorance and uncertainty, and the fragile yet lethal technology he has woven out of them, against the *terribilità* of nature and the capriciousness of fate—*this* may very well be to his everlasting sorrow.

CHAPTER V

The Lesson of the Thresher

It should be clear by now that safe, successful reactors will require the whole level of industrial workmanship, engineering, inspection, and quality control to be raised well above conventional levels. Even if safety were not a factor, common business sense recognizes that the plant that fails does not earn.

Whatever common sense recognizes, however, industrial management has fallen far short of the standard demanded of men, material, and machinery by this new phenomenon. Routine manufacturing and engineering practices prevail despite the awareness, and the experience, that such practices are utterly inadequate. The absence of an effective regulatory system, furthermore, has permitted those practices to prevail, and continuing disintegration of regulatory policy portends grave consequences if atomic power carries out its blueprint for the coming decade.

The nuclear power industry is a business, and the business of business is profit. While infinitely more sophisticated than the garment, auto, or meat-packing industries, the atomic industry is no more exempt than they from the pressures that force compromise for the sake of satisfying stockholders and customers. That such lapses, where such deadly forces are concerned, can be the forerunners of catastrophe seems to have registered with shockingly little force on government and industry, perhaps because no single individual is able to step far enough away to see how his own unimportant-seeming compromise may be the critical link in a chain of disaster.

In the electrical utility industry, the pressure begins with the consumer: His electricity needs must be satisfied. Because our population is expanding, and per capita use of electricity increasing too, demand for electric power in the United States is doubling every ten years.

The consumer's pressure is directed at the suppliers of electricity, the utilities, who must keep up with demand. If they fail, they pay three different penalties: (1) public criticism for betraying their commitment to consumer service; (2) stockholder action for losing money, or failing to take advantage of profitable opportunities; and (3) Government intervention, because unfilled electricity demand leads to overloaded circuits and large-scale power failures. The choice of power plant type to fill the demand—coal-fired, hydroelectric, nuclear, etc.—depends on many factors, but the overriding one is invariably economic: How can power be provided cheaply enough to satisfy consumers, yet profitably enough to satisfy stockholders?

Whichever form they choose, the utilities must make many steep commitments and investments: Construction and operating licenses must be obtained, land and right of way for plant and transmission lines secured, the community's power network prepared for the forthcoming delivery of electricity, designers and builders engaged, material and components ordered, etc. All such commitments revolve around a deadline, forcing utilities to exact deadline commitments in turn from local, state, or Federal licensing agencies, designers, manufacturers, and subcontractors.

In these ways, pressures originating with the consumer radiate through government and industry. Even from this thumbnail sketch it should be obvious that those pressures are incredibly complex and heavy. The opportunities for cutting corners are almost infinite, and when the pressure gets intense, resistance to temptation may drop. This is not to suggest that anyone in the nuclear power industry would set out to commit fraud or deliberately produce inferior work—though occasional instances of criminal or grossly negligent behavior in the utility field are by no means unknown. But it *is* to suggest that all too often, considerations of quality, service, and safety succumb to seemingly more urgent ones of delivery dates and profit margins. Even highly responsible executives, and companies with proud records of reliability, can give way under the frequently merciless pressures exerted in the business world.

In addition to those strains which the nuclear power industry shares with other industries, it is subject to some uniquely its own, arising out of our Government's avowed policy to make nuclear-generated electricity competitive with that produced by coal. We have portrayed how eagerly the Government has pursued this goal, and how heavily it has pressed industry to achieve it.

The trouble is that *under existing technology, a truly competitive atomic power industry is impossible— unless safety margins are reduced.*

By extending the analogy between reactors and prisons used in the previous chapter, the truth of these assertions can be seen more easily. An architect confronted by a state agency with orders for a prison that is at once escape-proof *and* economical might discover that these values were in conflict; add to that a short deadline, with financial penalties if construction did not meet timetables, and the pressures for corner-cutting might prove irresistible. By substituting thin bars for thick ones on cell windows and doors, brick for granite on walls, low-grade steel for better-grade on exit doors, etc., he can meet the state's deadline with only—to him—minor changes in the specifications. It may cross his mind that such compromises may one day make it easier for a prisoner to escape, but that abstract consideration flees before the state's unrelenting insistence that the building be occupied on the date agreed on.

The architect may not be the only person who compromises: A subcontractor may forge cell bars out of lower-grade metal than was called for in the specifications, or a state inspector may carelessly overlook construction flaws. Obviously, the odds against escape, which probably look high on paper, have been lowered immeasurably by compromises in design, poor material, unsatisfactory workmanship, and inadequate inspection. It can be imagined that with a few more ingredients—an incompetent guard at the cell block door, failure of the electrical system activating the building's alarm system, etc.—a determined prisoner just might make it to freedom.

Knowing these things, would you, living a quarter of a mile away from this prison, rest easily at night?

The same thought might have gnawed on the mind of an observer had he attended proceedings held on March 15, 1967, in Room AE-1 in the Capitol Building in Washington, D.C. Here, a little after 10 A.M., the Joint Committee on Atomic Energy convened, the Hon. Chet Holifield, Representative from California, presiding. Testifying before the seven members present was Milton Shaw, director of the AEC's Division of Reactor Development and Technology. The committee had been in session since January 25, conducting hearings on the AEC's authorization bill for the fiscal year 1968.

Shaw had just brought out that EBR-2, the experimental breeder reactor on which, since the Fermi plant failure, all of the Government's breeder hopes now rested, had recently suffered an unexpected setback. On March 2, 1967, copper deposits were found in the primary sodium system. This is how Shaw explained it:

MR. SHAW: We think we have found that the prime source of the copper is from the electrodes of an electromagnetic pump. It appears a total of perhaps 11 or 12 pounds of copper has been introduced into the sodium system. We must take steps to prevent further introduction of copper into the system. This, again, may be a problem with quality assurance. I understand that these electrodes should have been plated with a material that is not corrosive in the sodium environment. Nevertheless, they weren't plated properly. We are taking them out now and we will probably either plate them and put them back, or replace them.

REP. HOLIFIELD: Was that a fault of design? Knowing the tremendously corrosive properties of sodium, it seems to me that should have been done as a matter of routine.

MR. SHAW: Mr. Holifield, I think this is probably the most serious type of problem we face in the whole reactor business. There is so much information we have, so much we know that is not being applied, it is heartbreaking.

REP. HOLIFIELD: This was built by the Government, was it not?

MR. SHAW: Yes, sir, but this is both a Government and industry problem.

REP. HOLIFIELD: We had access to this knowledge. Why didn't the engineers in charge of the actual fabrication of this EBR-2 apply the things we know? We can understand why short-cuts might be made in the industry from the standpoint of saving money or from the standpoint of less background knowledge than we have in our in-house capability.

MR. SHAW: Mr. Holifield, I think the environment that has existed too frequently places emphasis on "We must rush through because we are going to miss something if we don't do this job quickly." We keep thinking we can get by whenever a problem develops without correcting the deficiency. Too frequently we find that something wasn't done, such as not taking the radiographs [X ray or similar photographs of components for the purpose of detecting faults], or the radiographs that were taken aren't clear. And the decision is made to move ahead, anyway.

Now these kinds of decisions are made on a very low level, in a sense, even though management may be aware of it, or management may not be. It is very clear that too many problems we are encountering across-the-board are due to not having written procedures or to people failing to follow written procedures.

It can be classified as a difference between a disciplined approach and an undisciplined approach to getting complex jobs accomplished. I believe we have paid a tremendous price for what I classify as an undisciplined approach in our reactor business. . . . I think this point is very important, Mr. Holifield. We must do a better job to exert this kind of discipline in our AEC projects, whether they are built by laboratory or industrial groups.

Shaw also described alarmingly hazardous inspection procedures. Illustrating these with the case of another experimental reactor, the Advanced Test Reactor, even the AEC representative spoke with something approaching indignation:

The ATR situation is deplorable. I say deplorable because the purpose of the ATR is to provide a test reactor for fuel. We can't even get the parts of the plant together long enough to get it tested properly. Of course, we had a strike out there which did hurt some. But the fact remains that too many of the components weren't built right in the first place. Because of the strike—we took the time to reexamine a number of the components to attempt to correct as many problems as we could during the strike period. We found that the people who apparently inspected and certified suitability of many of the components must have been blind.

Apparently, the inspectors were employees of the companies that made the components and were not obliged to report to the AEC; the contractor, in other words, was free to inspect and pass on his own item without responsibility to the regulatory authority. Asked by Representative Holifield whether the AEC had any system for inspecting such items after they are fabricated and certified by industrial contractors, Shaw had to admit "We do not have such a system set up in our reactor program right now. . . ." Apparently, quality control and inspection is often a matter of "understandings" and "assumptions" rather than stringent guidelines and forceful regulation. As a result, Shaw stated, "we get into the argument as to 'who is responsible for the malfunction of the valve,' or 'why didn't we tell the designer that the valve had to withstand vibration?' 'Show me the piece of paper that said the valve had to withstand vibration.' The piece of paper does not exist in the manufacturer's hands or in his contract," Shaw declared, "even though the understanding of the need clearly existed between ourselves and our laboratory, or between ourselves and our prime contractor."

Having few standards or strict regulatory procedures to heel to, some firms apparently feel free to cut corners. The extent to which this is done in an industry where whole populations depend on *square* corners is profoundly distressing, as this passage from Shaw's testimony demonstrates:

Let us remember that the reactor manufacturer has the option to change material and quality assurance procedures any time he wants to on the nuclear plant he is proposing to build for the utilities. His incentive may well be economic. Some of the problems are introduced into our development programs because of this flexibility. The lead-times associated with many of these safety programs may be 4, 5, or 6 years. Thus as we proceed down the road to develop the research and development information and get an understanding of the failure mechanism, the reactor manufacturers may decide not to use this [improved] material, or, worse yet, even though the reactor manufacturers decided to use the material, we know of cases where the subcontractor making the pipe decided that the specified material was too expensive, or not readily available, and substituted some other material. This is how the problems and the controversies start developing.

As well, Shaw might have added, as the calamities.

Inserted in the record of these hearings was a summary statement of the AEC's participation in the development of criteria, standards, and codes. This document is most disturbing in its revelation of the scant progress made in formulation of these vital standards. Reading it, one gets the sinking feeling that the reactors built to date do not reflect the application of many clear-cut guidelines, and those being built will not reflect many more. In one key passage, for example, the Commission tells us that the Nuclear Standards Board of the newly established U. S. A. Standards Institute has taken a number of steps to reactivate the nuclear standards program of the technical societies and trade associations. But "although these actions are expected to yield much increased emphasis to the development of commercial nuclear standards in the future," says the report, "the efforts are just getting underway."

To illustrate the magnitude of the standards problem, and the paucity of progress in that area, the AEC statement declared that *out of 2800 to 5000 standards necessary for a typical reactor power plant* in the areas of materials and testing, design, electrical gear and instrumentation, plant equipment and processes— *only about 100 recognized reactor standards had been approved as of March 1967!*

The transcript of these hearings is replete with statements by Shaw of the most alarming nature conceivable. Here is a handful:

. . . we know a safe and reliable fuel can be designed for the water reactor plants, if one doesn't extrapolate too far. However, there is no question but that the fuel warranties being provided right now far exceed the meaningful information which is available to us through the research and development programs.

Abundant concrete examples show that because of past failures to identify and invoke minimum engineering standards, neither the results of research and development programs, nor design and construction capabilities are being utilized as effectively as they should be.

The price must be paid—sooner or later. Example after example can be cited where failures of equipment have had to be corrected at great cost and time delays after a plant is built and operating.

. . . It is of deep concern when basic and important research and development objectives of the Commission's and industry's programs are not being realized in a predictable manner after costly investments because of insufficient engineering attention.

When a technological program comes a cropper, the technical problems invariably turn out to be reflections of deep defects in the agency that runs things. Obviously, the failures noted here are products of an agency whose goal of promoting atomic energy has overpowered considerations of caution. Further along in this book, the structure and policies of the Atomic Energy Commission will be examined in depth, but a glimpse at this point of some of the Commission's values may help us see how organizational flaws and technical ones correspond to one another.

David Lilienthal, in a *McCall's* article, "When the Atom Moves Next Door," described a bureaucracy as "any organization, private or public, primarily concerned with what happens to *it*." He was referring specifically to the Atomic Energy Commission. An early expression of this inverted value system was the AEC's formation, in the 1950s, of goal-oriented, deadline-controlled "plans" such as the Power Demonstration programs, the five-year achievement program of 1953, and the ten-year plan initiated at the end of the decade. While such undertakings are undoubtedly valuable for the way in which they systematize ends and spur efficiency, they also tend to focus attention on crossing the finish line on time, rather than crossing it with all components intact. Traditionally, the order of scientific progress has been (a) basic investigation; (b) technological application of the knowledge acquired; and (c) social use of the technological innovations. *The Integrity of Science,* a booklet published in 1965 by the American Association for the Advancement of Science, criticized the space program for commiting itself to particular technological achievements, even as to the date of accomplishment, "in advance of the orderly acquisition of the related basic knowledge." The identical reversal of priorities applies to the atomic power program.

In short, such "plans" and "programs" stress success instead of safety. When success finally comes, as it did when the AEC pump at last brought forth a flood of plant orders in 1966 and 1967, the regulatory agency may be unprepared to handle it. This is true of the Atomic Energy Commission. So geared to promotion was the Commission that its atrophied regulatory processes were incapable of dealing with applications in an orderly fashion. The backlog of unprocessed applications mounted rapidly. In 1965, one construction permit was issued out of six applications reviewed; in 1966, five permits were issued out of twenty applications reviewed; in 1967, fourteen permits were issued, but thirty-one remained unreviewed by year's end. The AEC, it seems, found itself in the position of the old oil prospector who at last strikes a gusher but realizes he forgot to bring barrels.

The Commission finally had to admit, in the midst of the deluge, that its licensing staff was not keeping up with applications, and new manpower was not going to be easy to come by. An "intensive recruitment effort" had been initiated, it was brought out at 1967 hearings, but the prospects were dim because qualified personnel were taking jobs with the equipment manufacturers and utilities, where the pay scale is higher.

As in any other commercial enterprise, there were only so many directions in which AEC "management" could move to accommodate its staff shortage. The proper one, one would think, would be to observe its statutory obligation to care and painstaking scrutiny and let the backlog pile up, placing caution above all other considerations in much the same way that flight traffic controllers did at some airports in 1968 when they called a slowdown to combat hazardous conditions in crowded air lanes. For obvious reasons, such a course was impossible for the Atomic Energy Commission.

The alternative was to streamline administrative and review procedures. There are inevitably loosely organized systems in any organization that can stand tightening up without suffering harm in quality. Unfortunately, the process in the case of the AEC goes far beyond the mere tightening up of systems; it actually streamlines caution out of the picture almost entirely, resulting in an unspoken, unwritten, but pervasive policy of corner-cutting which cannot help but dominate the behavior of everyone involved in the atomic energy program. In an interview published in the April 1967 issue of *Nucleonics,* for instance, Robert E. Hollingsworth, general manager of the Atomic Energy Commission and chief administrator of the seven-thousand-odd people who work for it, said: "I don't care for paperwork, and I make no bones about it. You can get a lot more done if you can get someone to boil down the issue and tell you orally what it's about. I've probably reduced the paperwork which has been coming into this office somewhere between 80 and 90%, and it's still too much. I work on the basis of their meeting with me or calling on the telephone. I'm hopeful that they are already taking action and just calling to inform me. I'm counting on them to keep as much paperwork from me as they can."

Hollingsworth boasted that his emphasis on action has paid off. "I think everyone around here knows that I won't put up with things getting bogged down," he declared. "We've speeded up everything—decisions, getting papers ready, taking actions, getting programs to move. This has been a speeding up of doing our business. We're going at a pretty fast clip now, and I intend to keep it that way."

Needless to say, it is essential that a Government agency be run with a firm hand, but is there not a serious danger, in an administration apparently preoccupied with the threat of paperwork, of confusing genuinely cautious deliberation with bureaucratic delay? Could not the pressures to increase productivity cause staff members to act hastily on crucial matters in order to keep paperwork off their backs? The answers are apparent in the congressional testimony that has been presented here.

The fact is that bureaucracies tend to order their values around paperwork rather than the functions and services the paperwork represents. Over a period of time, the administrators tend to lose touch with the nuts and bolts of their agency's operation. Paperwork has a tendency to make things look routine, and problems intellectual. The gravity of matters under the Commission's aegis has tended to lose weight as the novelty of atomic power wears off and the day-to-day drag of attending to paper problems becomes a dominant factor in the agency's attitudes and activities. A number of critics have pointed out how this kind of familiarity breeds a most hazardous contempt. David Lilienthal has expressed great alarm at the "downgrading of a great scientific discovery to 'just another government activity' run by 'just another' bureaucracy." Congressman Leonard Farbstein, in a speech in 1965 introducing a bill to make utilities and manufacturers more financially responsible for accident damages, said: "In the push for low-cost power, there is inherent a desire to save costs by placing atomic power plants near the center of power consumption and by reducing the cost of safety devices. I feel certain no utility would bow to such economic pressures at this stage of the development of atomic power. I do fear, however, that there may be a tendency to become complacent as the years go by, and I think the public is entitled to the protection which is inherent in some degree of financial responsibility for negligence." (The bill was unsuccessful, incidentally.)

Even AEC's Milton Shaw wistfully discussed this loss of intimate involvement:

> When the nuclear power program was in its infancy we had the personal involvement of many good top management people on one or two jobs at one time. During the Shippingport design and construction days, for example, we were at Pittsburgh about every week. Yet even then, . . . we felt we had to have the written and approved standards and specifications to make sure the job was done as required. Now there are many plants committed in many sections of the country. No matter how many good people are assigned to these jobs, they still won't get comparable management attention.

Equally disturbing are the occasions on which the Commission has denied, or sought to divest itself of, responsibility. One of the virtues of a bureaucracy, at least from its own viewpoint, is the way in which it disperses and obscures responsibility, both by delegating it down the chain of command until it vaporizes, and by leaving questions of jurisdiction open so that they can be shuffled up to industry or public or to other Government agencies when trouble arises.

The AEC has made it clear that the ultimate safety of nuclear power plants rests with reactor manufacturers and utilities operating such plants. ". . . we must reemphasize that the primary responsibility for safety must rest with the industry," said AEC Commissioner Ramey before the Joint Committee in 1967. And the

Advisory Committee on Reactor Safeguards has stated: "The ACRS believes that it is the reactor owner and operator who bears the ultimate responsibility for public safety and that he should satisfy himself fully in this respect." In pages to come the reader will see other instances of this sloughing off of responsibility, such as the AEC's referral to the Defense Department of questions of security against reactor sabotage, and to the Department of the Interior on matters of thermal pollution.

It can be seen clearly, then, that the lack of clear-cut standards and criteria in the atomic power industry, and the technical failures that result, are due to the bureaucratization of the Atomic Energy Commission. Former AEC Commissioner T. E. Murray spotlighted the issue when he wrote:

When we come right down to it, it is not easy to say precisely who makes atomic energy policy in the United States or how it is made. If one were to try to trace the making of a basic nuclear policy decision, he would have to go through a tortuous maze of governmental agencies that initiate or suggest policies, draft position papers on proposed policies, advise, dilute, compromise, and modify policy proposals. He would probably get lost or give up before he had completed his quest through the State Department, the Department of Defense, the Joint Committee, the National Security Council, the Operations Coordinating Board, the President's special staff assistants on scientific affairs, disarmament, and other matters, and the Atomic Energy Commission itself.

Vice-Admiral Hyman Rickover, Director of the AEC's Division of Naval Reactors, has wisely said "Unless you can point your finger at the man who was responsible when something goes wrong, then you have never had anyone really responsible." The disintegration of AEC control over the safety of the atomic power program can be illustrated most forcefully by simply asking: If something seriously went wrong with an atomic reactor, causing an accident of the magnitude we have been talking about—who would answer for it?

The answers may be gathered by considering the tragedy of the nuclear submarine USS *Thresher*, which while undergoing a deep test dive some two hundred miles off the Cape Cod coast in April 1963, went down with 112 naval personnel and 17 civilians and never came up again.

The previous October, Admiral Rickover gave a speech before the 44th Annual National Metal Congress in New York City. His prophetic statements are worth quoting at length because of their obvious and dismal parallels with commercial nuclear reactor technology:

Too often management is satisfied to sit in plush offices, far removed physically and mentally from the design and manufacturing areas, relying on paper reports for information about the status of design and production in the plant itself—the real center of the enterprise. This lack of firsthand evaluation results in poorly designed and manufactured equipment, late delivery, or both. During the past few years, hundreds of major conventional components, such as pressure vessels and steam generators, have been procured for naval nuclear propulsion plants. Less than 10 per cent have been delivered on time. Thirty per cent were delivered 6 months to a year or more later than promised. Even so, reinspection of these components after delivery showed that over 50 per cent of them had to be further reworked in order to meet contract specification requirements.

We have tried to improve matters by sending representatives of the naval reactors group to manufacturers' plants to make on-the-spot checks of engineering and production progress. Often our men discover extremely unsatisfactory conditions of which management is unaware. The usual management reaction is to disbelieve the facts submitted to them. Corrective action is therefore often taken too late. The most prevalent inadequacy found in our audits is failure to recognize that timely production of high-quality components requires almost infinite capacity for painstaking care and attention to detail by all elements of the organization, both management and non-management; this is as true for a so-called conventional "old line" product as for a new one. . . .

Time and again I have found that management is reluctant to depart from outdated practices; that it is not informed of what is actually going on in the plant; that it fails to provide the informed and strong leadership necessary to bring about improvements in engineering and production. It is not well enough understood that conventional components of advanced systems must necessarily meet higher standards. Yet it should be obvious that failures that would be trivial if they occurred in a conventional application will have serious consequences in a nuclear plant because here radioactivity is involved. Even in the non-nuclear parts of our plants we must have full reliability if the great endurance of nuclear power is to be realized. . . .

Rickover then took up specific instances of defects and malfunctions:

There have been many problems in material identification and control. Recently a reactor component failed to function properly. The plant had to be shut down for several weeks in order to remove this component, determine the cause of failure, and correct it—at considerable expense. We finally traced the cause of failure to the use of the wrong material in a small pin. The material actually used was not as hard as the material specified. . . .

Recently we discovered that a stainless steel fitting had been welded into a nickel-copper alloy piping system. The fitting had been certified by the manufacturer as nickel-copper, and had all the required certification data including chemistry and inspection results. In fact, the words "nickel-copper" were actually etched in the fitting. Yet it was the wrong material. The system was intended for sea water service; had it been placed in operation with this stainless steel fitting a serious casualty would have resulted. . . .

In another case we ordered electrical components that

are used to indicate whether a valve is open or closed. After several hundred of these had been installed several failures occurred. It was discovered that a small piece of insulation, required and specified in the drawings, had been left out by the manufacturer. . . .

Many quality control problems are traceable to lack of pride in workmanship. In one case a reactor component failure was caused by faulty brazing of two copper wires. We found the braze to be so poor that when the insulation was removed the two wires fell apart. . . .

"I assure you," concluded Rickover, "I am not exaggerating the situation; in fact, I have understated it. For every case I have given, I could cite a dozen more. . . ."

The 1964 hearings on the loss of the USS *Thresher* were full of similar criticisms. Admiral Rickover brought out, for example, that "during the recent stay of *Thresher* at Portsmouth about 5 per cent of her silver-brazed joints were ultrasonically inspected. These joints were in critical piping systems, 2-inch diameter or larger. The inspection revealed that about 10 per cent of those checked required repair or replacement. If the quality of the joints inspected were representative of all the *Thresher*'s silver-brazed joints this means that the ship had several hundred substandard joints when she last went to sea."

On March 15, 1967, in Room AE-1 of the Capitol Building, Admiral Rickover's name and reputation for fanatic devotion to quality control came up in a discussion of rigid inspection procedures. In addition to Milton Shaw there were present AEC Commissioner James T. Ramey and Assistant General Manager for Reactors George M. Kavanagh. And of all the testimony given at these hearings, none was more revealing than the following little dialogue:

REP. HOLIFIELD: This has been the greatest complaint against Admiral Rickover. The manufacturers do not want to deal with him because he has rejected defective parts, that is, defective according to his standard of values.

DR. KAVANAGH: The fact that he has done that consistently is one of the main ingredients of his general success.

MR. RAMEY: Yes, his reactors work.

REP. HOLIFIELD: That is right. It is one of the ingredients of his success and it may be an ingredient of some of these companies right now almost refusing to bid on some of his work.

MR. SHAW: Mr. Holifield, if a company has the option to turn out a product that does not require engineers and inspectors, compared to turning out one that does, there is no question, I think, what most industrial organizations will do.

In his foreword to the published transcript of hearings on the *Thresher* tragedy, Rhode Island Senator John O. Pastore, chairman of the joint committee holding those hearings, made an ominous statement: ". . . while nuclear power was revolutionizing the submarine as a weapons system during the past 10 years, the more conventional aspects of the submarine and its safety devices were not keeping pace with the more stringent performance requirements of greater endurance, higher speed, and deeper submergence. . . . It is extremely unfortunate that this tragedy had to occur to bring a number of unsatisfactory conditions into the open."

May not the same be said one day about the power industry's failure to accommodate the more conventional aspects of utility design and construction to the more stringent performance requirements demanded by nuclear power? Nuclear submarines have been described as "four-thousand-ton Swiss watches"; what image describes the infinitely larger and more complex commercial power reactor?

History, it appears, is well on the way to repeating itself. Just as there were warnings in the nuclear submarine program before the *Thresher* went down, the problems, defects, malfunctions, and accidents described in this book are clear warnings that the miscalculations, negligence, complacency, haste, and irresponsibility now being exhibited by our nation's leaders and by men in high authority in industry must precipitate a catastrophe if they go unchecked much longer. In a sense we are fortunate that only 129 men had to perish to underscore the lesson we must learn. Perhaps it is a fitting tribute that their deaths are of cosmic significance to the living. The lesson of the *Thresher* is written boldly and indelibly before every American citizen.

CHAPTER VI

Human Frailty and Inhuman Technology

Data processing people use an expressive acronym to describe how computer performance depends on human performance: GIGO. It stands for Garbage In, Garbage Out. It means that the quality of a computer's output is only as good as the instructions programmed into it. If you feed it garbage, it will turn out garbage. Stated another way, the flaws in a computer program will reflect exactly those of the men who fashion it.

The same holds true of any other technology: There is virtually no mechanical failure that cannot be traced to a human one. Furthermore, the more sophisticated the technology, the more precise will be the correspondence between the subtlest gradations of wisdom or ignorance, care or negligence, dedication or apathy, and that technology's success or failure. When meters, grams, and seconds are no longer good enough; when the specifications call for millimeters, milligrams, and milliseconds, the demands made on humans are accordingly refined. Minute human lapses that might be tolerable in a conventional industrial procedure will wreck the more exacting one.

And when, as in the case of atomic power plants, the technology is not only exacting but hazardous in the extreme, then a trivial misjudgment or a moment's inattention can spell doom. The word GIGO, then, takes on a special meaning in the context of nuclear power, for the smallest trace of human "garbage" that slips into a reactor's design, construction, or operation may very well manifest itself in a catastrophic eruption of radioactive garbage. We have seen how we are failing to engineer components to meet the cruel tolerances imposed by nuclear reactor technology; now let's examine how well *men* are engineered to meet them.

The sudden surge in orders for nuclear-powered utilities in 1966 caught science and industry by surprise and revealed labor shortages in every sector. An article in the January 1967 issue of *Nucleonics* described as "cliff-hanging" the ability of manufacturers to fulfill orders by promised delivery dates. An official at General Electric called it "touch and go for 1971," and Babcock & Wilcox said, "If the industry tries to get too many nuclear plants started up at once, there's going to be a bottleneck in constructors."

The yawning gap between orders and capacity precipitated a vast manhunt for new engineering and scientific talent as well as labor on a lower level. Westinghouse, for example, had about 650 professional and administrative employees on its atomic power staff in 1965, but forecast a 250 per cent increase to 1625 employees by 1969. Unable to find enough hands in the United States, Westinghouse began seeking them in England, Sweden, and elsewhere in Europe—where it found plenty of competition in that rapidly growing nuclear market. "We've gotten about twenty-five already," Westinghouse was able to boast a year or so later. Will Rowland, vice-president of Babcock & Wilcox's Nuclear Generation Department, said his company would have to train many of its conventional-service engineers for nuclear work.

Such explosive expansion negatively affects industrial personnel in a number of ways. We have already seen how it not only leads to errors and dangerous short cuts in the manufacture and assembly of components, but causes inspection oversights and relaxation of management quality control on the part of both those who sell equipment and those who buy it. We have also seen that the shortage of competent personnel in the Atomic Energy Commission itself has forced lowered vigilance in the very agency charged with regulating the industry.

It is not unreasonable to expect, then, that the pressures produced by rapid expansion of the industry will engender shortages in the personnel who operate and maintain nuclear plants, and in qualified supervisors and training directors. Even if a utility starts out with a sufficiency of such personnel, the high salaries operative in a seller's labor market might lead to competitor raids, leaving the victimized utility shorthanded and forcing it to replace highly skilled and experienced men with relatively inferior ones. Even if that does not happen, the usual dynamics of staff turnover will take their toll of top men. In his foreword to the *Thresher* hearings, Chairman Pastore raised this problem, saying, "Unless there is a drastic change in the present military technical management concepts, whereby competent individuals will be assigned technical responsibility for time periods commensurate with the time required to complete a technical project without adverse effect on their promotion opportunities, the high standards of efficiency and safety required will be most difficult to attain."

A "relatively inferior" operator or supervisor may be an extremely able individual whose only disadvantage is that he has not lived with the reactor from the outset. Under conventional circumstances familiarity with every tiny detail of a machine and its technological environment would not be an indispensable condition of safe and successful plant operation; in nuclear technology, however, a very good "second best" is nowhere near good enough.

As a matter of fact, it is dubious that "best" is even good enough. Consider first the operator, the man actually at the reactor's controls. In theory he is a thoroughly educated and trained individual whose AEC license guarantees a high level of technical competence. But why should we safely assume that company managers will have the time to train operators rigorously; that tests will not be made easier? There is little in industrial tradition to reassure us on these scores, and once again the *Thresher* hearings suggest that the problems are by no means speculative:

REP. HOLIFIELD: Admiral Rickover, I understand that before the *Thresher* incident at least there was quite a bit of pressure to get you to reduce some of your rather strict requirements in the selection of operators and the training of those operators. What is the status of that situation?

ADMIRAL RICKOVER: The attempts toward "degradation of specifications" on personnel—I will use that simple expression—still go on. . . .

Our real problem is in the submarine staffs where nearly all of the people are non-nuclear people some of whom have a deep resentment against the nuclear navy because it has put them out of business. They are constantly trying to get the personnel degraded. It takes a lot of fighting to keep it going.

But even if such unsettling conditions were not transferred into the commercial nuclear power field, it is nevertheless virtually impossible for even the best-trained, most experienced and alert operator to be prepared for, and capable of handling, every contingency that might confront him. If every commercial reactor is a one-of-a-kind phenomenon, possessing a unique and constantly changing personality, how can anyone be certain that an operator will be able to anticipate and deal correctly with eccentricities displaying themselves for the first time, with failures and combinations of failures so "incredible" that no precept in his training, no precedent in his experiences, tells him how to cope with them? As one survey noted, "The importance of operator error as an accident initiator arises from the intimate relationship which usually exists between the design of the plant, the control system, the operating procedures in use, and the personal attributes of the individual operator and his supervision." Is there any wisdom whatsoever in trusting that the personal attributes of the individual operator will *always* be up to sustaining this intimate relationship?

A reactor operator is, after all, not a god. Apart from his special skills, he is subject to the same physical, emotional, and mental strains as most other workers, and his every frailty constitutes one more unknown safety margin in any plant.

The AEC's licensing regulation 10 CFR 55 provides that the applicant for an operator's license "must pass a physical examination to show that his condition and general health are not such as to be expected to cause operational errors which might endanger public health and safety." Aside from the possibility that the examining physician could overlook or disregard a potentially serious condition, are there not countless ailments that might arise between mandatory examinations? Might not a head cold or severe indigestion or some other indisposition impair an operator's general efficiency or specific physiological functions such as eyesight or reflexes?

And what of examinations for psychological health? Is it not possible that an otherwise capable operator may bear some latent mental disorder that fructifies after he has been on the job awhile? Dr. Donald Oken, M.D., associate director of the Psychosomatic and Psychiatric Institute of Michael Reese Hospital in Chicago, pointed out some rather disturbing observations made in studies of reactor accidents:

> There are ample data indicating that most "accidents" are motivated acts subserving psychological needs. I do not, however, base my concern on data derived from other situations only. A review of reports of past criticality and reactor incidents and discussions held with some of the health personnel in charge reveal a number

of striking peculiarities in the behavior of many of those involved—in which they almost literally asked for trouble. This has occurred in the face of an Atomic Energy Commission safety program which has been pushed hard and has generally been highly effective. We know that some individuals have a particular psychological make-up leading to frequent accidents. These accident-prone people sometimes can be identified on psychological grounds. ... It seems evident, then, that the selection of scientists and personnel for sensitive work should include screening for this factor. ... Perhaps every installation should have, as a part of its health division, a psychiatrist or psychologist.

One need not get superanalytical to understand that the principle of the death wish, a well-accepted and documented explanation of human behavior, is operative in the accident-prone individual, and might be operative in the psyche of the fellow at the control console. He may normally be well in control of his darker impulses, but suppose he bears one morning a subconscious resentment against the company management for some real or imagined slight, or just wakes up, as everyone does from time to time, simply feeling uninvolved?

Other psychological pressures may also be present, as witness this account of a failure at Puerto Rico's Bonus reactor, as reported in the February 1965 issue of *Nucleonics:*

The operator closed the wrong valve—a bypass valve on a drain trap, in a line that at the time was being utilized as the flow path for steam from the reactor—rather than a valve in a line that was to be warmed up in preparation for the next experiment. Flow of superheated steam was reduced to about 20% of original value for about 2½ minutes until corrective action was taken—after a rapid rise in power level and reactor pressure were noticed. Corrective action was to check the rise in power by inserting one control rod 5 inches. However, Combustion [Combustion Engineering, designer of the reactor] evidently felt in retrospect that this was inadequate, since one of the nine measures reported to AEC as having been taken to prevent a recurrence is "an effort . . . to dispel an apparent subconscious reluctance on the part of reactor operators and shift supervisors to manually scram [shut down instantly] the reactor."

Aside from the death-wish theory, the "apparent subconscious reluctance" shown by the operators may be due to fear that they will be called on the carpet for causing the expensive delays which emergency shutdowns often entail. However one interprets their hesitation, though, the fact remains that such inaction in a crucial situation could prove fatal.

Even if psychological screening and periodic mental examinations were mandatory in this field, there would still be no way of anticipating temporary lapses of attention or momentary aberrations brought on by financial problems, domestic difficulties, bereavements, health worries, disputes with colleagues or supervisors, hangovers, or just plain daydreaming.

Nor has sufficient consideration been paid to what might be described as the psychopathology of accidents. Dr. Oken, quoted earlier in this chapter, stated in the same paper that ". . . accidents tend to occur in clusters during periods in which other signs of psychological stress are evident—the 'accident process' or 'accident syndrome.' " And Theos. J. Thompson has noted:

A surprisingly large fraction of these accidents happened at night, on weekends, or during startups after a vacation period. A typical example is the SL-1 accident which happened on the evening shift January 3, 1961, after a 10-day holiday shutdown. Enough others can be cited to indicate that judgment and alertness may be affected adversely on late shifts or on shifts where morale is likely to be low or where attention is wandering because of holidays or other reasons.

It can be argued that these factors obtain in all industries, not just the nuclear utility field. That may be so, but the one difference that makes *all* the difference lies in the magnitude of the consequences. We have pointed out that no industrial disaster can match the havoc produced by a nuclear power plant catastrophe, but this point is of such paramount importance that it is worth the risk of repetitiousness to fix it ineradicably in the reader's mind.

Indeed, this unique distinction charges the operator with two special responsibilities: He must not on the one hand become too self-conscious, nor must he on the other become too self-satisfied.

We know that excessive conscientiousness can itself bring about the very misfortune it aims to prevent: Might not an operator's acute awareness that a single slip-up can endanger thousands of lives and cost billions of dollars of damage prey so intensely on his mind that he freezes in a crisis? Thompson and Beckerley, in their *The Technology of Nuclear Reactor Safety,* state:

> Although designers can provide a variety of means for building safety into a reactor, these features may be negated by the operators. A safety device may go out of order, or a gauge yield an incorrect signal, or an operator ignore instrument responses that disclose malfunctions. Unless the operating organization is alert to all signs of abnormality, right down to the most subtle indications, the safety of the reactor is in jeopardy.

What an awful burden to lay on one man's shoulders!

Just as heavy is the opposite responsibility of not taking too much for granted; many accidents occur just when a company is patting itself complacently on the back. Again, the words of Thompson and Beckerley sound a tocsin:

> In reactor facilities one of the chief booby traps exists because there are so many safeties involved. Some acci-

dents have occurred because a relaxed or sloppy crew unknowingly has successively allowed various interlocks and safety measures to be breached one at a time; the logic of the operators always is that there are several and, therefore, the breaching of one is not important. Indeed, the results may be totally inconsequential until that time when the last in a long series is breached, and then the results may be very serious.

It is not always easy to document operator errors in assessing reactor accidents, since those errors may form only a barely perceptible—though no less vital—link in the chain of events. And, naturally, operators are no more eager than anyone else to step forward and accept responsibility for a mishap, especially if it is a costly one. An account of a Canadian reactor accident, however, illustrates how operator misjudgments can compound, if not actually precipitate, an incident of potentially devastating proportions:

The start-up procedure was to have been normal and the heavy water level was raised to a point for normal operation. An operator in the basement then by error opened three or four bypass valves thereby causing some of the shut-off rods to rise. This movement of the shut-off rods was noticed by the supervisor at the control desk who then went to the basement and corrected the situation. Apparently, however, some of these rods did not drop all the way back into position, although the signal lights at the control desk were cleared. The supervisor then instructed, by telephone, his assistant at the control desk to push specified control buttons; however, his instructions were partly in error, though normally the error would not have resulted in any difficulty. It became evident from the rate of rise of reactor power that the reactor was super-critical at a time when it was believed to be sub-critical. When the control button to insert the shut-off rods was pushed, it was found that all of the rods did not fall back into the reactor because of the earlier error in instructions, and also because of some mechanical difficulties. When it was observed that the reactor power was still increasing, the valve to re-

lease the heavy water into its storage tank was opened
and after a few seconds the reactor was shut down. . . .

Some 10,000 curies of long-lived fission products
were released into the heavy water as a result of this
emergency operation. By comparison, only some 1500
curies of radium had been produced in the world up to
the time of the accident.

Of course, the operator is but one member of a team
of employees. Even if his control of the operation is
impeccable, plenty of opportunities for error exist for
the more conventional breed of worker, and some of
these errors could be catastrophic. Although it is imperative that each worker perform his task with perfect
thoroughness, caution, and alertness, it is no more realistic to expect consistently high levels of performance
from pipe fitters or electricians than it is to expect it
from the ablest licensed operator. Because humans are
humans, accidents *will* happen. In fact, few of us realize the extent of industrial accidents, but an article in
the New York *Times* of September 1, 1968, written by
Howard A. Rusk, M.D., reported some startling statistics. In 1966, for instance, 2,200,000 Americans
suffered disabling injuries at work, the figures averaging
out to 55 persons killed, 8500 disabled, and 27,000
hurt less seriously *on every working day*. Accidents on
the job cause about ten times as many working days
away from work as do strikes and other work stop-
pages. But then that fatal difference rears its head again:
The kind of industrial accidents that happen all the time
in most other fields, resulting in limited damage or
injury or deaths, will have far-reaching effects when
they occur in a nuclear plant.

To give some idea of the weight placed on accidents
that would be considered trivial in another industry, the
AEC is legally obliged to report, and *has* reported in
annual summaries, such cases as:

> During the opening of a calorimeter can in an open
> laboratory, the lid blew off to a height of about two

feet above the table top. The sudden release of pressure forced radioactive dust (plutonium oxide) particles out into the room atmosphere. Five employees were in the room at the time. Contamination was dispersed throughout the laboratory and adjacent rooms. Decontamination costs were $4,243. . . .

A chemical process operator received a cut to his finger during cleanup work in a processing area.

A construction force was removing a plastic greenhouse enclosing a hood over a conveyor. . . . The workers, unaware that the tape which they were removing covered old tape which was placed over holes in the conveyor, removed the tape used to seal the greenhouse to the side of the conveyor and inadvertently removed the old tape also, causing the spread of radioactive contamination . . . (cost $5100).

After an experiment was completed, an employee was instructed to decontaminate glass apparatus used in the experiment. On the way back from the decontamination area, the employee carrying the glass apparatus containing polonium was accidentally bumped by another employee, causing him to drop a small glass tube. The tube shattered, spreading polonium contamination over the immediate area. . . . Operations in the building were down for approximately two-thirds of a day for decontamination.

Minuscule incidents like scratched fingers, lids popping off containers, and people bumping into each other would scarcely be worthy of mention in accident surveys of practically any other industry. That they are officially listed as "serious accidents" by the AEC, that they can shut down a company's operation for almost a day and cost four or five thousand dollars for decontamination, are good indications of how treacherous is the stuff we're dealing with. One would therefore think that no task, however tiny, involving nuclear material would be assigned to a worker not thoroughly familiar with the nature of that material or his duties.

Yet there are instances on record where potentially hazardous jobs were assigned to individuals utterly untrained or otherwise incompetent to perform them. On July 24, 1964, for example, Robert Peabody, an employee at United Nuclear Corporation, was given a plastic container five inches in diameter and sixty inches high, to rock on his shoulder to bring about a desired chemical mixture of radioactive material. He was then instructed to pour the contents from the safe shape of the plastic container into a mixing jar eighteen inches in diameter and twenty-six inches high, a shape capable of concentrating the mixture into a critical mass—one in which a runaway chain reaction of explosive energy is initiated. The violent reaction spattered him with radioactive liquid, and two days later he was dead. According to the account, Peabody had no training whatsoever in the field of chemical reprocessing of radioactive material.

If minor accidents committed by conventional laborers are of potentially major significance, what can be said of more serious examples of error and carelessness?

The AEC's Annual Reports to Congress reveal some unnerving examples of human negligence in AEC facilities. Perusal of the Reports for 1966 and 1967 discloses that 3844 pounds of uranium hexafluoride were lost due to an error in opening a cylinder; 50,000 pounds of non-radioactive mercury were spilled to the ground in an operational error; 10 gallons of waste solution were spilled on a floor during repair of a valve; approximately one-half pint of plutonium solution was spilled in an elevator; 100,000 pounds of non-radioactive sodium dichromate was spilled from a storage tank and drained into a sewer; a $220,000 fire in a heat exchanger cell of a Hanford Works, Washington, reactor was traced to the accidental tripping of valves by electricians during previous maintenance work, permitting oil to escape from the circulating pumps.

None of these accidents led to disaster; but who will warrant that, with the projected proliferation of power plants and their satellite industries in the coming decade, a similar "goof" will not trigger an event of disastrous magnitude?

Thus far we have been talking about "accidents," mishaps which occur despite our best conscious efforts to prevent them. But not all accidents are "accidental" —some are the product of deliberate human design and planning. Are our nuclear power facilities any better prepared to defend themselves against human hostility or malevolence than they are against human recklessness?

Consider labor trouble. The AEC's labor relations have been good, but "good" is not necessarily good enough. In 1967, about 182,000 man-hours were lost in operations and construction of nuclear-related facilities due to strikes against Government contractors. The worst of these, accounting for 104,969 man-hours, was a strike against Douglas United Nuclear by the Hanford Atomic Metal Trades Council, which ran from September 1 through December 12, affecting Hanford's "N" reactor.

These disputes were finally resolved peacefully. But unfortunately, even a non-violent strike can create extremely hazardous situations at a commercial nuclear power plant. Utilities must work around the clock. A work stoppage in a unionized department or division will, if past experience is any guide, force management personnel to take on jobs with which they are unfamiliar, or which they haven't tackled for years. The consequences in a nuclear plant are easy to imagine, but the record of strikes against defense installations, hospitals, and public services such as transit, garbage collection, fire and police departments shows plainly that organized labor can display remarkable insensitivity to public welfare if it believes its demands justified. This is not necessarily a criticism of organized labor, whose grievances against a utility's management might very well be responsible and justified. It is merely a statement of fact that strikes *will* occur, for good reasons or bad, but the best reasons in the world would be of no consequence in the light of a reactor accident at a struck nuclear plant.

Although few labor disputes end in violence, it would take only one ill-considered act of hostility to plunge a territory thousands of square miles in area into nightmare. The act might be perpetrated by one disgruntled employee or ex-employee without the sanction or even knowledge of responsible union leaders. The dispute might take a similar course to one that began in 1966 between the International Brotherhood of Electrical Workers and the Alabama Power Company, a utility powered by conventional fuel. On August 16 of that year, negotiations over a new contract with some 2400 members of the union broke down. Within the next thirteen days, saboteurs opened oil valves at four substations in the Jasper area, allowing an essential coolant and insulator to drain from the transformers. By late November of 1966, some forty-five acts of sabotage had been reported by the company, including the shattering of insulators and throwing of chains over high-voltage lines. White-collar workers were assigned double shifts to keep the power flowing, but some found their passage into the plant blocked by strikers.

Had Alabama Power been a nuclear utility, these hostilities would most assuredly have set the stage for a serious accident. Short-circuiting of power lines and destruction of transformers could cut off both regular and emergency power to the reactor and its backup safeguards. The burdens upon the handful of men operating the plant would enormously increase the possibility of serious error. The management might decide to shut the plant down until the strike was settled, but this does not guarantee that no accident would occur upon resumption of operations. We have read T. J. Thompson's observations on the special hazards present in nuclear plants during start-ups; the residual hostility and other emotional excesses affecting returning workers and operators might be contributing if not causative factors in an accident occurring at that time.

There is little evidence that commercial nuclear power plant management is allowing for such contingencies in plant plans, safeguard features, personnel deployment, and other security measures. References not merely against labor sabotage, but against political sabotage, civil disorders, and war are conspicuously absent from the many construction specifications, license applications, and safety reviews examined by the authors of this book. Why?

The reason, incredible as it may seem, is that the Atomic Energy Commission does not require such security provisions as criteria for issuance of construction and operating licenses.

In 1959 the possibility of sabotage in the nuclear field became a reality when—according to Robert Gannon in an article some years later entitled "What Really Happened to the *Thresher*," —cables on the submarine *Nautilus* were found cut. Nevertheless, the AEC did not require utility applicants to address themselves to the sabotage issue. It is not surprising that when the AEC submitted nuclear plant design criteria to W. B. Cottrell, director of Oak Ridge National Laboratory's Nuclear Safety Information Center, the very first of his long list of general comments was: "The ramifications of civil disobedience, riots, strikes, sabotage, and the like have not even been mentioned. With this vast potential risk in mind, should not the physical security of the plant be considered?"

As of this writing the AEC still does not seem to think so, though how it is able to reconcile its position with its explicit commitments under the Atomic Energy Act "to make the maximum contribution to the general welfare, subject at all times to the paramount objective of making the maximum contribution to the common defense and security"—it is impossible to explain. As a matter of fact, not content to leave its position flexible, it issued on February 11, 1967, a notice in the Federal

Register of its intention to amend several stipulations in its licensing and review procedures, so that in the future it would be clearly understood that:

> An applicant for a license to construct and operate a production or utilization facility, or for an amendment to such license, is not required to provide for design features or other measures for protection against the effects of attacks and destructive acts, including sabotage, directed against the facility by an enemy of the United States, whether a foreign government or other person.

By an intriguing coincidence, the AEC's amendment proposal was introduced in the midst of a legal action revolving around this very issue. It happens that on March 22, 1966, Florida Power & Light Company applied to the AEC to build two nuclear power reactors at Turkey Point in Dade County, some twenty-five miles south of downtown Miami. The following August, an attorney, Paul Siegel, wrote the AEC's Director of Regulation discussing the possibility of a bombing attack against the proposed reactors from Cuba. He suggested there might be little difference between dropping a nuclear bomb on one of Dade County's cities and using a smaller conventional bomb to breach the Turkey Point reactor's containment and coolant systems. His letter requested thorough exploration of these possibilities.

On January 25, 1967, the AEC issued a notice that a public hearing on the Turkey Point plants would be held in Miami. It is interesting that in an unrelated but by no means irrelevant event the very next day, a full-time employee of the right-wing Minutemen organization and six other men were arrested by the FBI in Seattle just as they were grouping to carry out a plot that called for, among other things, blowing up a power plant. In any event, Paul Siegel filed for a Petition for Leave to Intervene in the Turkey Point proceedings, asserting that his interests might be affected by accidental releases of radioactivity from the reactors and by intentional attempts to harm them. That the AEC would want to air his contentions seemed reasonable enough to him, considering the AEC's statutory dedication to public health and safety and to the common defense and security. But at the pre-hearing conference on February 10, the attorney for the Commission's regulatory staff said in effect that the AEC had never concerned itself with the effects of sabotage or enemy attack, and didn't plan to do so now. The AEC attorney then produced the proposed amendments cited above, which went into the Federal Register the next day. On the twentieth of that month, the Commission issued a Memorandum and Order stating that the Turkey Point hearings would not take up the matters raised by Paul Siegel. On April 27, 1967, provisional construction permits were issued to Florida Power & Light. Siegel filed exceptions. The AEC denied them, justifying its decision with the following legal and "practical" arguments:

Neither the Atomic Energy Act nor its legislative history suggests that hostile acts should be considered in the licensing process.

The Commission has the responsibility for interpreting the Act's general standards, and it has not and does not consider the common defense and security and public health and safety standards to refer to enemy attack and sabotage.

The protection of the United States against enemy acts is a responsibility of the defense establishment.

Designing reactors against the full range of the modern arsenal of weapons is not practicable.

The risk of enemy attack is shared by the nation as a whole and Congress has not indicated that reactors are to be treated differently from other structures.

Enemy attacks and sabotage are too speculative to warrant consideration.

Examination of the probability of and protection against attack and sabotage would involve sensitive information.

The fallacies in these arguments are so self-evident that they could be dismissed without comment were it not of the highest importance that every citizen understand unequivocally the consummate danger they represent to his life, health, and property. With the help of Paul Siegel's superbly argued briefs, some of these contentions can be examined more closely:

Take the argument that "the protection of the United States against enemy acts is a responsibility of the defense establishment." The Department of Defense's policy, as elaborated in its Directive #5160.54 dated June 26, 1965, is "to develop and promote industrial defense, to encourage industry to protect its facilities from sabotage and other hostile or destructive acts, and to provide industrial management with advice and guidance concerning the application of physical security and preparedness measures." In other words, the Defense Department is not specifically charged with protecting any industry from hostile acts, even an industry in which the explosion of a single conventional-sized bomb in a single installation could have effects as devastating as a multi-megaton atomic weapon. To make sure we understand this, part V-C of this DOD policy paper declares "The protection of property is an inherent responsibility of ownership. Accordingly, the Department of Defense does not assume primary responsibility for the physical security of privately-owned facilities, federally-owned facilities under the control of other Federal departments and agencies, or facilities owned by any state or political subdivision of any state."

In short, neither the AEC nor the Department of Defense is willing to assume the responsibility for nuclear facility security, but both have left it on the shoulders of private owners.

The Commission argues that designing reactors

"against the full range of the modern arsenal of weapons is simply not practicable." Paul Siegel replies:

> There is a continuum of potential missiles which might be aimed at a reactor containment vessel, going from a spitball delivered by a pea-shooter to a 100-megaton nuclear warhead delivered by intercontinental ballistic missile. It is ridiculous to say that because we might be unable to protect against the ultimate weapon on one end of this continuum, we need not protect against any form of enemy attack or sabotage.

Siegel might also have referred to a passage in the AEC's 1962 Report to the President on Civilian Nuclear Power stating: "Nuclear power could also improve our defense posture; . . . the containment required for safety reasons could, if desired, be achieved at little, if any, extra cost by underground installations, thus 'hardening' the plants against nuclear attack." Why is it no longer "practicable" to build A-bomb-proof plants underground, after the AEC's assertion that this could be done at little or no extra cost? Why has not a single American commercial reactor been designed or built underground? Why has not the AEC steered, if not pushed, commercial utility companies in that direction?

These and dozens of other equally forceful considerations have not prevailed with the AEC. On September 19, 1967, the Commission adopted its proposed amendments, making its position with respect to sabotage and destructive acts official. Paul Siegel took his fight to the United States Court of Appeals. The Court upheld the AEC.

The last word on the unreliability of the human element in nuclear power belongs to the renowned, Dr. Edward Teller, who stated in an article published in 1960:

> A single major mishap in a nuclear reactor could cause extreme damage, not because of the explosive force, but because of the radioactive contamination. . . .

So far we have been extremely lucky. . . . But with the spread of industrialization, with the greater number of simians monkeying around with things that they do not completely understand, sooner or later a fool will prove greater than the proof even in a foolproof system.

CHAPTER VII

Near to the Madding Crowd

The Brookhaven Report, as we have seen, estimated the worst consequences of a major atomic plant accident to be 3400 deaths, 43,000 casualties, and $7 billion worth of property damage, give or take a few hundred tormented souls and a few million dollars in devastation. Conditions, however, have changed radically since the relatively horse-and-buggy days of atomic technology in 1957, when the Report was issued. Today, mammoth reactors, containing many times the uranium inventory of this nation's first generation of power reactors, and located much closer to population centers than was envisioned in the 1950s, are being built or planned. But proposals to issue an updated Brookhaven Report, bringing casualty and damage figures into line with these vastly altered circumstances, have been mercilessly squashed by the nuclear power establishment, fearful of the dread such revelations might provoke.

What would an updated Brookhaven Report look like?

It is impossible, of course, to calculate accurately the damages resulting from an event for which there is no historical precedent, and it would only dignify the original Brookhaven Report to attempt the same kind of statistical reckoning. But if we contrived a hypothetical reactor of a size and site similar to those that are being designed to go on line in the next decade, the reader might get some idea of the magnitude of the threat he will be confronted with tomorrow, if he is not already confronted with it today.

Consider three fundamental plant features.

The first is the size of the reactor. It is a well-known fact that the larger a power plant is, the more economical is its operation. That fact was familiar to the men who drew up the Brookhaven Report, who said: ". . . since all the cost analyses that have been performed on reactors show that the cost per kilowatt-hour of electricity decreases with increase in reactor power, it is expected that the power level of future reactors will tend to be large." Nevertheless, the Brookhaven Report postulated a plant of only 100,000 or 200,000 kilowatts.

On July 10, 1968, the AEC released a report on the status of the U.S. civilian nuclear power program. It stated that as of June 30, 1968, 102 reactor power plants were operable, being built, or planned, for a total kilowatt capacity of 72,939,700. Fifteen of the 102 were already operable, and their total capacity was 2,798,700 kilowatts—an average of 186,000 kilowatts per plant, which falls roughly between the 100,-000-kilowatt minimum and 200,000-kilowatt maximum hypothesized by the Brookhaven Report. But how large will future reactors be?

The total capacity of the thirty-one plants being built was to be 22,501,000 kilowatts. That means an average of 725,800 kilowatts per plant, which is 3.4 to 7.2 times larger than the Brookhaven Report's hypothetical machine.

Forty-two more reactors in the planning stage averaged 832,000 kilowatts.

Fourteen more, planned but without reactors ordered as yet, averaged 904,300 kilowatts.

Thus, not counting the reactors now operable, the eighty-seven reactors scheduled for the late 1960s and early seventies average 806,200 kilowatts: *four to eight times the capacity of the hypothetical reactor described in the Brookhaven Report.* And of course, the bigger the generating capacity, the more atomic fuel is required.

But those are just averages. Some of the plants being built or scheduled are 1,000,000 kilowatts or larger. Commonwealth Edison has applied for two units at Zion Station in Illinois that are 1,050,000 kilowatts each; Pacific Gas & Electric has applied for a station in Diablo Canyon, California, that will be 1,060,000 kilowatts; the Tennessee Valley Authority is building two units, and applying for a third, in Decatur, Alabama, that will each be 1,065,000 kilowatts; and Consolidated Edison of New York has just announced intentions to build four units of 1,000,000 kilowatts each on an island just off New Rochelle in teeming Westchester County—*four* nuclear reactors, each with a capacity five to ten times the imaginary machine described in the Brookhaven Report!

It might be innocently assumed that in order to build a 1,000,000-kilowatt plant, you simply have to make everything ten times bigger than a 100,000-kilowatt plant. This is like saying that to build an airplane with a ten-thousand-mile range, you merely have to scale up ten times an airplane with a thousand-mile range. In reality, the extrapolations from small systems to large are at the very least enormously complicated, and sometimes they are impossible. A metal capable of withstanding the heat of a small reactor may not hold up under fire in a large one; a valve that contains small-reactor pressures cannot simply be scaled up to accommodate big-reactor ones. The know-how required to build plants 50, 100, 1000 per cent bigger than any built before amounts to an entire new technology. And because experience with 1,000,000-kilowatt reactors will be gained not from test projects sited in remote regions, but from commercial operations only a few miles from population centers, these plants must—we repeat—be regarded as nothing more, and nothing less, than gigantic experiments.

Aside from the obvious fact that bigger reactors use more fuel, and therefore pose a bigger quantitative threat to the community, bigger reactors also make higher demands on safety features and the time margins in which they must operate to be effective. This fact was brought out in a statement to the Joint Committee on Atomic Energy submitted in 1967 by Dr. David Okrent, the 1966 chairman of the Advisory Committee on Reactor Safeguards, and Nunzio J. Palladino, the 1967 ACRS chairman:

Increases in power density lead to a reduction in the time available for initiation of emergency measures in the unlikely event of a large primary system rupture. The requirements placed on the emergency core cooling systems are more stringent for any size rupture. More precise knowledge is needed both about the course of events during the postulated accident and the damage limits that can be tolerated. This is so because less margin is available with which to handle unexpected events.

Associated with the matter of making fuel cores bigger is that of making them more efficient, for naturally an increase in performance spells an increase in profits. But, as is usually the case, the profits are taken out of the box marked *Safety*. After describing technically how greater efficiency may be extracted from a fuel core, Thompson and Beckerley in their book on reactor safety state that "Pressures to increase core performance tend to force reactor designers to move closer to burnout conditions and to operate on narrower margins of safety as far as fuel is concerned. . . . As the safety margins are narrowed, it may be necessary to devise improved in-core instrumentation or to develop new means of burnout indication. To date efforts in this area have been limited; clearly, as performance has increased, such efforts become more and more necessary."

Just how critical these issues are may be gathered from the fact that they caused, early in 1967, a member of the AEC's Advisory Committee on Reactor Safeguards to file a public dissent on the Committee's recommendation of a go-ahead on the TVA's application to build two titanic nuclear units at Browns Ferry, near Decatur, Alabama. It was the first time such action had been taken by a Committee member in AEC history. The Committee, though expressing concern that the average power core densities would be about 40 per cent higher than any previously planned light water reactor, that the calculated number of fuel elements reaching undesirably high temperatures was greater, and that the time margin available for putting emergency core cooling systems into operation was less— nevertheless gave its green light to TVA, saying merely that many of the unresolved questions about the plant "warrant careful attention" before an operating license is issued. Stephen H. Hanauer of the Oak Ridge National Laboratory bravely, but futilely, took the position that the Committee had not gone far enough. Interestingly, Hanauer's dissent followed by only a few days an indication by Milton Shaw, director of AEC's Division of Reactor Development and Technology, that the atomic power program, while proceeding at great speed, was not always giving proper attention to quality.

Another feature of today's "new, improved" reactor that bears comparison with the Brookhaven Report's modest machine is the fuel cycle. As we have seen, during operation the uranium fuel elements in the reactor core produce an inventory of radioactive fission products which eventually interfere with smooth functioning of the fuel. The fuel elements must then be removed from the reactor and new ones substituted while the old ones are being reprocessed. The time it takes for fuel elements to build up a fission product inventory so high that they must be replaced is known as the fuel cycle. The cycle for the Brookhaven Report's reactor was 180 days—six months.

The replacement of fuel elements in a reactor core is a fantastically delicate operation. Each element is a bundle of slim tubes containing uranium fuel. Once these bundles are irradiated their removal calls for infinite care, for they burn with hundreds of millions of curies of deadly radiation. The replacement process may therefore take a month or longer. At Con Edison's Indian Point #1 Plant at Buchanan, New York, it took six weeks to replace 40 of the 120 fuel elements, each of which weighed nearly four tons. Just removing the fifty bolts from the reactor's cover took a week.

Obviously, it is not profitable to shut a plant down for four to six weeks every 180 days, and therefore longer fuel cycles become highly desirable—at least from the accountant's viewpoint. Technologists have thus managed to extend the fuel lifetime of reactors by three or more times the 180 days of the Brookhaven Report's typical reactor. But while this is economically advantageous, it also means that the fission product inventory in a big reactor will be proportionately greater, having had three times as long to build up. Since there is more uranium in there to begin with, the total amount of radioactive poison in a modern nuclear furnace, especially toward the end of its fuel cycle, is staggering. An accident occurring late in that cycle would, if poorly contained, spew far greater amounts of radioisotopes into the environment than one happening at the end of a smaller reactor's cycle.

By far the most significant distinction between yesterday's reactor and tomorrow's, however, lies in its distance from population centers.

Until the atomic power program began, in the mid-1950s, moving away from the hypothetical and closer to the practical, few gave excessive thought to the matter of how close reactors should be placed to population centers. The main thrust of the Government's effort in the field was toward getting reactors built and operating at any cost, just to show potential investors that nuclear power worked. But as the 1950s turned the corner into the 1960s, and the Government was able to demonstrate that its small experimental and demonstration reactors worked (more or less), the emphasis began to shift to answering the question: Do they work profitably?

One of the reasons why the Government stammered when it tried to answer that one was that it knew that reactors built far from the electricity consumer are uneconomical. Because the costs of purchasing right of way on which to build transmission lines, and the costs of the transmission lines and supporting equipment themselves, are tremendous, long-distance power transmission adds both to the capital and operating expenses of a utility. One authority stated that the costs of rural transmission lines range between $50,000 and $150,-000 per mile, exclusive of right of way. So there are powerful economic incentives to move reactors as close to major centers of electricity use as possible, and early in the 1960s industrialists and investors began to reach out for them. In the words of Clifford K. Beck, AEC's Deputy Director of Regulation, speaking before the 1963 Annual Convention of the Federal Bar Association, "competitive prices for electricity from nuclear reactors began to come within 'smelling range' [around 1962] and efforts to eliminate unnecessary costs, e.g., long transmission lines and large reactor sites, increased."

But there was a slight conflict here, because in its 1962 Report to the President on Civilian Nuclear Power, a major policy statement, the AEC had declared: ". . . for safety reasons, prudence now dictates placing large reactors fairly far away from population centers."

Luckily for the AEC, its major policy statements, when it comes to safety, do not have very much relevance to actual practice, for while it was preaching caution on the one hand, it was encouraging economic expediency on the other, urging utilities to put up monster-sized reactors and not discouraging them from putting them up near population centers.

In April 1962 the AEC formally adopted and published its guides to reactor site selection, guides which today are still in effect. These defined the estimate of upper limits of fission product releases, the containment capabilities of the facility, meteorological characteristics, and potential exposure doses permissible for any site. Of course, "permissible" suggests that these guidelines were enforceable. They were later to prove just suggestions, take 'em or leave 'em.

As Beck pointed out, publication of the guides had a crystallizing effect on siting philosophy. Designers and utility operators, who had been asking what they had to do to get their reactors profitably situated near a population center, now interpreted the guidelines as concrete instructions. "If we can build our containment structure to meet *this* guideline, and design an emergency cooling system to meet *that* one, then our plant will be safe at a distance of X miles from the city," was the way they reasoned. The AEC's guidelines, which should have kept reactors out, had the opposite effect of attracting them to come in. Beck's exposition of this dynamic is worth repeating in depth:

> . . . a very great change has taken place in the concept of the maximum credible accident. For many older reactors, the maximum credible accidents described were pretty far out in the realms of incredibility, both in the opinions of the proposers and of the reviewers. The reactors were remotely located anyway, and even if this horrendous incredible accident created no tolerable hazards, then any credible situations, posing lesser hazards, would also be acceptable. Now the situation is different; there is an obvious (economic) reason for the upper limit of anticipated hazard to be as realistic as possible: *assumptions that larger accidents might happen cost money.*

The italics are most emphatically ours.
Beck went on to say:

> Accident experience to date has been very reassuring.

Every reactor, when it is finished and fully evaluated, is confidently expected to operate throughout its lifetime without serious accidents and there is a firm basis for confidence in this expectation. But I would not, and I doubt that many other people would, at the present stage of reactor development, depend on this expectation alone when the reactor is located in the midst of people and the consequences of a misjudgment could be so severe. We are not yet to the point where dependence on the low probability of a serious accident alone can be taken as the only barrier against disaster. . . .

And yet on December 10, 1962—only twenty days after the AEC's Report to the President stating ". . . for safety reasons, prudence now dictates placing large reactors fairly far away from population centers," and nine months *before* Clifford Beck stated "We are not yet to the point where dependence on the low probability of a serious accident alone can be taken as the only barrier against disaster"—on December 10, 1962, Con Edison of New York announced its proposal to build a 1,000,000-kilowatt nuclear plant in Ravenswood, Queens, one of New York City's five boroughs. In other words, a reactor squarely in the heart of a population of millions, a reactor five or ten times the size of our little friend in the Brookhaven Report!

One would think the AEC would have come down on this reckless proposal with hobnail boots, for it violated every scruple the Commission had ever enunciated, including the one it had made less than three weeks earlier. Yet for thirteen months the Commission walked around it, considering.

Why did the AEC hesitate? One possible reason, as we have seen, is that atomic energy was on trial in 1962, and the AEC was urgently looking for a power plant that would vindicate all the time, money, and labor this nation had sunk into making nuclear power facilities economically viable. *Nucleonics,* reporting the month-to-month developments, quickly went to the heart of the matter, stating in its January 1963 issue:

By so doing, Con Ed clearly threw down the gauntlet on the long-controversial question of siting reactors near population centers. If the site, in the middle of the United States' biggest city, is approved and the plant built, Con Ed will have succeeded in making nuclear power an entirely conventional, routinely accepted thing.

And, in it's next month's issue:

The process will be closely watched by the entire nuclear industry. . . . For if nuclear power is to become commonplace and gain an equal footing with coal and oil power, it must gain acceptance for plant location close to or in large cities.

Opposition to the plant was ferocious, and took on a somewhat sensational aspect when none less than David E. Lilienthal, the former first head of the AEC, declared he "would not dream of living in Queens if a huge nuclear plant were located there." He was promptly attacked for his "head in the sand" attitude and, since he hadn't been associated with the Commission for thirteen years, for fuddy-duddyism. One newspaper ran an editorial saying "the generation of nuclear power for civilian community use has passed the visionary and experimental stages and progress in the development of such powers should not be barred by merely uninformed emotionalism or antiquated fears." And Con Ed's chairman actually bragged, "We are confident that a nuclear power plant can be built in Long Island City, or in Times Square for that matter, without hazard to our own employees working in the plant or to the community."

Just what processes worked to cause Con Ed to withdraw in January 1964 cannot be clearly ascertained, but what they said in effect when they pulled out was "We'll be back."

Con Ed's test was both too sensational and too premature. But while Con Ed was licking its wounds, a number of other companies were more quietly setting up shop close to population centers around the United States, and by 1967 Dr. Beck would have to confess to the Joint Congressional Committee on Atomic Energy that "Connecticut Yankee, Connecticut Power and Light Company, the Malibu location, the Rochester Gas and Electric and Con Edison No. 2 of New York, and others, and Niagara Mohawk have been approved with lower distances than our general guides would have indicated when they were approved."

Remembering that the Brookhaven Report, published in 1957, placed its hypothetical reactor thirty miles from a major city, let's see just how close tomorrow's reactors will be to us.

It is important to bear in mind a distinction between distance from a major city and distance from a densely populated area. A reactor may be thirty miles from a major city, but only a few miles from a densely populated minor one, or a heavily settled suburb. It is more realistic, then, to ask how far a reactor is from a *population center,* which is officially defined by the AEC as the nearest boundary of a densely populated area containing more than 25,000 residents. Thus, while New York State's Indian Point units are officially some twenty-four miles from New York City, *they are actually one mile from a population center!* And the estimated population within ten miles of those plants is 155,510. It need only be recalled that the Brookhaven Report foresaw people being killed by a major radioactive release at distances up to *fifteen miles* to realize the significance of these figures.

In a recent study of nuclear plant siting made by W. K. Davis and J. E. Robb of the Bechtel Corporation of San Francisco, the locations of forty-two nuclear power plants were examined, the criterion being the distance between the reactor and the boundary of the nearest population center inhabited by more than 25,000 residents. Their conclusions are flabbergasting. They found that only *two* plants in operation or planned are more than thirty miles from a population center. Of the rest, fourteen are between twenty and twenty-seven miles away, fifteen between ten and sixteen miles, and eleven between one and nine miles.

A May 15, 1968, U. S. Public Health Service paper provides a look at the population densities within ten miles of some reactors currently operating. The list is worth reproducing in full:

Reactor	Location	Population Within 10 Miles
Browns Ferry	Athens, Alabama	22,040
Brookwood	Brookwood, New York	27,480
Dresden	Morris, Illinois	22,600
Diablo Canyon	San Luis Obispo County, California	1,570 permanent 3,500 summer
Fort Calhoun	Blair, Nebraska	24,270
Ft. St. Vrain	Weld County, Colorado	8,384
Indian Point	Buchanan, New York	155,510
Millstone	New London, Connecticut	95,864 permanent 118,000 summer
Monticello	Monticello, Minnesota	9,712
Oconee	Keewee Dam, South Carolina	36,334
Oyster Creek	Lacey Township, New Jersey	13,108 permanent 64,200 summer
Quad Cities	Cordova, Illinois	39,488
Turkey Point	Homestead, Florida	42,397
Vermont Yankee	Vernon, Vermont	31,038

One siting case is of interest: the Burlington, New Jersey, station proposed by Public Service Electric & Gas Company was recently slated for relocation, the only case on recent record. Evidently it was so flagrantly close to big population concentrations that the AEC finally drew the line. The Burlington plant was to be within one mile from some of the city's buildings, and the whole city would have been contained within one and a half miles of the site. Population within a radius of two miles of the plant was estimated as reaching 27,263 by 1970, and, within a three-mile radius, 75,080 by 1970. The reactor was to have been eleven miles from Trenton in one direction, and seventeen miles from Philadelphia-Camden in the other. Significantly, *on December 10, 1968, an earthquake whose shock center was traced to Burlington County, New Jersey, jolted the Philadelphia area.*

The implications of these reckless siting policies are not difficult to imagine. A breeze just a few miles per hour higher than average, or an unpredicted shift in wind direction, might be all that is necessary to convert a local accident into widespread disaster. For example, though Bodega Head, California, is fifty miles up the coast from San Francisco, some twenty miles farther from a major population center than the distance hypothesized in the Brookhaven Report, an accident at the proposed Bodega Head power plant might have seriously affected San Francisco's population under weather conditions only slightly different from those postulated in the Report. The Bodega Head Association one day released fifteen hundred balloons from the reactor site, each carrying the message: "This balloon could represent a radioactive molecule of strontium 90 or iodine 131." Some landed in Marin County, Petaluma and Napa and a few in Richmond, all in the San Francisco Bay area.

It was calculated that external doses of radiation to San Franciscans on the first day of exposure could be almost four times the *yearly* permissible dose, and within ninety days about twenty-five times the yearly permissible dose. Radiation levels of that intensity would, if Brookhaven Report criteria were applied, officially call for "probable destruction of standing crops, restrictions on agriculture for the first year." *That* in some of the most valuable farm country in the United States.

It is obvious that our Government has not addressed

itself to the philosophical questions relating to nuclear plant siting and safety. Aside from the big question of putting mammoth reactors near great cities, a number of lesser but nonetheless crucial ones remain unexplored. For example, it is a fact that population densities in most metropolitan areas are growing rapidly: How does one justify placing a reactor near a low-density area, knowing that its population will soon swell to high density? Or: By what logical process does our Government conclude that it is "better" to risk destruction of a small rural town of 10,000 people than a large city of 1,000,000? And: Would not a "minor" release of radioactive material into a highly populated area cause as much harm as a major release occurring in a reactor much farther away from the same city?

But even if we can set aside these moral questions as easily as our Government seems to have done, the technological questions remain as insoluble today as they ever were. Testifying before the Joint Committee on Atomic Energy in the spring of 1967, Dr. Clifford K. Beck, AEC's Deputy Director of Regulation, stated:

> The actual experience with reactors in general is still quite limited and *with large reactors of the type now being considered, it is non-existent.* Therefore, because there would be a large number of people close by and because of lack of experience, . . . *it is a matter of judgment and prudence at present to locate reactors where the protection of distance will be present.* [Emphasis ours.]

Beck's statement is mild compared to that made in the same hearings by Nunzio J. Palladino, chairman of the AEC's Advisory Committee on Reactor Safeguards for 1967, and Dr. David Okrent, the chairman for 1966:

> . . . the ACRS believes that placing large nuclear reactors close to population centers will require considerable further improvements in safety, and that *none of*

the large power reactors now under construction is considered suitable for location in metropolitan areas. [Emphasis ours.]

But these grave, grave doubts on the part of these highly placed officials no longer hold sway with a utility industry now strongly attracted to the smell of profit. The giant reactors are going up everywhere, and are going up just outside our city limits.

It is interesting to note that among the biggest of these is the 4,000,000-kilowatt multiple-unit plant proposed by Con Edison for David's Island, the present site of Fort Slocum. Four years before Con Ed's 1968 announcement of the Fort Slocum scheme, the utility company had retreated from its Ravenswood, Queens, debacle warning it would be back.

On a clear day, you can see Fort Slocum from the Empire State Building.

CHAPTER VIII

Don't Bother Running

Considering what has been said so far, no one could be blamed for being seized with the impulse to flee. Unfortunately, even if it *were* possible to relocate out of range of all atomic installations planned for the next few decades—which is doubtful in itself—the pursuing atom will eventually place even the remotest regions in jeopardy. There will be no place left to hide.

By the 1970s, thousands of tons of nuclear fuel will be traveling by train, truck, ship, and plane to stoke reactor furnaces around the globe; giant reactors will propel naval and commercial ships across the oceans and into ports a stone's throw from the hearts of the world's great seaside metropolises; millions of gallons of seething radioactive poison will travel through or near our nation's towns and cities on their way to underground storage sites.

All of the problems, perils, and probabilities characterizing stationary nuclear facilities exist in ones that move around. In addition there are some unique to a mobile nuclear technology. That these will grow to monumental proportions is easy enough to visualize merely by taking some of the incidents that have already occurred and extrapolating them for an industry hundreds of times bigger tomorrow than it is today.

Massive efforts to power aircraft and land vehicles by means of nuclear reactors have not gotten past the experimental stage, thankfully. For once, recognition of hazards seems to have been a controlling factor. From what we've seen thus far, however, it obviously takes only a little economic incentive to blind the most sensible man to risk, and one suspects that as soon as someone develops a way to make nuclear air and land propulsion economically feasible—or, to put it more accurately, to make it *appear* economically feasible—caution will undoubtedly be thrown to the winds.

Esquire magazine's editors succumbed not long ago to such a siren song, presenting in the June 1968 issue a serious and ostensibly attractive proposal for a "cruise ship of the air," a nuclear-powered intercontinental dirigible combining the best features of jet airliner and conventional ocean liner. The caption of a lavish, full-color illustration of this ship, moored above midtown of a thronging city, concludes thus:

> ... For the occasions when she does land, gliding down in perfect silence, without fuss, vibration or dirt, a mooring mast can be built *in the heart of a city without disturbing anyone around.* ...
>
> The possibilities of a nuclear airship are being seriously studied now at Boston University's Department of Aerospace Engineering, and in the Department of Defense, at Goodyear Aircraft, General Electric, and other centers here and in West Germany. When and if she is built, the nuclear airship will restore our right-thinking belief that transportation can be for the comfort and convenience of people, instead of the other way about. Look at her beauty, lineage, and construction. Doesn't the whole idea beat jet lag, not to mention a tray on the lap? [Emphasis ours.]

The enthusiastic editors apparently forgot the lesson of the *Hindenburg:* that dirigibles, like brainstorms, must prove they can get effectively down to earth.

Experiments in nuclear jet and rocket propulsion, and in use of radioactive fuel for generating electricity in satellites, are actively being carried out today, but hopes for their success have engaged scientific attention far more thoroughly than concern for possible effects of their failure. In one experiment, a B-36 bomber was loaded with a 1000-kilowatt reactor. Forty-seven three-hundred-mile flights, between Fort Worth, Texas, and Roswell, New Mexico, were carried out. The reactor was not used to power the plane, but just to find out some things about radiation behavior under airborne conditions.

A lot might have been learned about radiation behavior under crash conditions too, but luckily no such thing occurred. Later on, the crashes of nuclear weapons-bearing military aircraft in Spain and Greenland provided ample data to fill our information gap on the behavior of radioactive material—and of humans—when nuclear pay loads fall from the sky.

An ill-considered and ill-fated experiment occurred on April 21, 1964, when the AEC "lost" 2.2 pounds of plutonium 238, described as a "fiendishly toxic" isotope, when a transit navigational satellite failed to go into orbit. The plutonium's function was to run the satellite's electrical systems, but because someone forgot to throw a switch, the rocket went awry. For some time nobody knew quite where it had gone. Some experts said the rocket had re-entered the atmosphere and burned up along with its nuclear pay load. But nobody actually saw the rocket re-enter, and, the Commission acknowledged, "anomalies" can sometimes occur in which metal parts reach the earth without burning up. The maximum permissible dose of plutonium 238 in the bodies of atomic workers is two billionths of a gram. For all anyone knew, enough of the stuff to reverse the Afro-Asian population explosion was mucking about the Eastern Hemisphere. Eventually, unusually strong traces of the element were detected in the upper atmosphere, indicating that the pay load had indeed vaporized. Some scientists hailed the discovery as a Good Thing because it afforded them an extraordinary opportunity to track meteorological conditions. At the same time, humanity's radiation budget, already progressing toward exhaustion, was reduced to the tune of 2.2 pounds of plutonium.

While equipping of planes and cars with nuclear reactors is still thankfully low on man's agenda for systematic self-destruction, the outfitting of ocean vessels with them is something else again. Here, near-total disregard for the resources of the sea and the welfare of the people on its shores presents a whole new dimension to the issues before us.

Although military applications of nuclear material aren't strictly germane to this book, a brief look at naval experience with atomic reactors can shed much light on the dangers of a seaborne nuclear technology.

The special functions of warships demand special reactor consideratons, and these in turn present special problems, problems of containment and cooling, problems of radioactive waste control, and of course problems of shielding against military action. A power reactor operating in a ship does not possess the margin of an exclusion distance, the safe zone between it and the personnel operating it. Therefore adequate shielding of the containment vessel is a must. Yet excessive shielding adds weight, a distinct disadvantage either in a merchant or a military vessel. Leakage rates of radioactivity must be severely restricted, yet because the structure is subject to movement, there will be difficulty maintaining tightness of joints, pipes, and cables. Ventilation control, especially in a nuclear submarine, is a most important matter. The facts that naval reactors commonly use a more concentrated form of uranium fuel and that the cooling system functions by means of pressurized water present unique challenges to technologists. These facts take on new significance when we consider the potential tally of victims should a serious reactor eruption occur in a large port city. Recognizing this threat, some foreign Governments have closed their harbors to nuclear ships, or strongly protested their entry despite the most vigorous reassurances on the part of the Navy and AEC.

These reassurances have been undercut, however, by alleged instances of radiation leaks by our nuclear ships anchored off the shores of host countries. In May 1968, for instance, Japan's Premier Sato told the United States that, because of increased radioactivity measured in the waters of Sasebo Harbor during a visit of the *Swordfish,* a nuclear-powered sub, Japan could no longer permit American nuclear vessels to call at her ports unless their safety was guaranteed.

The fact that the radioactivity of this alleged discharge may have been low is utterly beside the point. Of far greater pertinence is the proximity of the reactor to a population center. For even if land reactors were located at sensible distances from metropolises—if there *is* a sensible distance—the presence of a nuclear-fueled ship in a harbor represents a flagrant violation of every official siting guideline in existence. *It means atomic reactors within, or virtually within, city limits.*

What can happen to a nuclear ship in harbor? A better question is, what *can't* happen to one?

For one thing, the same design and workmanship errors that Admiral Rickover complained so bitterly about in congressional hearings could militate to cause a reactor explosion capable of breaching containment structures, releasing fission products into the water and air.

Secondly, sabotage is not only a possibility for nuclear ships, it should be considered a likelihood, even if those ships are non-military. Not only are they strategic military targets, but an incident in a foreign port could have profoundly damaging effects on our political relations with the host country, its neighbors, and all other nations where our fleets cast their anchors. Many demonstrations and bloody protests, some anti-American and others anti-nuclear, have been aimed at our atomic submarines overseas, and one of these could result in an attempt to storm and wreck one of them dockside. Damage to safeguards could conceivably bring about the very results feared by the demonstrators.

A third possibility is human error. Manpower shortages in the Navy can lead to the same hazards mentioned in connection with land-based reactors. In 1963, according to a New York *Times* article by military expert Hanson W. Baldwin, "many officers aboard nuclear submarines were being forced to serve 'inordinately long' tours of sea duty and many were under great strain, because there was an insufficient number of qualified officers to relieve them." Indeed, the nuclear submarine force had tripled the number of personnel required. The Navy initiated an accelerated training program that year, but in March 1965, 124 naval officers out of 493 men specially selected for nuclear power training resigned from the Navy, or indicated their intention to resign when their hitches were up, threatening to plunge the nuclear fleet back into manpower shortages that could one day open the sea valves to a flood of disastrous human error.

It is even possible that hurricanes, typhoons, and earthquake-induced tidal waves could cause unexpected and unexpectedly severe damage to a nuclear vessel in port. By a weird irony, in the very same week that Japanese reporters screamed "Yankee, go home!" at American experts investigating allegations of the *Swordfish* radiation leak, Japan's biggest earthquake since 1923 shook a six-hundred-mile stretch of seaboard, touching off tidal waves and causing widespread damage.

Nuclear vessels can also suffer damage on the high seas, of course. At first glance such damage would appear to threaten only the crew, but a reactor-driven ship partially immobilized by mishap or enemy action would be an extremely hazardous proposition to bring into port, for a nuclear runaway in progress in the ship's bowels could fulminate just as the vessel came within range of population concentrations.

If the ship sank, damaged fuel elements would release dangerous radioactive contaminants among shellfish, food fish, and other marine life on which man directly or indirectly depends, to say nothing of subtler genetic effects the radiation would have on marine biology and ecology.

The ships of our nuclear fleet are heavily safeguarded and armored, but they are by no means indestructible in this age of superweapons. Even setting aside the question of damages sustained in warfare, however, there is sufficient record of damages sustained in noncombat situations to make potential investors in commercial nuclear ships hesitate—at least for a few moments. On October 13, 1965, for example, two nuclearpowered subs, the *Sargo* and the *Barb,* collided off Oahu, Hawaii, while on submerged maneuvers. There were fortunately no casualties and only superficial damage. Still, if *two* nuclear subs could bump into each other with all that ocean to navigate in . . .

With respect to the merchant fleet, the annual reports issued by the Liverpool Underwriters Association, a leading British insurance group, state that every third merchant ship in service in any year will suffer some sort of disabling event. According to the 1965 edition of its survey, for example, 8317 out of 24,028 merchant ships of five hundred tons or more throughout the world suffered collisons, weather damage, stranding, fires, explosions, damage to machinery, and contact damage in 1964-34.6 per cent of the total. This figure was up 1.4 per cent from the previous year, 2.4 per cent from 1960. And these statistics don't even include the 117 vessels listed as totally lost that year.

What is the status of our nuclear merchant marine? At present the only American nuclear-propelled merchant ship in existence is the *Savannah,* belonging to First Atomic Ship Transport, Inc., a wholly owned subsidiary of American Export Isbrandtsen Lines. Shippers everywhere had watched the *Savannah*'s performance carefully in the hope that it would fulfill its promise of high efficiency and low cost. But early in 1967 it was announced that the streamlined beauty would be retired: It just wasn't pulling down a profit.

In addition to the technical difficulties of staffing the

Savannah with highly trained crew members—and note how this problem comes up in sector after sector of the nuclear industry—the company's management had been plagued with heavy liability expenses. A lot of countries had simply forbidden the *Savannah* entry until it was indemnified against serious nuclear mishap. And that meant a guarantee of up to five hundred million dollars per country.

Despite its poor showing, many of America's mercantile hopes were riding on the *Savannah,* and its retirement was no sooner announced than a large number of shipping men, labor leaders, members of Congress, and other public figures assaulted the decision. On June 13, 1967, the Maritime Agency reversed its stand, allowing the vessel one year's reprieve. Borne on the momentum of its victory, this coalition began pushing for a major national effort toward the creation of a nuclear merchant fleet.

How competitive it would be depended on how much backing the Government, and thus the taxpayer, could be expected to put up. In the autumn of 1967, Senator Warren G. Magnuson introduced a bill in Congress providing for a three-billion-dollar crash program of merchant shipbuilding over a five-year period. The measure called for a nuclear ship program that would afford sufficient Federal assistance to make it possible for qualified operators to buy a nuclear ship at the price of a conventional vessel.

At this writing the legislation is still pending; heavy budget cuts have taken their toll of many such developmental programs. But the bills may also be stalled because Congress is growing a bit tired of subsidizing so many aspects of the nuclear industry. Perhaps nuclear ships will have to pay their own way without benefit of subsidy. If so, we can expect the same response that we have seen in the utility field: Cut corners on safeguards.

This very argument was put forward on November 18, 1967, by George L. West, Jr., professor of marine and nuclear engineering at the University of Michigan, and Lieutenant E. J. Roland of the Coast Guard, at the annual meeting of the Society of Naval Architects and Marine Engineers. These gentlemen suggested that "by simply doing away" with many of the present design and operational safety requirements, "many of the first cost items, such as containment and filtration systems, warning and backup systems could be eliminated." Their paper also suggested that many safety requirements be liberalized in the areas of pressure suppression, pressure venting, and low-pressure containments.

The most interesting response to these suggestions came from the *Savannah* itself. One week after West and Roland advanced their moneysaving proposal, the ship had to be brought back to its Hoboken pier after its instruments indicated a possible leak in the ship's secondary cooling system. Whether there really was a leak, or whether one of the gauges was out of kilter, is a matter of conjecture. But the incident did seem to be telling us something about secondary safeguard systems.

There is no doubt that our merchant marine needs a shot in the arm. Whether it is desirable that this "shot" be administered by nuclear reactors is another matter. A nuclear fleet *can* be made competitive and economical *if* the taxpayer supports it with heavy insurance coverage and the high cost of safeguards; it can also be made competitive without taxpayer help if some of the safeguards are dropped and insurance premiums skimped. It cannot, however, be made economical *and* safe without something giving somewhere.

Even if the shipping lobby fails to get a nuclear merchant fleet launched, there will nevertheless be plenty of radioactive material on the high seas. It can take a number of forms: Partially refined uranium will be shipped to the United States by foreign countries for enrichment in gaseous diffusion plants; the enriched fuel will go back to the countries of origin for use in reactors; irradiated fuel will be shipped here for reprocessing; reprocessed fuel will be shipped back for reuse in reactors; and of course, importation and exportation of radioisotopes for a wide variety of purposes will be a thriving form of trade.

Actually, shipping of nuclear material is already a respectably sized business. As of mid-1967, the AEC had distributed abroad through sale, lease, and deferred payment special nuclear and other materials valued at approximately $266.4 million, bringing in revenues of $171 million. Much of this was uranium 235—more than 10,000 kilograms of it, or about 10 metric tons. In February 1966 President Johnson increased the allocation of enriched uranium for distribution abroad to 250,000 kilograms—about 270 tons. In 1967 legislation was enacted to permit the AEC to transfer to the European Atomic Energy Community 1000 kilograms of plutonium in addition to the 500 kilograms previously authorized, and 145,000 kilograms of U-235 in addition to the 70,000 kilograms previously authorized. This stuff will have to cross water to get to Europe, obviously.

The United States was also vigorously pursuing business in the area of enrichment of foreign fuel, and reprocessing. So there will be lots of international comings and goings of radioactive material in the next few decades, with the odds that one ship out of three bearing it will be disabled—and one out of two hundred won't survive at all. Forty-four major American ports have been cleared for receipt of irradiated fuels.

Of course, not all nuclear material will be going abroad by sea. Some of it will go in planes, as it already does domestically and internationally under AEC, International Commerce Commission, and Federal Aviation Agency regulations. On July 12, 1966, the ICC issued a revision of its regulations providing rules for shipping fissile material as a routine commodity in transportation, including air transportation. The AEC's handbook of Federal regulations applying to transportation of radioactive materials contains stringent guidelines for shipments, but Leo Goodman reported to a public health luncheon that: "One official in ICC told me that though apparently adequate standards were established for the transportation of radioactive materials, the staff of the ICC had been advised to 'play ball' with AEC and not be too tough with the application of the standards and regulations."

So much for stringent guidelines. Those who find it disturbing that our airlines are supersaturated, and the skies over our cities mobbed with planes, can now rest even less easily with the knowledge that some of those aircraft may be bearing radioactive material.

Upsetting as these pictures of radioactivity in the air and on the sea may be, they form only two panels in our triptych of recklessness, callousness, and ineptitude. The third and center panel, featuring shipments by land, is a compelling study of human madness meriting comparison with the most tormented productions of Hieronymus Bosch.

Before gazing upon it, a bit of background is necessary.

One of the fundamental rationales of atomic power is the cheapness of fuel transportation. Proponents of atomic power point out that a tremendous percentage of the cost of conventionally generated electricity paid by the consumer owes to the expense of bringing coal, oil, and gas by train, truck, boat, or pipeline to the utility. But because one ton of uranium delivers as much energy as about seventeen thousand tons of coal, uranium shipping charges are an inconsequential fraction of your electric bill. Time and again one reads such statements as the following, made by an AEC official in February 1968 before an American Public Power Association gathering: "The relatively minor cost of transportation of nuclear fuel provides greater flexibility in the location of generating plants and thus influences decisions with respect to long-distance transmission."

Apart from the current trend for conventionally fueled utilities to construct power plants directly on mine and refinery sites wherever possible, thus sharply reducing fuel transportation costs, the AEC's transportation argument is grossly misleading in all that it fails to take into account.

First of all, uranium *does* travel all over the place. In *Atomic Fuel,* an AEC information pamphlet, a section endearingly entitled "The Odyssey of Uranium" informs us that "once the uranium has been separated from the ore dross, it is ready to travel, and travel it does. For example, material mined and milled in Utah may be refined in Missouri, enriched in Kentucky, converted in Pennsylvania, fabricated in California, used to generate power in Massachusetts, and reprocessed in New York!"

Second, it is never stressed that as the ore is refined, enriched, converted, fabricated, shipped to the user, and shipped back to the reprocessor, the radioactive content gets higher and higher, the attendant hazards steeper and steeper.

Third, no mention is made of the enormous expense involved in shipping the huge quantities of radioactive waste to storage sites, some of which are located in the State of Washington, three thousand miles west of Eastern Seaboard utilities. Special containers must be fabricated to contain this supremely toxic liquid against the contingencies of transportation, and other special precautions taken to ensure uneventful delivery to the turbulent caldrons in which it is to be stored for centuries. Ritchie Calder, in *Living with the Atom,* stated that transportation of high-level and extremely dangerous radioactive wastes required trips of over two million miles annually—and that was in 1962. He surmised that by the year 2000, the amount of fission products on the highways will be 980,000,000 curies, "a mighty lot of curies to be roaming around a populated country!"

Finally, when atomic power proponents talk about cheap transportation, little mention is ever made of the fact that much of the savings generated is due to the absence or inadequacy of insurance coverage. A recent study made by the Southern Interstate Nuclear Board found three major obstacles currently affecting transportation of radioactive materials. As reported in an AEC Division of Industrial Participation book, these obstacles are:

> (1) the refusal of the eastern railroads to transport fissile materials as common carriers; (2) the lack of satisfactory nuclear indemnification for movements on the high seas and by means of air transport; and (3) the lack of indemnification which, in the view of bridge, tunnel and turnpike authorities, would enable them to offer the use of their facilities as applied to other types of cargo.

Thus, the way to keep transport costs down, is by not buying insurance. In the AEC publication just referred to, one may read: "Air transportation of radioactive materials has frequently been the only solution to shipping cold nuclear fuels [meaning uranium sealed in metal tubes] and radioactive materials overseas because of the difficulty in obtaining indemnification for steamship service." Another passage informs us that it cost about $2.50 and $3.00 per kilogram respectively to transport irradiated fuel from the Yankee and Dresden power plants to the Nuclear Fuel Services reprocessing facility at West Valley, New York. These prices included cask rental, but "Insurance was not required in these instances." The NFS facility is where used fuel is divested of its intensely radioactive fission products. Thus violently lethal material traveled on public thoroughfares to New York from Illinois and Massachusetts totally without indemnification.

It is estimated that the annual transportation charges associated with nuclear plants alone may reach fifty to eighty million dollars in the nuclear economy projected for the late 1970s. That's a lot of money, but it wouldn't begin to cover the cost of damages, say, if a truck bearing irradiated waste products turned over, breaking the seals on the casks inside and spilling its cargo into a city's water supply.

If that seems an unlikely possibility, a glimpse of transportation mishaps in the nuclear field may give skeptics pause.

For anyone with a sense of black humor, the AEC's annual supplements to its Summary of Industrial Accidents have more entertainment value than the annual special edition of *Variety*. A typical harvest of transportation accidents involving release of radioactive material, reaped from the 1963-64 supplement, includes:

During transit, plutonium-contaminated liquid leaked from a glass carboy (with a loose-fitting ceramic stopper) and contaminated several trailers, truck terminals, a number of packages of other materials and several persons handling the materials. . . . The 13-gallon glass carboy was in a large wooden box. The box was marked "this end up," so that during transit the carboy would remain upright. However, the presence of pallets on the box apparently suggested to the carrier that the box should be placed on its side, resting on the pallets, which allowed the material to leak slowly from the container and the wooden box. (The carboy was not surrounded on all sides by an absorbent material sufficient to absorb the entire liquid contents.) . . . Decontamination was carried out successfully in the truck terminals, trailers, and on the cargo at a cost of approximately $27,500. (Jersey City, New Jersey)

A 55-gallon drum, containing 5 polyethylene bottles of radioactive material, was damaged during transit. . . . During transit, the ring bolts loosened on two drums (lying on their sides) and the lids came off, allowing 4 bottles containing 93% enriched uranium to escape from one drum. (Kansas City, Missouri)

During railroad yard switching operation, a railroad car door broke open and two drums, containing 0.947 enriched uranium, fell out. Part of the contents of one of the drums spilled. The entire shipment constituted 251 drums. (Madison, Illinois)

Upon arrival at destination, an autoclave housed in a lined shipping cask and containing nine unclad fuel pins in 432 cc's of water was discovered to have leaked during transit. The leak occurred when a broken valve allowed contaminated water inside the autoclave to leak into the shielded container and then seep out onto the floor of the truck. (Chicago, Illinois)

On top of these, the supplement described a large number of accidents in which no radioactivity releases occurred. Such as:

Truck transporting fuel elements involved in accident with private car.

Tractor-trailer carrying interplant shipment of radioactive materials tipped over when forced off road by oncoming traffic.

Train derailed. Coach carrying radioactive materials remained upright.

Truck transporting radioactive material jackknifed.

Truck carrying radioactive materials slid into ditch.

The fact that no releases occurred in these accidents is certainly no assurance that they will not occur in the future. All it means is that so far, accidents involving radioactive material in transit have not been severe enough. But the laws of averages are working against the shippers. In April 1968, for example, it was announced by the National Transportation Safety Board that the number of train accidents had increased from 4149 in 1961 to 7089 in 1967—a zooming rise of 71 per cent. Of the total number of accidents in 1966, 4447 were derailments and 1552 were collisions. In a letter to the Federal Railroad Administration, the Board's chairman, Joseph J. O'Connell, Jr., stated that in the future the accident rate might get worse because of higher speeds, longer and heavier trains, and the *increased hauling of hazardous materials.* Nor have we considered sabotage. The aforementioned shipment of 251 drums of highly enriched uranium, two of which rolled out of their railroad car, would have made a compelling target for the saboteur's bomb.

Considering the enormous annual increase in nuclear industry activities, there is a reasonably good chance that one day in the 1970s a truck or railroad car containing radioactive material will be blown sky-high, or will dump its cargo in the midst of a town or city population, or in a drinking or sewage water system.

The inadvertent or intentional cracking open of casks containing nuclear material is just one eventuality we can expect if we permit the peacetime atom to come of age in the 1970s. Another is the loss or theft of such material. Yes, it *can* be lost. And yes, it *has* been stolen! Leo Goodman, who has fought a courageous battle to keep tabs on, and publicize, the misadventures of the atomic industry, stated in a 1967 speech that his tabulations showed eighty-eight capsules of radioactive fuel lost or stolen up to then.

An instance of loss in 1966 received wide coverage in the newspapers. A one-inch-long cylinder containing three hundred milligrams of radium was lost in a shipment between Fort Worth, Texas, and Queens, New York. That the capsule had been poorly packed, enabling it to escape both from its lead container and the box in which the container was contained, was bad enough. But the real headache owed to the fact that authorities hunting for the capsule found it impossible to trace the route along which it had been shipped. "We are really disturbed," said a spokesman for the United States Public Health Service in Washington, "that the route of this hazardous shipment should be so hard to identify." Nevertheless, after monitoring a number of potential routes and terminals, searchers had to give up. The capsule is still—somewhere. In 1620 years it will have lost half its radioactivity.

Six weeks later a second capsule was misplaced in much the same fashion.

Sometimes lost radioactive material is found. In March 1962 a little boy named Henry Espindola, playing in a town dump outside of Mexico City, found a container and managed to pry it open. It contained seven pellets of radioactive cobalt apparently lost by a nuclear engineer some time earlier. The container was kept around the Espindola house as decoration. On April 17, the grandmother, Augustina Ibarra, noticed the drinking glasses in the kitchen darkening. By April 29, Henry was dead. The mother died July 19. The cause of death was recognized and the capsule removed July 22. Nevertheless, Henry's sister died on August 18, and his grandmother October 15.

But with increased movement of radioactive material along world traffic lanes, a new and incomparably frightening hazard poses itself: piracy.

But what, you ask with a nervous laugh, can they do with a shipment of uranium—make a bomb with it?

An article on the front page of the June 13, 1968, edition of the *Wall Street Journal* may provide an answer. The article descibed a report prepared by a nine-member panel formed by the AEC in which it was predicted that a nuclear black market is likely to develop. "An atomic bomb can't be built without the right materials, of course," the article explained, "but atomic scientists say that as these materials gain increasing use, the opportunities for stealing them will multiply. Indeed, even now large shipments of nuclear material are regularly trucked in ordinary unarmed rigs through rural America, where hijacking would be relatively simple, and by 1970 these shipments will be sharply increased. Similarly, tremendous transatlantic air shipments of nuclear material for Europe's burgeoning nuclear power industry already are frequent."

The panel surmised that these shipments could attract criminal organizations that might divert the enriched uranium or plutonium. The once secret information needed to build nuclear bombs was unclassified years ago, and the *Journal* quoted Theodore Taylor, a nuclear physicist who headed the Defense Department's atomic bomb design and testing program for seven years, as saying, "I've been worried about how easy it is to build bombs ever since I built my first one."

Whether the matter is as simple as Taylor suggests is open to question, for the problems of handling, fuel separation, etc. are probably beyond the financial or technical means of any criminal syndicate, and undoubtedly beyond those of an individual criminal, revolutionary, or lunatic. They are not, however, beyond those of a nation, and the possibility that some countries could build—if they have not already built—secret installations for the purpose of producing atomic weapons from "diverted" material has been raised by reliable observers.

In any event, the *Journal* mentioned two incidents that had made a vivid impression on the members of the AEC-appointed panel. In one, two workers at a London plant stole twenty fuel element rods containing enriched uranium, dropping them over a fence for a pickup. The plot was discovered before the fuel elements were removed from the site.

In the second incident, a plant that makes fuel elements, reviewing its inventory, discovered that more than 100 kilograms of enriched uranium, totaling about 6 per cent of the amount handled by the company over a six-year period, was missing. "At first," the account explains, "it appeared conceivable that the missing material had been diverted into bomb production somewhere. After a long hunt at the plant, however, a fraction of the material was found. The AEC then assumed that the rest was lost in normal processing—blown out vents, tracked out on shoes or buried as scrap." Delmar L. Crowson, director of the AEC Office of Safeguards and Material Management, stated that "We have no reason to believe the material got away from the plant," but some Federal officials, the *Journal* stated, were not quite as sanguine as Crowson.

There is no fully effective means of policing the peaceful atomic activities of our own or foreign nations. Indeed, the New York *World Journal Tribune* of April 16, 1967, pointed out that "Nuclear reactors are sprouting so fast all over the world that it is almost impossible for the International Atomic Energy Agency to keep an accurate census of what is being built and what is planned." Thus the projected proliferation of civilian nuclear power plants presents mankind with the bitterest irony imaginable. For it may well turn out that the atomic weapon that triggers the next and final world war will be fashioned from fissionable material "diverted" from a power plant dedicated to the innocent purpose of producing electricity.

Advocates of Atoms for Peace have much to think about.

CHAPTER IX

We Interrupt This Broadcast . . .

"We interrupt this broadcast . . ."—words guaranteed to accelerate the pulse and stay the breath. Fingers go to lips and conversation dies rapidly. Everyone leans forward and listens apprehensively, conditioned to expect bad news.

At first, the announcer's words leave his audience more puzzled than anything else: "An explosion occurred one hour ago at the nuclear power plant north of this city. Radiological experts are now considering the extent of damage, but city officials have been informed that evacuation of the surrounding area may have to be undertaken due to the possibility of radioactive contamination."

His next statement, however, would undoubtedly send hearts racing with terror: "A nuclear physicist interviewed by this station reports that under certain weather conditions, an area as large as a hundred miles in diameter could be affected, raising the possibility that the entire population of this city, as well as those of all communities within fifty miles of the reactor site . . ."

Then, inevitably, the words: "Residents of this area are advised to remain calm and stay tuned to this station for further bulletins."

Are you prepared for this announcement? Is your community? Your city hospitals and health services? Your civil defense? Your state or Federal government? From all indications, the answer is No: This situation would catch every sector of the public unprepared.

151

Clearly, no plan can be devised to cope, or even begin to cope, with a disaster of this magnitude. Indeed, it is practically impossible merely to contemplate the consequences. Perhaps, however, the most effective way to illustrate our unpreparedness for a major accident of this type is to describe the inadequacy of preparations for accidents of far more modest dimensions.

The Atomic Energy Commission's literature presents a reassuring picture of a program for radiological emergencies. Plans to be used by personnel at nuclear facilities are considered before operating licenses are issued; such plans usually include procedures for notifying and co-operating with state and local police, state health officials, and the nearest AEC operations office. AEC compliance inspectors visiting the facility periodically review the adequacy of these plans and procedures. The Commission also maintains emergency teams under its Radiological Assistance Plan, and may call on other Federal agencies for supplementary action if necessary.

While this description sounds as if the Commission has all possibilities covered, confidence dwindles when some vital questions go unanswered.

The Commission's Radiological Assistance Program is organized to respond to an emergency anywhere in the United States, but it is limited in personnel and equipment. Between July 1958 and December 1967, the Program received 715 requests for assistance, of which 468 involved radioactive material. F. Raymond Zintz, Radiological Assistance Coordinator of the AEC's Division of Operational Safety, describes the incidents as "quite diversified. The Atomic Energy Commission has responded to requests for assistance in incidents ranging from fake packages of radioactive materials to the actual contamination of buildings, public roads, railroads and other property." Certainly, as the atomic power program soars to projected heights in the 1970s, the number, kinds, and extent of incidents can be expected to soar with it. Will the AEC's emergency teams be able to handle all contingencies?

Transportation accidents alone may pose staggering challenges. At a 1963 symposium on radiation accidents and emergencies, it was brought out that of 223 requests for radiological assistance handled by the AEC's special emergency teams between 1960 and 1963, 40 per cent involved transportation incidents. Yet few state or local jurisdictions had the knowledge, instruments, or competence to handle them. A large crowd of police, firemen, medical emergency personnel, and bystanders could easily be fatally exposed before anyone became aware of the presence of harmful radiation. "Take a transportation accident that happens in the middle of a cornfield somewhere," said one of the panelists. "The nearest hospital has got to have some sort of preparation for taking care of this. It may be unlikely to happen, but still it may. I know several radium installations not too far from here where I'm sure there has not been the slightest preplanning for what would happen if there was a spread of contamination." Another participant in the symposium stated flatly: "The emergencies that can and do occur en route within our transportation systems necessitate broader planning and more elaborate preparation by the responsible state agencies."

"Action initiated by trained state police officers prior to the arrival of a radiological emergency team," the same panelist went on to say, "could very well transform a potential tragedy into a minor accident." It is unsettling to contemplate the converse of that statement.

Obviously, the Radiological Assistance Program is not an adequate substitute for the local competency required in atomic emergencies. Recognizing this fact, the AEC has done what it can to encourage states and major cities to provide local orientation training and emergency teams which could be available within minutes. But as Donald R. Chadwick, then chief of the Division of Radiological Health, pointed out in a speech prepared for a seminar on the Protection of the

Public in the Event of Radiation Accidents held in Geneva November 18-22, 1963: "Currently over half the states provide emergency team assistance and about one-third provide orientation training to ancillary personnel" such as police and firemen.

The situation has scarcely improved since Dr. Chadwick spoke in 1963. According to the latest figures available from the U. S. Public Health Service, thirty-five State Health Departments, plus the cities of New York and Philadelphia, and Puerto Rico, the Virgin Islands, and the District of Columbia, have Radiological Emergency Protection Plans. Fifteen states, then, almost one third of the total, are without such plans; only two major cities and the District of Columbia have them; and countless communities across the nation, where reactors will be sited or trains and trucks laden with "hot" material will be routed, will have little if any formal plan for the contingency of a nuclear incident.

With regard to the number of states providing orientation training for police and firemen, the AEC and Office of Civil Defense have stated they do not have such information and hence couldn't update Dr. Chadwick's statement that about "one third" of the states provide training of this nature. Clearly, neither local officials nor local police and fire departments are prepared to handle even small nuclear plant accidents and nuclear transportation accidents.

But if police and firemen, who are usually first on the scene of any accident, are unprepared to deal with a radiation emergency, the situation with regard to hospitals is even more deplorable, and it has not significantly changed since Dr. George LeRoy asserted in 1963: "I would guess that major installations such as the big power reactors or large processing plants are unlikely to have in their vicinity hospitals with people who already have knowledge about the care needed in radiation accidents."

Dr. LeRoy went on to say, "I can imagine nothing but sheer confusion created by taking a person to the

nearest hospital without its having any prior information and asking them on an *ad hoc* basis to develop a
plan for dealing with a radiation accident." Just how
prophetically accurate his words were was demonstrated the following year when Robert Peabody, whose
case we mentioned earlier, died when he unwittingly
poured radioactive material into a container improperly
shaped to hold it, and the material exploded. Leo
Goodman's description of the events that followed is an
object lesson in community unpreparedness:

> As the radioactive liquid had splattered over his body,
> he ran out of the plant screaming but had enough pres-
> ence of mind to disrobe as he approached the plant
> gate, prancing around because of the effects of the radio-
> active liquid on his body. There were no facilities to
> meet his immediate medical needs until a volunteer am-
> bulance from Westerly, Rhode Island, could be called
> and have time to drive to the plant. . . .
>
> The ambulance driver logically drove to the nearest
> hospital. On arrival, he advised the admitting officer of
> the nature of the patient's illness. The hospital refused
> to admit the patient. Only after telephone communication
> was the decision made as to where the patient should be
> taken for possible treatment. . . .
>
> After an extensive automobile ride to Providence,
> Rhode Island, the patient, Mr. Peabody, was admitted
> to the Rhode Island Hospital in Providence. A fellow
> worker named Spencer rode with the driver, and both
> received extensive contamination from radioactivity on
> the patient's body. No facilities for transporting radio-
> active patients were available. The medical reports re-
> garding the following 45 hours . . . state that "Dr. Karas
> and others did the decontamination without gloves and
> had considerable difficulty cleaning themselves later."

In brief, there were no medical facilities near the
United Nuclear plant to meet the needs of victims of
such occurrences; no medical program had been
devised to handle accidents in an area where atomic
industry is rapidly developing; nor had the state

prepared its medical personnel for treatment of radioactively contaminated patients.

Similar failures have been reported in the western states. Dr. George L. Voelz, assistant director for health services at AEC's Idaho Operations Office, has told of a dismaying lack of radiological knowledge displayed by eighty hospital administrators, X-ray technicians and emergency-room nurses who attended a one-day seminar on problems of radiocontamination:

> We concluded that there is a very serious need for radiation accident information among this type of hospital personnel. I thought that it had been widely disseminated by literature, but there were few people among this type of hospital personnel who knew that a radiation emergency plan existed. For example, if they had been faced with a transportation accident involving radioactive substances with a truck or with an airplane crash, of those eighty people only four would have known that the U. S. Atomic Energy Commission has emergency plans and that the hospitals could get help from them.

We have seen ample evidence of how strongly the AEC promotes the construction and operation of nuclear power plants all over the country. How much attention is this same agency, which has been entrusted by the Atomic Energy Acts with the health and safety of the public in the area of atomic power, giving to preparation of state personnel?

The AEC's Annual Report to Congress for 1967 devotes all of four paragraphs to the matter headed "Training for State Personnel." The first of the four declares that "Adequate numbers of well-trained and experienced personnel are one of the most important factors in a State radiation program. The AEC, therefore, provides State personnel with technical training in radiation protection and orientation in the AEC's regulatory practices and procedures." What follows this build-up, however, is a big letdown:

Twelve people from nine States participated in the annual 10-week course in health physics and radiation protection given by Oak Ridge Associated Universities (ORAU). In addition, a 3-week course in applied health physics was presented by ORAU in the spring for 12 other persons from nine States. This course provides practical experience for students with theoretical training but limited experience in health physics.

Two orientation courses in AEC regulatory practices and procedures were attended by 22 persons from 16 States.

A special 1-week course in the regulatory and health physics aspects of nuclear medicine was given at the University of Florida, Gainesville, for State personnel in the southeastern United States, with 19 persons from seven states participating.

In other words, according to this report, only sixty-five people participated in the AEC's training programs for state personnel in the area of radiological health and regulation. Similar inadequacies seem to exist in the AEC's training of medical personnel. In a memo dated August 2, 1968, directed to field office managers, on the subject of "Training of Physicians to Treat Radiation Accident Victims," Martin B. Biles, director of the AEC's Division of Operational Safety, stated that "As part of a broad program to assure that adequate medical support is available at each nuclear facility, AEC plans to present a series of training seminars for responsible physicians" in such areas as diagnosis and general treatment of acute radiation illness, general care of acute internal and external exposure, and radiation control to minimize contamination of hospital staff and vehicles. Two seminars were scheduled, one for physicians east of Chicago and one for those west, but after giving details of application procedures, Mr. Biles announced that "Attendance at the seminars will be limited to 30 physicians." This seems like a woefully small number, and scarcely one calculated to "assure that adequate medical support is available" in the enormous complex of AEC atomic facilities and related institutions now in existence and the far greater one in the private sector projected for the coming decade.

Nor can additional courses offered by the U. S. Public Health Service be considered adequate. According to a catalogue prepared by the National Center for Radiological Health on "Training Courses Scheduled Through July 4, 1969," only three courses were specifically directed toward "Management of Radiation Accidents," the rest being devoted to things like "Basic Radiological Health," "Occupational Radiation Protection," etc. Two of those three accident courses were five days long, the third twelve days.

It can be safely assumed that little taught in the courses, classes, and seminars we have mentioned touches on the matter of disaster, and disclaimers such as this one by Dr. Robert Landauer, in a paper published in a collection entitled *Radiation Accidents and Emergencies,* must be common: "It should be stated here that this discussion is not to be construed as a plan for dealing with a military holocaust; such, I think, would be impossible to handle for most civilian hospitals. Plans may be made, however, for the sorting and reception of a hundred or so victims, 30 per cent of whom may be contaminated."

It is doubtful, then, that even with much broader training programs, we will ever be able to prepare for radiation accidents involving several hundred victims, much less for one involving injury to thousands, tens of thousands, or hundreds of thousands. Nevertheless it is imperative that the public and its legislative representatives recognize that the current programs of the AEC and the U. S. Public Health Service hold little promise against the possible harm in an accident of *any* serious scale.

One of the biggest problems that would arise in the case of such an accident is that of decontamination. Unless medical personnel were completely informed and trained, plentiful equipment at the ready, and a well-thought-out plan drawn up and impressed on the minds of regular hospital staff and volunteers, the initial catastrophe could be multiplied by hysteria and gross confusion as non-irradiated individuals did their best to avoid being contaminated by victims rushing to them for aid.

It should be noted that people may be injured by radiation without actually contacting radioactive material or debris. Radiation sickness is not contagious; one person cannot "catch it" from another. On the other hand, when the victim has been directly exposed to fallout—very small particles of radioactive material attached to dust and other matter suspended in the air—the victim himself, along with his clothing, is a "carrier," capable of irradiating other persons. Clothing must be removed and decontaminated, and the victim washed down to remove radioactive dust from all skin surfaces, otherwise he can expose countless other people.

The complications are many and difficult to overcome. For instance, referring to the room to which victims are originally taken, Dr. Landauer observed:

> If the room is connected with a general air conditioning system means must be provided for a "disconnect" to prevent the dissemination of radioactive material throughout the hospital. It is important always to remember to "contain" radioactive material, not to spread it. This applies to the decontamination team personnel as well. These people should not leave the area without first ascertaining that they themselves are not contaminated. There have been several instances of physicians spreading radioactivity all over a hospital and even into their homes.

Another fearful complication arises when one considers the procedure of washing down the bodies of contaminated persons. For while it is feasible for minor transportation or nuclear plant accidents in which radioactivity does not escape into the environment at large, it would be far less feasible, and perhaps impos-

sible, in the vicinity of a large nuclear plant accident
where fission products and gases were released outside
the utility structure—*because the water supply itself
might be contaminated*. Bear in mind that nuclear plants
must be located on the banks and shores of large water
sources for cooling purposes, and those water sources
invariably supply drinking and bathing water to nearby
communities.

As H. M. Parker and J. W. Healy pointed out
several years ago:

> Contamination of bodies of water will occur both by
> direct fallout and by secondary leaching of the materials
> into the streams. Direct fallout could render bodies of
> water reasonably close to the reactor unfit for use until
> the material is carried away. . . .
>
> The possibility of rainout into a stream near the re-
> actor site exists, with severe contamination resulting,
> depending upon the rate of washout from the cloud and
> the stream flow characteristics. Of more concern in at
> least some cases is the possibility of the escape of reac-
> tor coolant containing a significant quantity of fission
> products. Such a mishap would bring about a band of
> grossly contaminated water, depending again upon the
> flow characteristics of the stream, which could cause
> severe contamination of water plants or other equipment
> downstream and in special cases could lead to serious
> radiation dosages to people using the water for sanitary
> purposes.

More recently, writing about the effects of a nuclear
attack, a disaster which would not differ substantially in
its effects on water supplies from a major nuclear plant
release of radiation, Tom Stonier stated:

> Water supplies may also become temporarily unusable
> as a result of heavy fallout contamination. In Westchester
> County [a suburb of New York City], for example,
> about 90 per cent of the population uses water from
> open surface sources, and if fallout were fairly heavy,
> this water would not be fit even for emergency con-

sumption for days or possibly weeks. It would probably be acceptable for emergency use thereafter, because fission products in fallout appear to be in an insoluble form, and tend to be removed by sedimentation and filtration. However, even this "uncontaminated" water might not be entirely safe, since it could still produce considerable long-term biological damage, particularly from radioactive iodine.

It must also be remembered that in the event of a major reactor accident, hospitals and clinics in the area might themselves be severely contaminated and require evacuation.

In fact, a moment's thought produces the realization that scores of fundamental questions remain unassessed. For instance, what if the accident occurs late at night, catching most of the public asleep? Some communities might be able to resort to air-raid sirens and the like to alert citizens, but is there any assurance that that measure would be taken, or that its meaning would be comprehended? How many cities have established evacuation routes for civil or military emergencies, to prevent the rampant hysteria that would quickly develop when mobs poured into main arteries? Without organization and discipline, a panicky citizenry could inflict dreadful injury on itself even if contamination hazard was not present.

What would be the reaction of surrounding communities to the prospect of countless numbers of fleeing, and possibly contaminated, individuals? It has been pointed out, for example, that during the plague that struck London in 1665, surrounding towns padlocked water wells, closed shops, and posted armed guards on the roads from the city to bar fleeing refugees. And in the 1950s, when fear of nuclear war ran highest in this country, it was common to hear talk of means of repelling survivors from affected areas, slaying them in self-defense or in protection of food, medical supplies, etc.

Another possibility unconsidered is that people living near other nuclear reactors—and of course there will scarcely be a population concentration in this country *not* within reach of radiation releases—may very well become infected with panic, creating disorders throughout the land. Operators of other power plants might become jumpy and detonate yet other accidents, a possibility which many psychologists, examining the mysterious clusters of accidents occurring from time to time such as airplane crashes, believe to have a substantial basis in human behavior. Our Government might have to call for a temporary shutdown of all atomic plants—especially if there is suspicion of sabotage—pending investigation or until the first wave of panic subsides. In an age when one fourth or one half of our electricity will be generated by nuclear energy, as has been forecast, what effects would these massive shutdowns have on the economy and the public welfare?

The fact that this country's fire, police, medical, and governmental personnel are inadequately prepared for a reactor plant or nuclear transportation accident of any magnitude, and its citizenry utterly in the dark about even the most elementary do's and don't's in protection of self and property, in recognition or detection of radioactive contamination, in medical or evacuation procedure, is one of the most reprehensible aspects of the atomic power program. And it explains why it is so difficult for the average person to get any information about what to do if there is a serious incident. To illustrate this one need only try to get some information from the local Civil Defense office on procedure in such an event.

An acquaintance of one of the authors, for instance, called New York City's Civil Defense Office and asked what she should do if a serious nuclear plant accident occurred. She was told to "stay where you are." Assuming this instruction meant for her to hold on while the clerk checked with a superior for further directions, the caller waited. Some time later, another clerk picked up the phone and asked: "Are you waiting for something?" The lady explained she'd been told to stay where she was. The clerk's response nearly floored her: "Well, those *are* the instructions: Stay where you are."

Even conceding that this meant to remain in place until further instructions could be broadcast to the public, it hardly answers the question. "Where she was" could have been a phone booth.

The authors fared no better. In response to our call to the Civil Defense Disaster Control Office in New York City, we were told: "If anything like that happened, the AEC would step in."

Someone wishing literature on the subject will be astonished to learn that no booklet clearly outlining the first essential steps to take in a reactor emergency has ever, to our knowledge, been published. One little-known booklet, "Radiological Emergency Procedures for the Non-Specialist", was published in 1964 by the AEC, but it largely concerned itself with transportation accidents and provided instructions to those first "on the scene." It did not attempt to inform the public on fundamental steps to be taken should an accident, major or minor, or even a "scare," occur at a nuclear plant a short distance away.

In fact, a recent—March 1968—booklet prepared by the Office of Civil Defense, "In Time of Emergency: A Citizen's Handbook on Nuclear Attack, Natural Disasters," omits all mention of peacetime nuclear emergencies, even though such emergencies have occurred a number of times in recent years and are far more probable than a nuclear attack. Remember that the AEC, between July 1958 and December 1967, received an average of six requests a month for assistance through its Radiological Assistance Program, an average of four a month involving radioactive material.

Is it unduly cynical to wonder whether these incredible omissions are effective ways of evading questions the public would otherwise have raised long ago about the wisdom of our atomic power program? And is it alarmist to suggest that the first instructions citizens ever receive about what to do in a reactor emergency may begin with the blood-curdling words: "We interrupt this broadcast . . ."?

CHAPTER X

The Thousand-Year Curse

"How fortunate it is that our discovery of radiation is paralleled by our knowledge of its deleterious effects. . . . Otherwise, ignorance of the consequences of irradiating man might induce great recklessness." The passage is taken from *Radiation* by Professors Jack Schubert and Ralph E. Lapp.

There is scarcely anything in our histories to reassure us that man is capable of conducting himself wisely in the presence of known lethal hazards. Indeed, in their own book, Schubert and Lapp portray instance after instance of human carelessness with radioactive emitters despite the abundance of well-documented dangers. One can only assume that when they wrote that poignantly wishful passage, they were desperately hoping that in the future man would have learned enough to proceed with greater caution in coping with the unprecedented hazards of radiation.

Thus far this book has dealt with the possibilities and potential consequences of disasters at reactor and other atomic facilities or in transit. It must be recognized, however, that even if such massive emissions could somehow be prevented, our population will be exposed to a sharply increasing amount of radiation which the Government and atomic power industry foresee as the unavoidable by-product of tomorrow's peacetime atomic activities. Disturbingly, these emissions are labeled "planned releases." Furthermore, stored in fragile and unsafe tanks will be hundreds of millions of gallons of savagely toxic nuclear waste material, seething with many times the amount of radiation necessary to destroy all life on earth. The technology for neutralizing this radiation is unknown and, even to the best scientific minds, practically unimaginable; the technology for safely disposing of it is scarcely well enough advanced to make a difference in the crucial decades ahead; and the technology for merely containing it is so studded with unknowns and hazards as to make it utterly unreliable.

Despite all preventive efforts, future atomic facilities will be releasing enough radiation into our environment to present a clear-cut danger to every living thing on this planet. Ritchie Calder, in his book *Living with the Atom,* describes an "audit" of environmental radiation which he and his colleagues, meeting at a symposium in Chicago, drew up to assess then current and future amounts of radioactivity released into atmosphere and water. The audit covered the period 1955–65 (the book was published in 1962), and because atomic power was negligible then compared to the prospects for the 1970s and beyond, the high figures on the ledgers are most significant.

The members of Calder's group assumed that in the period 1955–65, "the figures for land-based power reactors might be a thousand or ten thousand megawatts of heat which, in turn, means that locked in the total system there would be a thousand or ten thousand million curies of radiation. And the 'planned release' (the acceptable amount of 'leakage,' given all precautions) would be a millionth of that." Of course, "a millionth of that" comes to ten thousand curies per year. By 1980, Calder estimated, the annual leakage would be around a hundred thousand curies. This figure did *not* allow for radioactive releases due to serious reactor accidents, however.

Nuclear ships were then considered, including both military vessels—over thirty nuclear submarines were under construction at that writing—and commercial, such as the N.S. *Savannah.* The symposium team estimated that sixty million curies of radioactivity would be present on or under the high seas in ship reactors, and "planned release" would come to three thousand curies.

Nuclear aircraft propulsion, which at the time of the symposium was still being seriously weighed by our Government, was regarded by the "auditors" as capable of releasing at least one million curies annually into the atmosphere, and by 1980 the figure could rise as high as a hundred million. Fortunately, that area of research and development was dropped, though nuclear propulsion of rocket ships is a present field of investigation. Also, reactors were being designed and used to provide power for instruments and radio communications in satellites. "If we have a lot of megawatt auxiliary power units in space vehicles by 1980," Calder wrote, "flying all around outer space but occasionally entering the atmosphere as live reactors, we might have something of the order of a million curies of fission products introduced into the environment."

The audit examined research and test reactors (as opposed to electricity-generating commercial reactors). "In the United States, these already represent something like 1,000 megawatts and, therefore, 1,000 million curies. Of these about a hundred thousand curies escape every year," Calder stated. He continued:

There are the plutonium factories. These release into the environment something like a million curies a year, in the form of low-level wastes. . . . The uranium mills seem to be releasing about 1,000 curies of radium per year into the rivers of the United States. . . . There are also the fuel reprocessing plants. There are the radio-isotopes which are being distributed all over the world for research and industrial uses and for medical treatment. These are under control, but by 1965 they will represent 10 million curies. The absolute safety of these depends upon the responsibility and training of those handling them. They are stored in impenetrable vessels but sometimes they get loose. . . .

The final tally made by Calder's group was most disquieting: "By the time we had added up all thé curies which might predictably be released, by all those peaceful uses, into the environment, it came to about 13 million curies per annum."

Calder went on to say, as if to belittle this figure, that several thousand times that number of curies had been released into the atmosphere in each of the five years of active testing of nuclear weapons prior to 1962. But that assertion not only does little to comfort us, it actually raises even sharper anxieties, for it means that the unnatural radiation in our environment was already extremely high by the time peacetime uses of nuclear power began releasing radioactivity.

The thirteen-million-curie annual "planned release" figure included nuclear aircraft propulsion, which currently is not a serious consideration and can be discounted. On the other hand, the audit did *not* include serious reactor accidents; it did *not* include experimental programs in which some radiation inevitably would be released, such as the "Plowshare" program of AEC-conducted explosions exploring the use of atomic energy to excavate harbors and canals; it did *not* include potential accidents involving transportation, on land, on sea, and in the air, of nuclear materials; it did *not* assess the contribution of radioactive fallout due to bomb testing, testing which still is carried out today by non-signatories of the Nuclear Test Ban Treaty. And it did *not* include possible escape of stored high-level radioactive wastes, the implications of which were awesome to contemplate: ". . . what kept nagging us," Calder said, "was the question of waste disposal and of the remaining radioactivity which must not get loose. We were told that the dangerous waste, which is kept in storage, amounted to 10,000 million curies. If you want to play 'the numbers game' as an irresponsible exercise, you could divide this by the population of the world and find that it is over 3 curies for every individual."

Irresponsible or not, Calder's "numbers game" gives a clear indication of how much lethally radioactive material must be contained without mishap; just as important, it indicates the impressive amount of radioactivity that is being and will be released under so-called "controlled" conditions even if no mishap should occur—a most dubious proposition.

A detailed look at the ways in which the environment is contaminated by normal functioning of nuclear power plants and related facilities is enlightening.

In a typical reactor, as we have seen, the concentration of uranium fuel in the core produces intense heat to convert water into steam, which in turn powers electricity-producing turbines.

At the same time that the uranium is generating heat energy, however, it is generating another form of energy, radioactivity, the emission of rays such as beta, gamma, and X rays. The radioactivity has a number of negative effects on the material inside the reactor. One of these is swelling, warping, or destruction of the metal tubes containing the uranium. Another is irradiation of the reactor components. Trace impurities in the metal cladding of the fuel tubes, for instance, or in the coolant, become radioactive, and once they do they interfere with the efficient energy production of the uranium. After a while, the accumulation of these "fission products" makes it impossible to keep the reactor running economically. Also, the neutron bombardment of fertile U-238 by fissionable U-235 is creating plutonium, and it is desirable to separate that plutonium from time to time and utilize it as weapon or commercial fuel material.

Thus because some fuel tubes may be damaged, and because the uranium fuel has become contaminated by fission products, and because it is desirable to recover the plutonium by-product, the fuel in the reactor's core must be replaced periodically. It is interesting to note that replacement occurs when only a tiny fraction of the fuel has been burned up.

The intensely radioactive spent fuel elements are removed from the reactor and stored under water for several months to allow some of the radioactivity to die down. Then they are loaded into heavily shielded casks and shipped to a fuel reprocessing plant. There, by means of remote control equipment, the metal cladding is stripped from the fuel, the fuel dissolved in acid, and the acid solution subjected to chemical separation processes. During these cycles, the noxious fission products are first removed from the fuel, then the uranium and plutonium are separated from each other and processed for reuse. The highly radioactive solutions from the extracting process are collected and boiled down to reduce their volume, and the concentrate is stored in large underground tanks.

Described in this abbreviated form, the whole process sounds sensible, safe, streamlined, and sterile, which is exactly what proponents of nuclear power would like us to believe. Pamphlets put out by government and industry describing the Magical Odyssey of Uranium are replete with photos of white-clad workers in aseptic surroundings, cheerfully carrying out their tasks as if they were packaging candy bars. A closer look at these processes, however, is nowhere near as soothing.

Taking reactor operation first, it must be pointed out that the technology for trapping every last radioactive particle released by the uranium fuel is either unperfected or too costly. While most of these contaminating radionuclides are trapped by processing the air and water, then concentrated and shipped to storage areas, minute quantities are issued into the environment. These are known as "low level" wastes, and we are told that such releases are undertaken in such a way as to ensure dilution sufficient to prevent any predictable human exposure above levels expected to produce deleterious consequences. Gaseous wastes are sent through a stack presumably high enough to ensure atmospheric dispersion. Liquid residues are spilled into the river, lake, or sea and presumably diluted to the point of harmlessness.

Thus when reactor operators are asked about the dangers of contaminating the environment, they cite the above techniques and the seemingly tiny amounts of radioactivity involved, as evidence of the complete absence of risk in nuclear power technology.

These arguments are seriously misleading. As will presently be detailed, (a) a number of radioactive waste products released at reactor sites do not decay for dozens or even hundreds of years, which means that the accumulation of radioactivity in our environment from *all* sources will increase; and (b) many of these released radioisotopes tend to concentrate in human and other organic systems, eventually building up formidable doses of what Walter Schneir, in *The Reporter,* so aptly described as "the atom's poisonous garbage."

The second major aspect of the atomic waste problem comes in the reprocessing of the fuel used in reactors. Until 1966, the task of reprocessing spent fuel was strictly a Government affair, having mostly to do with plutonium for defense purposes. The small volume of civilian reprocessing business did not justify the existence of a commercial reprocessing plant. But it is predicted that by 1980 there will be over three thousand tons per year of spent fuel to be reprocessed, and by the year 2000 that figure will jump ten times, to thirty thousand tons.

In anticipation of the vast increase in nuclear power in the 1970s, W. R. Grace & Co. and American Machine & Foundry Company formed an 80-20 partnership to erect the world's first commercial fuel reprocessing plant, sited about thirty miles south of Buffalo, New York. This thirty-two-million-dollar Nuclear Fuel Services, Inc., plant has a capacity of 1000 kilograms of fuel a day, about a quarter of a ton, and has an arrangement with the New York State Atomic Research and Development Authority for related radioactive waste storage facilities.

In December 1966, *Nucleonics,* a nuclear industry journal, chirped:

> The world's first commercial fuel-reprocessing plant handled its initial 100 tons of spent fuel in a smooth and routine fashion—a remarkable accomplishment for a facility relying largely on remote operation.

One group that became interested in this plant was the Rochester Committee for Scientific Information, particularly its Radioactive Pollution Subcommittee headed by Dr. George Berg and Dr. E. Grant Pike. The RCSI was worried that NFS Inc. was exceeding the official guidelines for effluent radioactivity established by the state and Federal governments.

The Subcommittee arranged for one Wayne Harris to collect water samples from Buttermilk Creek below the NFS plant. Buttermilk Creek is a tributary of Cattaraugus Creek, which forms a reservoir at Springville, then continues on to Lake Erie.

The group had the samples analyzed, and on February 24 and 28, 1968, the RCSI published its findings. We mention here only those for strontium 90, the long-lived bone-seeking isotope, though other isotopes were reported on as well.

The maximum limit of soluble strontium 90 allowed by New York State and Federal law is three hundred picocuries per liter.

On December 16, 1967, the Committee and the New York Health and Safety Laboratory of the U. S. Atomic Energy Commission, measuring the amount of strontium 90 at the NFS sewage outlet, found a concentration of 86,900 picocuries per liter. This would amount to some 290 times the legal limit. The amount of strontium 90 measured in Buttermilk Creek on that date was 4010 picocuries per liter, or about thirteen times the legal limit.

The average concentration of strontium 90 in the creek between December 1966 and May 2, 1967, was

655 picocuries per liter, or twice the legal limit. These findings would seem to confirm a State of New York Department of Health Radioactivity Bulletin issued in February 1967 in which "gross beta levels" of radioactivity in water downstream from the NFS plant, measured in November 1966, ran between 26 and 328 times the average measured at other water stations in the area.

The U. S. Congressional Joint Committee on Atomic Energy had criticized the AEC and Nuclear Fuel Services for inadequate attention to certain safeguards. Now Buttermilk Creek was adding its testimony. "The Nuclear Fuel Services Plant," the Rochester Committee concluded in its report, "is currently operating at a fraction of its licensed capacity. . . . If the plant has not managed to clean up its outflow after a year under minimum load, the RCSI sees reason for serious concern about its performance under full load."

And well it might.

It would be a pleasure to report that the worst part of the story had been told. But a survey of the perils of nuclear peace is like a Dantean survey of hell: One leaves each level certain that he has seen the worst, but ahead lie scenes more fiendish still. In order to complete our picture of the threat of radioactivity in the environment, we have to descend into that ring of Hades called Waste Storage.

It has been estimated that a ton of processed fuel will produce anywhere from forty to several hundred gallons of waste. This brew is a violently lethal mixture of short- and long-lived isotopes. It would take five cubic miles of water to dilute the waste from just one ton of fuel to the maximum permissible concentration. Or, if we permitted it to decay naturally until it reached that safe level, consider this: Just one of the isotopes, strontium 90, growing feebler by half every 27.4 years, would still be too hot to handle 1000 years from now, when it will have only one seventeen billionth of its current potency.

There is no way to reduce the toxicity of these radioisotopes; they must decay naturally, meaning *virtually perpetual containment.*

Unfortunately, mankind has practically no experience in perpetual creations, and the procedures for radioactive waste containment therefore leave a lot, if not everything, to be desired. Between 1945 and 1960, according to a speech made by Dr. Joseph A. Lieberman, chief of the AEC's Environmental and Sanitary Engineering Branch, some fourteen thousand curies of radioactive waste were dumped into the Pacific, and eight thousand into the Atlantic, contained in very much less than perpetual metal casks. In 1959 Herbert Parker, manager of the Hanford Laboratories of the AEC, told the Congressional Joint Committee on Atomic Energy that some three billion gallons of intermediate level wastes had been admitted to the ground at Hanford.

The most common practice, however, is to store the concentrates in large steel tanks shielded by earth and concrete. This method has been employed for some twenty years, and over seventy-five million gallons of waste is now in storage in some two hundred tanks. This "liquor" generates so much heat it boils by itself for years.

Most of the inventory in these caldrons is waste from weapons production, but as we approach the year 2000 the accumulation from commercial nuclear power will accelerate sharply. An article in the December 1959 issue of *Nuclear Information* stated that "If nuclear power grows in the United States at the rate now predicted, we shall have accumulated 6 billion curies of strontium-90 by the end of this century. That's 30 times as much strontium-90 as would be released by the nuclear war envisioned by the May 1959 Congressional hearings on nuclear war. . . . The significance of the expected amount of strontium-90 in radioactive wastes in the year 2000—6 billion curies—can be judged from the fact that the absorption of less than one curie of strontium-90 is lethal to a human being."

And that's just one isotope, strontium 90. Tens of billions of curies of radioactivity from other elements, some of which remain lethal for thousands of years, will have accumulated as well. Dr. Donald R. Chadwick, chief of the Division of Radiological Health of the U. S. Public Health Service, estimated in 1963 that the accumulated volume of these wastes would come to *two billion gallons* in 1995.

It is not just the volume that fills one with apprehension, but the ugly disposition of this material. David Lilienthal put his finger on the crux of the matter when he stated:

> These huge quantities of radioactive wastes must somehow be removed from the reactors, must—without mishap—be put into containers that will never rupture; then these vast quantities of poisonous stuff must be moved either to a burial ground or to reprocessing and concentration plants, handled again, and disposed of, by burial or otherwise, with a risk of human error at every step.

It cannot be stressed strongly enough that we are not discussing days, months, or even a few years. We are talking about periods "longer," in the words of AEC Commissioner Wilfred E. Johnson, "than the history of most governments that the world has seen." Nor can it be overemphasized that we are not talking about typical industrial pollution, requiring millions of gallons of waste to befoul a lake or river. We are talking about a material so potent that a few gallons released in a city's watershed could cause death and chaos on a scale comparable only to the havoc of modern warfare.

Bearing these things in mind, would we not be safe in assuming that safeguards no less fanatic than those surrounding the release of nuclear missiles would be operative in the case of nuclear waste management?

We would not.

In an article entitled "Radioactive Waste Management," published in the January 1965 issue of *Reactor Technology,* an AEC publication, W. G. Belter and D. W. Pearce cited no fewer than 9 cases of tank failure out of 183 tanks located in Washington, South Carolina, and Idaho. More recently, and most disturbingly, a passage in the AEC's Authorizing Legislation for 1968 called for funding of $2,500,000 for the replacement of failed and failing tanks in Richland, Washington:

> A total of 149 tanks with about 95 million gallons capacity have been built [the report stated]. Prior to 1964, five tanks have been withdrawn from service because of leaks. Since 1964, one tank has failed and four more have developed indications of incipient failure. . . . The waste storage situation has been further aggravated by recent temperature control problems which have occurred in a tank being filled with the Purex self-boiling wastes. The tank bottom temperatures began exceeding the design control limits and further filling of this tank has been stopped which reduces planned waste storage space.

The urgency of the situation could not be disguised by the bureaucratic language in which the plea was couched:

> . . . There is no assurance that the need for new waste storage tanks can be forestalled.

Here then are tanks which have failed after twenty years. Twenty years is a respectable period as industrial processes go, but in the life of a radioisotope it may be but a moment, for some isotopes, as we have seen, can outlast ten, twenty, fifty, or more transfers of waste over hundreds and hundreds of years to come. It is beyond belief that this burden of centuries can be borne without some collapses. The individual tanks require elaborate supporting facilities. Special cooling apparatus is needed, itself subject to heavy contamination. Special pumps are needed to recirculate the waste to prevent ferocious surges of boiling. Switching and access equipment is needed to direct or divert flow from one tank to another.

Furthermore, these so-called "tank farms" are vulnerable to natural catastrophes such as earthquakes, and to man-made ones such as sabotage or plain human error. And what about the long-term legal and financial responsibilities? In 1959 the Joint Committee on Atomic Energy of the U. S. Congress, examining industrial radioactive waste disposal, predicted a capital outlay of two hundred million dollars for these atomic sepulchers, plus six million dollars a year to maintain them. Cannot private companies fail, or Government administrations withdraw support for a program?

One needn't look into a crystal ball for a glimpse of what could happen if someone failed to hold up his end of the bargain in the matter of waste maintenance; it has already happened. On February 2, 1967, the St. Louis *Post-Dispatch* reported that a mining company had defaulted on an AEC loan to buy some 100,000 tons of uranium ore residue located on a field in Missouri's St. Louis County. It therefore became necessary to put the stuff up for auction—*repeat,* put it up for auction! It was picked up by a loan corporation and was still waiting for someone with sufficient financial backing to take it over and reprocess it. Title to 100,-000 tons of radioactive waste—kicking around like a pawnshop ticket!

Efforts are of course being made for the effective handling of the waste problem. The most promising proposal would reduce the wastes to solid form, enclose them in concrete or glassy material, and store the blocks in abandoned salt mines proved to have no access to underground water systems. But while this is nice in theory, many technological barriers remain before the problem is licked. It is easy for AEC Commissioner Wilfred Johnson to toss off: "The Commission is now looking at the challenge of long-term waste management and I am certain we will have effective means in hand to meet it well in advance of the need." But his optimism has no basis in solid fact.

Meanwhile, millions and millions of gallons boil furiously inside their frail tanks, tanks whose seams groan under strains metal was never meant to bear, and men go on building power plants to feed ever more of this corrosive ichor into its nuclear garbage dumps.

Industrial waste is not peculiar to the nuclear industry. It is a phenomenon of every major industrial process. But the waste of the nuclear industry is unique in three ways. It cannot be disposed of in any conventional sense of the term. Its toxicity is not immediately apparent to human senses. And finally, the longevity of certain waste isotopes poses storage and disposal problems unparalleled in industrial history.

These unique circumstances place intolerable burdens on Government regulatory agencies and on the individuals in private industry whose task it is to supervise the waste management operations; and the load they place on future generations is unmitigatedly cruel. Joel A. Snow, writing in *Scientist and Citizen*, put it well when he wrote, "Over periods of hundreds of years it is impossible to ensure that society will remain responsive to the problems created by the legacy of nuclear waste which we have left behind."

"Legacy" is one way of stating it, but "curse" seems far more appropriate, for at the very least we are saddling our children with the perpetual custodianship of our atomic refuse. But it could be much, much worse than that, as we may be dooming them to any of a galaxy of horrors should the frail reservoirs we are building today release their virulent stew tomorrow.

We have little time left to reflect on our alternatives, for the time must soon come when no reversal will be possible. Dr. L. P. Hatch of Brookhaven National Laboratory vividly made this point when he told the Joint Committee on Atomic Energy:

... If we were to go on for 50 years in the atomic power industry, and find that we had reached an impasse, that we had been doing the wrong thing with the wastes and we would like to reconsider the disposal methods, it would be entirely too late, because the problem would exist and nothing could be done to change that fact for the next, say, 600 or a thousand years.

To which might be added the following paralyzing thought stated by Dr. David Price of the U. S. Public Health Service:

We all live under the haunting fear that something may corrupt the environment to the point where man joins the dinosaurs as an obsolete form of life. And what makes these thoughts all the more disturbing is the knowledge that our fate could perhaps be sealed twenty or more years before the development of symptoms.

How fortunate, as Professors Schubert and Lapp said, that our discovery of radiation is paralleled by our knowledge of its deleterious effects. Otherwise, ignorance of the consequences of irradiating man might induce great recklessness.

CHAPTER XI

The Waters Ignited

Early in 1963, shortly after the nuclear power station at Indian Point, New York, began operation, an unusually large number of crows began concentrating at a refuse dump near the plant. Curious sportsmen investigating the phenomenon were astounded to find that the crows had been attracted by dead striped bass—tens of thousands of them. "They were piled," according to one observer, "to a depth of several feet. They covered an area encompassing more than a city lot."

What grim fate had befallen these fish? And who had carried them to the dump to rot as crow fodder?

Following their noses to a dock on the Hudson River, just below the power station, the sportsmen learned the answer to the first question. The dock was located at the shoreline where heated water, which had been used to cool the plant's atomic reactor, was being discharged back into the river. Beneath the dock was a ghastly scene: Countless dead and dying fish floated on their sides, their eyes bulging.

The stripers apparently had been attracted by the hot water flow around the discharge pipe, then became trapped within the wharf and water intake structures at the plant. Further inquiry revealed that Consolidated Edison, which operated the Indian Point facility, was using two trucks to haul the dead fish to the dump.

The Great Indian Point Fish Kill, as that grisly episode has been called, is a nauseating but by no means atypical example of the devastating effects of what has come to be called thermal pollution. To recognize heat as a form of water pollution may require a bit of mental exercise, since we normally associate pollution with dirt and other visible contaminants. But if we define a pollutant as *any* factor whose introduction into the environment is detrimental or ruinous, then heat can surely be included in the growing list. For it was heat that drew those striped bass to the dock, and the hairsplitting explanation by one Con Edison official that the fish "were not *injured* by warm water—they were killed by the mechanical device" in no way diminishes the gravity of the thermal pollution issue.

A rise in the temperature of a river can kill in many ways, some of them far more subtle than the outright slaughter that took place at Indian Point. The ecology of any given area—the relationship of each plant or animal to every other organism in the environment—is always an extremely complex and delicately balanced system. An apparently insignificant change in one branch of that system can have astonishingly significant effects on another, and indeed on interrelationships of *all* parts. The eradication of a large portion of a river's fish population, then, is not merely pathetic in terms of the fish and the humans who directly depend on them for food and sport; it may be tragic in the many unpredictably dire consequences suffered by all life in the environment.

Not even a professional ecologist will attempt to predict any but the more obvious results of a disturbance in an environment; too often he finds out only when the effects become clearly manifest, and even then it may take sharp detective work to trace effects back to their causes. But the obvious results are disturbing enough to merit a detailed look at some of the known relationships between temperature rises in large bodies of water and the quality of life in the environment.

In the first place, heat has a profound effect upon the composition of water itself. Warm water can hold less oxygen dissolved in solution than cooler water. Since fish must obtain needed oxygen from water by means of their gills, a drop in the oxygen content of water leads to suffocation and death. When a body of water already contains toxicants of other kinds near the maximum allowable tolerances—as is the case with an increasing number of America's waterways—even a relatively small rise in temperature can have disastrous consequences.

The implications can best be seen in the case of salmon, which, along with other fish of the salmon family such as trout, are particularly sensitive to temperature changes. The Pacific Northwest's Columbia River Basin is a major salmon spawning ground, but it is also the site of considerable nuclear reactor activity. Scientists now calculate that this activity will raise the temperature of the river to 85 degrees Fahrenheit, a full *five degrees above the maximum temperature tolerable by salmon even for a few hours*. Even a temperature of anything approaching 85 degrees, then, could result in nothing less than the complete extirpation of the river's salmon population, sending one of the most valuable natural resources on the North American continent to the same fate as the extinct, or all but extinct, bison, sperm whale, alligator, and passenger pigeon.

The collateral effects of water temperature changes are no less dangerous. Warmer waters produce much heavier growths of aquatic algae and other undesirable vegetation that turn clear and sparkling swimming areas into scum-ridden morasses. Of more immediate danger to wildlife, however, is that a rise of only a few degrees can enable formerly dormant fungi and parasitic organisms to flourish. Such has recently been observed in the Columbia River, due essentially to the discharges of the Hanford reactors. The net effect has been the growth of a deadly, but hitherto dormant, bacterial fish disease, columnaris. The disease has taken a heavy toll of salmon swimming upstream toward their spawning grounds.

Even if these fish are not slaughtered outright by excessive heat or columnaris, or even if excessive heat can be controlled, the fish population is nevertheless endangered by even moderate rises in water temperature. Cyclical changes in water temperature are vital to the reproductive processes of such fish as bass, trout, salmon, and walleyes. Unless they experience the natural rhythm of seasonal variations, their reproductive mechanisms will be disoriented, disrupted, or destroyed. Furthermore, a relatively slight upward change in water temperature can prove fatal to fish eggs and small fry, so that the attainment of the desired spawning grounds—an incredibly difficult struggle for many varieties of fish under the best of circumstances—does not guarantee the hatching of eggs or the development of the fry.

Just how great a problem is thermal pollution? Is it only a matter of killing salmon in Washington or stripers in New York? Scarcely, for *virtually every large fresh-water system in our country is earmarked for nuclear plant cooling purposes!* A statement made by Dr. Gerald F. Tape, an AEC commissioner, at a 1968 Arkansas meeting of the Southern Interstate Nuclear Board, that "There is no basis for statements that 'thermal pollution from nuclear plants has been responsible for serious damage to marine ecology,'" is therefore puzzling.

Of course, reactors are not the only thermal polluters; many other industrial processes, including conventionally fueled electricity production, spill high quantities of hot water into rivers and streams. However, a report by J. G. Terrill, Jr., to the American Society of Civil Engineers establishes that "fossil fuel plants currently have a thermal efficiency of about 36 percent as compared to an efficiency for nuclear plants of about 25 percent. This results in a somewhat higher thermal load being placed on the receiving stream from a nuclear plant for a given electrical generating capacity." As a result, nuclear-powered stations require up to 40 per cent more water to cool their apparatus than do their fossil-fueled counterparts—as much as half a million gallons of water *per minute*.

The deluge is pumped back into its source at temperatures as high as 115 degrees, and has been known to heat the entire river to a temperature of 95 degrees as far as five miles downstream! What is more, the stream of hot water remains separate from the stream of surrounding cooler water, so that a utility wishing to prove that no serious thermal pollution had been created could measure the cooler part of the river.

There *is* one way to combat thermal pollution, and that is by means of "cooling towers" designed to lower the temperature of the water emerging from reactors before it is returned to its source. Since these cost millions of dollars, however, utilities seek to avoid adding them to their facilities. The AEC does not require them as standard equipment.

Scientists estimate that by 1980 the plants producing the nation's electric power will require some two hundred billion gallons of water per day, nearly all of it for cooling purposes. As noted in the January-February 1968 issue of the *Sport Fishing Institute Bulletin,* "This amount of water compares to an annual nationwide runoff totalling 1,200 billion gallons per day. In other words, a quantity of coolant equivalent to *one-sixth of the total amount of available fresh water will be necessary for cooling the steam-electric power-producing plants.* More ominously, during the two thirds of the year when flood flows are generally lacking, about *half the total fresh-water runoff will be required* for [steam-electric station] cooling purposes at inland locations. On certain heavily populated and industrialized northeastern U.S. watersheds, moreover, *100 percent of available flows may be passed through the various power-generating stations* within the watersheds during low-flow periods." [Emphasis ours.]

And that takes us up only to 1980.

What has the Atomic Energy Commission done to check the thermal destruction of our streams and estuaries? Its most vigorous action has been a monumental shoulder-shrug, disowning any regulatory responsibility in this area whatsoever. The AEC contends that the problem falls within the authority and jurisdiction of state agencies, so that it is "unnecessary, and therefore undesirable, to involve the AEC. . . ." Some officials have euphemistically termed the temperature effects of reactor discharges "thermal enrichment," and AEC Commissioner James T. Ramey told a congressional hearing in 1967 that "One point of view says it improves the fishing."

If the AEC, then, thinks it "unnecessary" and "undesirable" to get involved in the question, what about the Department of the Interior? Might not its Fish and Wildlife Service bear the burden of responsibility? Interior seems to pass the hot potato back to the AEC. For a while it looked as if *someone* at last was going to take the job on, for in April 1966 Interior wrote the AEC entreating it to join in resolving their differences and settling on a mutually agreeable policy in the near future. Strangely, however, when Representative John D. Dingell of Michigan submitted legislation that year authorizing the Department of the Interior to make a study of the effects of thermal pollution on fish and wildlife, Interior said no. Instead, it joined the AEC in supporting legislation delegating all authority concerning non-radiological aspects of power plant operation to yet *another* agency, the Federal Power Commission.

Thus the issue floats on an increasingly polluted no man's sea lying, apparently, beyond the jurisdiction of any one Government entity. In February 1968 the Senate Subcommittee on Air and Water Pollution held a series of meetings to determine whether new legislation was needed to regulate thermal pollution by nuclear power plants. Chairman Edmund S. Muskie of Maine found that while "Nuclear power plants are licensed by a Federal agency, and, therefore, can and should be expected to conform with applicable water quality standards and a concept of water quality enhancement," things just weren't working out that way. In fact, Muskie went so far as to declare that often the activities of Federal agencies "actually condone pollution rather than encouraging water quality enhancement."

Muskie may have had in mind a forceful move made by the AEC just a few months earlier. That move was reported in the December 7, 1967, issue of *National Coal Policy Conference Newsletter*:

> At a time when increasing concern is being expressed in and out of Congress over thermal pollution of the Nation's rivers and lakes by nuclear power plants, the Atomic Energy Commission is proposing to adopt new rules which would have the effect of *barring testimony on this subject at public hearings to consider the licensing of new atomic installations.*
>
> The AEC's proposed new rules would specifically prohibit witnesses from discussing subjects which are outside the agency's jurisdiction. Thermal pollution is, AEC has ruled, outside its jurisdiction and, therefore, should not be considered as one of the factors determining whether the licensing of a nuclear plant is in the public interest.
>
> Despite the fact that AEC denies it has the authority to take thermal pollution into consideration, it nevertheless has been cool to suggestions that the law be amended to give it specific authority or to give the regulatory authority over thermal pollution to some other agency such as the Interior Department or Federal Power Commission. . . .
>
> *If the AEC approves the proposed new rules, they will have the effect of formally barring the question of thermal pollution from being raised in future cases.* [Emphasis theirs.]

Early in 1968 the Department of the Interior of the United States finally came up with a plan to undertake a two-year study of thermal effects along the entire Columbia River, with an eye to establishing some scientific basis for determining permissible variations in water temperatures above natural levels. What will have become of the salmon population by the time the study's results are published and by the time action—if any—is taken on them, is most unpleasant to contemplate. And the destiny of fresh-water fish everywhere else in our country is far more than unpleasant, to put it mildly: Two Rutgers University experts have estimated that, at the present rate of heat discharge into American rivers, some of those rivers might reach their boiling point by 1980 and evaporate by 2010.

CHAPTER XII

Man's Dwindling Radiation Budget

In the last chapter it was mentioned that some utilities have proposed to build "cooling towers" to alleviate the problems of thermal pollution. It can be asserted, however, that those devices may be used to cool something other than water: namely, community hostility to atomic reactors. Although the cost of building cooling towers is one no utility cares to pay, agreement to build one may make the public feel the utility is genuinely trying to meet the community halfway. Similar agreements may be made in matters of land beautification, such as building parks around nuclear facilities or offering to bury transmission cables underground. The community comes away feeling it has wrung a valuable concession out of the utility people, and relaxes pressure or abandons the fight altogether. Meanwhile, attention has been distracted from a threat far more insidious even than the overheating of water resources: that of radiological pollution of the environment.

Apparently the public, for want of information, thinks in conventional terms about this form of pollution. There are many indications that numerous utility executives labor under a similar impression. In any event, this error has enabled power companies to play down the importance of low-level emissions of radioactivity into air and water and rule them out as valid grounds for opposition to nuclear plants. It is imperative that this gross misapprehension be corrected.

In the first place, and foremost, is the fact that many waste radionuclides take an extraordinary long time to decay.* Cobalt 60 has a half life of over five years, strontium 90 of over twenty-seven years, and cesium 137 of over thirty years. A few take far, far longer. A pound of carbon 14, could it have been placed in the tomb of Narmer, Egypt's first known pharaoh, around 3200 B.C., would still have more than half its potency today. A gram of plutonium 239 buried today will have lost only half its radioactivity in the year 25,969.

Thus, even though these long-lived isotopes may be widely dispersed in air or diluted in water, their radio-activity does not cease. It remains, and over a period of time accumulates. It is therefore not pertinent to talk about the safety of any single release of radioactive effluents into the environment. *At issue, rather, is their duration and cumulative radioactivity.*

For another thing, scientists do not understand all the ways in which radiation from specific isotopes affects human and other life. There are some two hundred isotopes created in the heart of a reactor, but analyses of their biological effects are scarcely complete, to say the least. The fact that effects of atomic experiments and programs are often totally unexpected and discovered only after radioactivity has been introduced in quantity into the environment was brought out in "Test Fallout and Water Pollution," an article by Dr. Barry Commoner which appeared in the December 1964 issue of *Scientist and Citizen*. Dr. Commoner said: "Massive nuclear testing which began with the development of the hydrogen bomb in 1953 was well under way before most of its biological consequences were appreciated. The unanticipated tendency of world-wide fallout to deposit preferentially in the North Temperate Zone was unknown until 1956; the hazard from radio-

---

*Decay in a radioactive element is described in terms of its "half life"—the time it will take for half of its atoms to disintegrate through fission. The isotope ruthenium 106, for example, has a half life of one year, meaning that one pound of it at the start of 1970 will be one half pound at the start of 1971 and one quarter pound at the start of 1972, etc.

active iodine and carbon-14 was not brought to light until 1957; the special ecological factors which amplify the fallout hazard in the Arctic were elucidated for the first time in 1960; experiments which suggest that strontium-90 may cause hereditary damage by becoming concentrated in the chromosomes were first reported in 1963."

A perfect example of this "information lag" may be seen in a story related by Dr. Commoner, who is Chairman of Botany and director of the Center for the Biology of Natural Systems at Washington University, St. Louis, Missouri. Speaking before a conference on Nuclear Power and Environment held in Vermont in September 1968 (which the AEC declined to attend, incidentally), he told his audience of an important biological observation which, though several years old, seemingly had received little attention—in any event, he had just learned about it. It concerned the radioactive isotope of iodine, iodine 131.

Iodine 131 is one of the inevitable products of nuclear reactions, whether in bomb or reactor. It is relatively short-lived, with a half life of only about eight days, so that after a few weeks any iodine 131 released into the environment decays thoroughly.

Because of its short life, I-131 contamination from nuclear explosions was for a long time neglected, Dr. Commoner pointed out. In due time it was realized that actually it was among the most hazardous of all fission products because iodine is concentrated in the thyroid gland, and even low concentrations of the radioactive variety would, in the process of decay, severely damage the thyroid and cause harmful biological changes, among which is thyroid cancer.

One would think that in the absence of extensive nuclear weapons-testing or serious reactor accidents, the environment would be completely free of fast-decaying I-131. Dr. Commoner, however, had only recently been reminded of a test by investigators at the University of Nevada, who studied the I-131 content of cattle thyroids during a period (1959-61) in which there were only rare environmental intrusions of radioactive iodine from nuclear tests. "Much to their surprise," said Dr. Commoner, "—and I must confess, mine as well—they found, consistently, that even when there were no nuclear tests, cattle thyroids always contained *some* I-131."

What was most surprising was that the I-131 levels in the cattle thyroids are constant—month after month. Since I-131 decays so fast, it means that new I-131 is entering the thyroid as fast as the original I-131 decays. There must be a constant introduction of radioactive iodine into the environment, then—from a source other than nuclear explosions, which were ruled out because of their infrequency at this time.

After considering all possible sources, the University of Nevada investigators concluded: "The principal known source of I-131 that could contribute to this level is exhaust gases from nuclear reactors and associated fuel processing plants."

Similar data, Dr. Commoner added, suggest that this situation is widespread, *involving at least the western third of the United States.*

Another example of the sketchiness of our knowledge of the effects of certain radioisotopes is tritium. Tritium is a radioactive isotope of hydrogen which, if absorbed by the human body in place of stable, nonradioactive hydrogen, might have deleterious effects. Since it has a relatively long half life, twelve and a half years, and its distribution into body tissues would be as wide as its parent element hydrogen, its presence in reactor effluents dictates the highest caution. Yet in his keynote address to the Health Physics Society Symposium at Atlanta, Georgia, on January 24, 1968, AEC Commissioner Wilfred E. Johnson admitted that the release into the atmosphere of tritium and noble gases such as the ten-year half life krypton 85 would be a problem in the future, and that as yet scientists had not devised a way of solving it.

The other isotope Commissioner Johnson mentioned, krypton 85, gives us even greater cause for concern. This isotope, with a half life of about ten years, is particularly difficult to extract from the effluvia of reactor operations. J. R. Coleman and R. Liberace of the Radiological Health Division of the U. S. Public Health Service stated in an official report dated November 1966 that removal of krypton 85 from reactor wastes involved "costly techniques which are reasonable only if very small volumes or flow rates are used"—a condition that does not apply to the big reactors now built or presently to go into operation. And so instead of spending money to remove krypton 85, and thus raising the cost of "cheap electricity" to a realistic price that embraces health safeguards, reactor operators have no choice but to let the gas go into the air.

Although some radioactive elements seek particular tissues and organs when taken into the system, krypton 85, with its tendency to dissolve in fatty tissue, is distributed fairly evenly throughout the human body, raising over-all internal radiation and the attendant chances of cancer induction, genetic damage, and shortening of life.

By what amount will krypton 85 raise exposure levels? According to the highly detailed but conservative report made by Coleman and Liberace, the human whole-body dose from this isotope will be between twenty to a hundred millirads per year by 2060. It is not necessary to define a millirad in this context, but merely to point out that the National Committee on Radiation Protection and Measurement has set 170 millirads per year, above natural background radiation, as the maximum amount of radiation from any and all sources to which the general population should be exposed.

Thus the release of krypton 85 alone may exhaust about three fifths of the human radiation "budget" within the next century!

Considering, therefore, that krypton 85 is but one of

a compendium of some two hundred radioactive elements produced by reactors, the reassurance that carefully monitored releases of low-level radioactivity into the environment are not harmful is nonsense.

Such reassurances are deceptive in another way. While, as we've seen, some radioactive elements taken into the body are distributed evenly, others are absorbed into specific tissues and tend to build up concentrations. Iodine 131, for instance, seeks the thyroid gland; strontium 90 collects in the bones; cesium 137 tends to accumulate in muscle. Many of these isotopes have long half lives, some measurable in decades. Human intake of these poisonous isotopes does not, therefore, lead merely to general distribution throughout the body. It leads instead to build-ups in the specific tissues or organs to which those isotopes are attracted, thus increasing by many times the exposure dosage in those local areas of the body.

Man is by no means the only creature in whom radioactive isotopes may concentrate. Indeed, the dietary needs of all vegetable and animal life dictate the intake of specific elements. Those elements, whether radioactive or not, will concentrate even in the lowest and most basic forms of life. They are then passed up food chains, chains such as grass-to-cattle-to-milk-to-man. As they progress up these chains, the concentrations increase, sometimes by hundreds of thousands of times. Norman Lansdell, in his book *The Atom and the Energy Revolution,* reports a study of the Columbia River in the western United States in which it was found that while the radioactivity of the water was relatively insignificant,

1) the radioactivity of the river plankton was 2000 times greater;
2) the radioactivity of the fish and ducks feeding on the plankton was 15,000 and 40,000 times greater respectively;
3) the radioactivity of young swallows fed on insects

caught by their parents in the river was 500,000
times greater; and
4) the radioactivity of the egg yolks of water birds was
more than a million times greater.

A closer look at this amplification process is enlightening. Take zinc 65. Zinc 65 is produced in a reactor
when chain-reaction neutrons interact with zinc in reactor components. Some of this radioactive isotope is
released into the waters surrounding reactors. Studies of
numerous sites downriver from reactors, such as the
Columbia River on which the Hanford, Washington
reactor is located, or Connecticut's Thames below the
Groton nuclear submarine station, have disclosed concentrations of zinc 65 (among other isotopes) in algae,
fish, oysters, vegetation, and animals that feed or prey
on those foods.

Scrutiny of the wildlife in a pond receiving runoff
from the Savannah River plant near Aiken, South Carolina, demonstrated that while the water in that pond
contained only twenty-five thousandths of a picocurie
per gram of zinc 65, the algae that lived on the water
had a concentration of 148 picocuries per gram, an
increase of 5820 times. The bones of bluegills, an
omnivorous fish that fed both on the algae and on fish
that ate the algae, had 218 picocuries per gram, a
concentration of 8270 times the amount of zinc 65
found in the water. Another example: In 1958 when
Columbia River water had about 188 picocuries per
kilogram, oyster samples at the mouth of the river had
concentrations as high as 63,500 picocuries per kilogram, a 330-fold concentration.

Studies of humans in the Columbia River area drive
the point home. Measurement of radioactive zinc in the
bodies of people who drink Columbia River water
showed that these people have 57 picocuries of zinc 65
per kilogram of body weight—more than 4000 picocuries in a 154-pound man. A man drinking three
glasses of milk and eating about a quarter of a pound

of meat daily from the Columbia River Valley would have nine times that amount of radiation in his system —which is greater than that measured in some persons working in atomic energy installations.

Here then are clear illustrations of the ways in which almost undetectable traces of radioactivity in air, water, and land may be progressively concentrated so that by the time they end up on man's plate or in his glass they have become a tidy package of poison. This is to say nothing, by the way, of genetic effects and bizarre transformations about which practically nothing is known. Dr. Robert Pendleton, molecular and genetic biologist of the University of Utah, has stated that at Oak Ridge, Tennessee, "very small amounts of radioactive waste were dumped into . . . White Oak Lake. Fish that appeared afterward . . . were fantastic. They changed into many grotesque shapes and sizes. The most amazing thing was not the genetic mutations but the fact that some fish were found many miles downstream from the lake glowing like Christmas trees."

That "low level" waste is, in the light of these discussions, a grossly deceptive term is obvious. The level is low only if one thinks of the dispersion of radioactive particles into air or water on a single occasion. If one considers instead the accumulation of long-lived isotopes released over decades by scores of reactors and other sources, and if one considers the reassembly of those scattered particles in growing concentrations up the stages of the food chain, and if one considers their further concentration in bones, muscles, glands, and other tissues and organs of the human body—where, then, is your "low level"?

This gross misconception has led to formulation of a very dangerous and deceptive system of radiation guidelines established by various groups and adopted by our Government. Altogether, these guidelines lay down a "maximum permissible dose" which an individual can receive from any single radioactive source without suffering harmful effects.

The fallacy in the "maximum permissible dose" system is that the guidelines fail to take into account the *total* accumulation of radiation we receive from *all* emitting sources. Ritchie Calder expressed it clearly when he said ". . . radiation adds up to a sum. For example, when a series of operations feeds legalized waste into a common stream, the contribution of each may be insignificant but the total may be really significant. Our common environment is like that stream."

The maximum permissible levels of radiation exposure used in the AEC's regulations are based on the recommendations of the National Council (originally Committee) on Radiation Protection and Measurements —the NCRP. This private organization, founded in 1929, has been the principal standard-setter for radiation protection in the United States. But although it is known as a body of distinguished and cautious scientists and engineers who try to perform their functions conscientiously and objectively, there is a flaw in its fundamental approach which is not widely recognized. That flaw is decribed by Harold P. Green in an article published in the November 1967 *Bulletin of the Atomic Scientists*:

> Despite the competence, conservatism, and integrity of the NCRP, its role raises significant questions of public policy. Its public pronouncements explicitly reflect the policy of "calculated risk"; in making its recommendations, it balances the benefits of radiation technology against its hazards. It endeavors to adopt levels of permissible exposure which will protect the public but which will not, at the same time, stifle the radiation industry. As Dr. Lauriston Taylor, for many years the head of NCRP, has pointed out, NCRP and its international counterpart are ". . . scientific and technical in their makeup and hence do not attempt to solve the social problems that radiation control may introduce," and ". . . the establishment of permissible levels of radiation exposure is not basically a scientific problem . . . it is more a matter of philosophy, of morality, and of

sheer wisdom." Despite these disclaimers of competence the NCRP has, largely by default of others, undertaken to make recommendations as to "maximum permissible dose."

Green's conclusion is of the highest importance to our discussions: "It is apparent that NCRP, in adopting radiation protection standards which are arrived at through the balancing of social values, and which are more or less automatically incorporated into government regulations and used as standards by the courts, is performing a legislative function. As such it is unrepresentative, since it consists only of scientists and engineers, without membership from other disciplines (law, psychiatry, the clergy, economists, etc.) and societal interests. Nor does NCRP have political accountability of the kind that should be inherent in lawmaking bodies."

The fallacy of the "maximum permissible dose" can lead society far astray from the path of safety and health. "A case in point," states Walter Schneir in an article in *The Reporter,* "is the pollution of the Animas River in Colorado and New Mexico, where the water used by thirty thousand people was found by the Public Health Service to contain radium far in excess of maximum permissible levels. For a proper assessment of the danger from the wastes, the Public Health Service sought to learn what other man-made radiation the people of the area were exposed to. By unhappy coincidence, the peas, cabbages, lettuce, and other vegetables grown in this area were also discovered to have extremely large amounts of strontium-90 from fallout."

The National Committee on Radiation Protection and Measurements, in an article in *Science,* advocated that "The levels should be set so that the typical person in the area will not receive more than the established permissible dose when all sources are combined." And Dr. Theodore Rice, laboratory director of the U. S. Bureau of Marine Fisheries, Radio-Biological Lab,

Pivers Island, Beaufort, North Carolina, was reported as stating that at present the AEC Code of Federal Regulations, Title 10, Part 20, on maximum permissible limits of release of radioactive wastes, was so flexible as to be no regulations at all. "Although safe levels of radiation are determined on the basis of intake of drinking water, if we get additional amounts from food and other sources, we get more than the maximum level."

The great danger in having flexible guidelines set by groups sensitive to scientific or governmental needs—or incapable of overruling them in the name of humanity—is that those guidelines could be raised if it were thought expedient to do so to further the interests of atomic energy proponents and promoters. This was expressed by Dr. Paul Tompkins, executive director of the Federal Radiation Council, who observed that if our population was receiving frequent or continuous exposure to iodine 131, it might "justify an adjustment upward of the total estimated dose that would be acceptable without taking protective action."

At the conclusion of this book will be presented an increasingly influential scientific view that new guidelines must be set fixing hard and fast levels—a radiation "budget" as it were—which could not be exceeded without the most scrupulous consideration by a body of qualified individuals. It should be clear from the foregoing, however, that the current system of guidelines and acceptable levels and maximum permissible doses establishes a most unrealistic framework of criteria for our radiological security.

As stated earlier, many conservation issues such as thermal pollution are unwittingly serving as red herrings to divert the public's eyes from the perils arising from radioactive discharges from atomic facilities. Though those issues are by no means insignificant, it is absolutely necessary that we recognize that radioactivity is the chief hazard by far. Time and again, following announcement of a utility's plans for constructing a nuclear facility, one can read newspaper stories and editorials expressing disturbance about land and wild-life conservation, yet saying not a word about radiological hazards. On August 20, 1968, to cite just one instance, the New York *Times* published a feature story titled "Nuclear Plant Plan Stirs Controversy." It told of the public outcry in Fairfield County, Connecticut, because of United Illuminating Company's plans for a nuclear station on Cockenoe Island, just offshore in Long Island Sound. Cockenoe is four miles from Westport, four from Norwalk, a little over five from Darien, eight from New Canaan, and about a dozen each from Bridgeport and the north shore of Long Island. It is also within casualty- and property-damage-inflicting distance of New Haven and New York City. Yet not a single one of the thousand or so words devoted to the controversy mentioned radioactive hazards.

The point is not that the preservation of natural resources, of scenic wildlife preserves, of places where humans can go and be at peace, escape metropolitan tensions, do some thinking—the point is not that these issues are unimportant. The erection of even a conventional plant on this island would be offensive from a conservation viewpoint in any event.

The point is that people have *missed* the point. That responsible and presumably well-informed citizens and newspaper people can be so utterly unaware that an accident at the Cockenoe plant could wipe out the lives and property of thousands upon thousands of souls in the densely populated Connecticut-Long Island area—does this not illustrate the need for greater public airing of the hazards of atomic power?

If the Save Cockenoe Committee really wants some ammunition for its conservation arguments, the following matters should be considered.

Our seas are grand but they are not of infinite capacity. They can accommodate a huge amount of waste and flotsam, but, as we are discovering with all natural systems on our planet, they have limits. It might take a good deal of radioactivity to contaminate the seas, but the enormous potency of nuclear material, its longevity and cumulative lethality, could in time raise radiation levels by a small but undesirable, if not alarming, amount. Runoff of radioactive effluents and bomb tests or peacetime nuclear excavation, the sinking of nuclear ships or of ships and planes bearing nuclear material, large-scale releases resulting from accidents on land- or island-based reactors, and of course the continued ocean-dumping of enormous quantities of atomic waste —these can all make their contributions.

In recent years scientists have been looking with increased hope to the sea as a source of food and other resources. Under the Pacific Ocean alone, it has been estimated, there is enough aluminum to last at the present world rate of consumption for *eighty thousand years*, compared to a hundred years of reserves known on land; enough manganese for *four hundred thousand years,* compared to land reserves of a hundred years, and enough copper for *six thousand years*, compared to land reserves of only forty years. Mismanagement of the oceans and sea beds, however, may render it more difficult if not impossible to harvest this incredible bounty.

This fact is seen most clearly in the contamination of plankton, the minute plant and animal organisms that float on or near the surface of the sea. A recent article in *The Nation* found the plankton at one site to be 150,000 times more radioactive than the water. But while the contamination of such microscopic lowlife would not, at first glance, seem to have much bearing on the fate of our planet, the upshot could range from the "merely" catastrophic to the totally apocalyptic.

It has long been known that protein-rich plankton is one of the prime sources of food for fish. Radioactive poisoning of this food, therefore, could eradicate it as completely as a flood eradicates a farm crop, leading to starvation of whole species of sea life and turbulent changes in marine ecologies. Even if the plankton were not actually poisoned out of existence, its ingestion by fish, and the concentration of radioisotopes in their bones, tissues, and organs, could lead to wholesale extermination or deadly mutations eventuating in extermination. In either case the life of the sea, and the life that depends on it, would be radically affected by radiological contamination of this elemental life form.

But that is not all. Efforts are now under way to harvest plankton as a potentially vast source of protein for a humanity that is growing by one million persons per week. Even if nothing is said about loss of edible fish to world markets as a result of radioactive contamination, the loss of edible plankton would strike a grave blow to a major hope for the relief of future famines.

Yet even this prospect is eclipsed by a potential hazard of awesome proportions—one which threatens to transform the very air we breathe.

One man who has considered these possibilities is Dr. LaMont Cole, professor of ecology at Cornell University. Most of us who got through high school biology may still be familiar with the cycle by which oxygen and nitrogen are kept in immutable balance in the atmosphere. Green plants produce oxygen with the help of sunlight during photosynthesis. Nitrogen is produced and released in the decay of dead plants and other organic life. Plants and animals need both elements to form their proteins.

Professor Cole has pointed out that over 70 per cent of the world's photosynthetic oxygen is produced by marine micro-organisms floating on or near ocean surfaces. Introduction of biologically active materials such as radioisotopes, to which the ocean's living forms have never before had to try adapting, could prove calamitous. "No more than a minute fraction of these substances or the combinations of them have been tested for toxicity to life," says Dr. Cole, "—to the diatoms, the microscopic marine plants that produce most of the earth's oxygen, or to the bacteria and micro-organisms involved in the nitrogen cycle."

We can speculate on what would happen if, as a result of unregulated contamination of the seas, men finally succeeded in destroying or inhibiting the oxygen-producing capability of, say, 10 per cent of the sea's plants. It would mean a reduction of one twentieth of our oxygen supply; the air we breathe would then consist of roughly 19 per cent oxygen instead of the current 20 per cent. This may seem little to make ado over, except for the fact that the "current" ratio has prevailed for some four hundred million years.

If this is not bearding the gods, what is?

CHAPTER XIII

Absolute Power

As we have seen, the Atomic Energy Commission woke up in the mid-1960s to discover that the robot it had for twenty years attempted to breathe life into had risen from the table and was marching on the nation's cities. Almost all of the hazards to which this nation is now subject owe to the fact that the regulatory forces which ordinarily would have contained the monster had been subdued, permitted to atrophy, or actually enlisted into the service of atomic power's advocates. A detailed examination of this process will place those perils into the context of the policies that created them.

Four areas stand out distinctly in this connection: (1) the internal components of the Atomic Energy Commission itself, such as advisory committees and review boards; (2) the congressional committee charged with review of the AEC's activities; (3) the state and local governments; and (4) the public at large.

The first area in which the AEC's near-omnipotence is manifest is in its relationships with its own advisory groups. The Atomic Energy Act of 1954 authorizes the AEC to establish subcommittees to conduct administrative proceedings, public hearings, safety examinations, licensing reviews, and so on. Several of these groups are implicitly designed to provide conservative drag on any tendencies to accelerate the commercial reactor program hazardously.

In practice, however, that conservatism is all but non-existent. The AEC is not obliged to confer final jurisdiction on subcommittees, nor to accept their recommendations. The Commission is entitled to disregard or overrule adverse findings, and has even, as we have seen, sought to suppress them on at least one occasion. The statutes make it possible for the Commission to bestow diluted responsibilities on subcommittees so that their reports often constitute a virtual playback of the Commission's positions.

Such is not uncommon practice in a hierarchical system of administration. However, in an area as supremely delicate as atomic power, advisory and review groups must have the widest possible latitude in determining the suitability—or, more to the point, the *un*suitability—of plant blueprints, reactor safeguards, sites, radiological security, inspection procedures, and the like. Adverse finding in these areas made by a subcommittee must be given profound weight when the Commission considers issuance of a license; in fact, such adverse findings should, one would think, be tantamount to an automatic red light. One could go yet further to suggest that even if a subcommittee gives its *approval* to an application, the minority report of dissenting members should cause the parent Commission seriously to hesitate, though the minority report be filed by but one member.

This breakdown of caution may be seen most clearly in the AEC's licensing and regulation procedures. On numerous occasions concerned congressmen have proposed splitting the bodies that conduct these procedures away from the main Commission in order to permit safety considerations their fullest day in court. But on each occasion the Commission has rejected the proposal, usually on the grounds that such an arrangement would make communication between the Commission and the regulatory group difficult. If some quarrels on record between the Commission and its advisory bodies are any indication, the proposed "two party" system would end up with the two parties not communicating with each other at all. The dilemma is well expressed by Harold P. Green, professor of law and director of the law, science, and technology program of the George Washington University National Law Center. In an article in the June 1968 issue of *Notre Dame Lawyer,* he stated that a principal basis for the AEC's rejection of an autonomous regulatory body has been that

> ... such a new regulatory agency might become preoccupied by safety considerations and not give adequate recognition to the need for pioneering the diverse peaceful uses of atomic energy, thus creating the possibility of "policy deadlocks" between the new agency and the AEC. Implicit in this policy justification is the premise that licensing and regulatory actions should reflect the need for pioneering. Putting this another way, it seems to be national policy that the regulatory program should not be single-mindedly safety oriented, but that some risks should be tolerated for the sake of rapid technological advance.

The AEC has good reason to be satisfied with the present system, in which "communications" are smooth indeed. When a utility application is filed for construction of a nuclear plant, it is accompanied by the company's analysis of the safety features to be incorporated. This analysis is submitted by the AEC to two groups: its own regulatory staff, and the Advisory Committee on Reactor Safeguards. The two groups review the safety features and file their findings with a three-man Atomic Safety and Licensing Board, consisting of a lawyer and two technically qualified persons drawn from a twenty-six-member panel established by the AEC. The latter holds a hearing based mainly on documentary evidence, and unless the case is contested, or one of the two AEC review groups (or both of them) report adversely on the application, the Atomic Safety and Licensing Board will give the go-ahead to the applicant.

The system sounds well safeguarded against manipulation by over-eager proponents of nuclear power, but close examination reveals many discrepancies.

For one thing, disputes between these two groups are kept most strictly "in the family." In January 1965 the AEC appointed a seven-man Regulatory Review Panel "from outside the Government" to review the Commission's policies and procedures for licensing nuclear reactors. The chairman was formerly the AEC's general counsel, and the other six were scientists, engineers, and executives drawn from the nuclear industry. It is not, then, surprising to learn that one of the Panel's recommendations was that every effort be made to conceal from the public any differences of opinion between the ACRS and the AEC's regulatory staff.

But there is other and far more serious evidence that the Commission's safety review groups have little independence. Approval by the AEC's regulatory staff of an application has, it has been asserted, become more and more predictable. As Harold P. Green points out in describing the regulatory staff safety report, "The report characteristically concludes with a judgment that safety standards are met and a recommendation that the construction permit be issued."

The Advisory Committee on Reactor Safeguards seems slightly more independent than the AEC regulatory staff, but its rubber-stamp okay of virtually every application is ensured by the concept of the "provisional construction permit." Before describing it, a little background will be helpful.

The ACRS is a prestigious group of technical experts which, though its members are appointed by the AEC, has tried to maintain a critical, conservative, and independent posture. Unfortunately, over the past ten or twelve years, the ACRS has had a steadily decreasing influence over the AEC. And yet, so important does Congress regard the ACRS's function that in 1957 it passed legislation placing the Committee under the legislature's aegis, making it mandatory for the Committee to report on reactor safety, and making the report part of the public record of proceedings. The idea behind this extraordinary move by Congress, obviously, was to create a "conscience" for the AEC, and to make sure the parent organization did not with impunity dismiss the urgings of that conscience. Congress knew what it was doing, for not long after the Atomic Energy Act of 1954 went into effect, the AEC found itself suffering from rather distressing pangs of "conscience."

The struggle reached a climax in 1956 with the review of the construction license application for the Fermi plant. In that case, as we saw in the opening chapter, the ACRS reported to the AEC that ". . . the Committee believes there is insufficient information available at this time to give assurance that the PRDC reactor can be operated at this site without public hazard." Pressed heavily by the applicant, committed to a timetable, and, fearful that the negative report might spook everybody preparing to put money in the atomic power program, the AEC not only overruled the ACRS, but, to use Representative Holifield's word, "suppressed" the report. The voice of expediency was clearly evident in the AEC's ruling:

> We believe the public interest in the development of the fast breeder reactor, the time to be saved in proceeding with construction while the remaining technical and safety problems are being solved, and our responsibilities under the Atomic Energy Act of 1954, are better served by continuing the permit.

Although we have recorded the angry reaction of Senator Clinton Anderson, then chairman of the Congressional Joint Committee on Atomic Energy, when he learned of Strauss's action, it is worth repeating for its relevance to the issues we are taking up in this chapter:

> The issuance of this construction permit, in my opinion, sets a dangerous pattern in the early stages of AEC regulative and quasi-judicial activity. . . . From a practical standpoint, AEC might feel obligated to go through with a bad deal with respect to public safety because they will have permitted the expenditure of huge sums

under the construction permit. It is my belief that decisions on safety should be made without any examination of dollars involved, but only from the standpoint of human lives.

Senator Anderson, of course, helped organize the opposition to Fermi. But the fact that the Supreme Court upheld the Fermi applicants strengthened immeasurably the AEC's power—even though the nearly catastrophic failure of the reactor vindicated all of the ACRS's worries.

Most important of all, the AEC's triumph in the Fermi case established the concept of the provisional construction permit. This permit acknowledges that the applicant's safety proposals are not adequate, or the technology for certain proposed safety features is not fully perfected, but nevertheless permits the applicant to proceed with construction *in the expectation that the problems will be resolved by the time the plant is up and ready to apply for an operating license.* This provisional scheme serves everybody's purpose very nicely. It enables the applicant to go through with construction without having to resolve important safety problems first, or without having to wait for technology to resolve them for him. It does not commit the AEC to approve all proposals for safety components until the plant is finished; and, theoretically at least, it forces the builder to proceed at his own risk, because there is no guarantee that approval by the AEC will be automatic when the plant is finished. Of course, in practice, "momentum is on the side of the applicant, not on the side of the public," as the minority report in the Supreme Court's Fermi decision expressed it. The utility, having a huge investment to protect, and itself under pressure from the community to get the plant in operation before a power shortage occurs, is undoubtedly going to push very hard for final approval. The whole process is helped along by the fact that *neither a public hearing nor a review by an atomic safety and licensing board is required when, after construction is finished, the utility applies for an operating license!*

Finally, the provisional setup saves the face of the Advisory Committee on Reactor Safeguards. It enables the Committee to raise the alarm on inadequate safeguards just as loudly as it cares to—yet by granting conditional approval anyway, the Committee manages to avoid running athwart of Big Brother AEC.

The provisional permit scheme stands close to center in the galaxy of reckless procedures described in this book. In their standard work *The Technology of Nuclear Reactor Safety,* T. J. Thompson and J. G. Beckerley clearly point out that

> The important economic and safety decisions are made early in the reactor design stage. There may be no retreat from poorly made initial decisions. It is therefore essential that considerations of safety are given a vital role at this stage of a reactor project.

The book from which this passage is quoted was published under the auspices of the AEC.

The Commission, of course, publicly proclaims its support of this principle. In answer to a question posed by the Joint Committee on Atomic Energy in its 1967 hearings, for example, AEC Chairman Glenn Seaborg stated:

> From the regulatory standpoint, it is important that a comprehensive safety review be conducted before large financial commitments have been made, designs frozen or construction accomplished. From the industry's point of view, it is equally important that this review be accomplished before irrevocable commitments have been made.

But while the necessity for correct initial decisions on reactor design is acknowledged at congressional hearings, the *practice* of insisting on safe design before construction begins is obliterated by the provisional construction permit. On Tuesday, May 28, 1968, for instance, the Advisory Committee on Reactor Safeguards reported to the AEC on five proposed nuclear power plant projects it had reviewed. Though the layman may not be qualified to judge the technical merits of the Committee's reports, it is by no means beyond the man in the street's grasp that extremely serious dangers were ascertained by the Committee. Here are excerpts from four of the five reports:

The Committee believes that the proposed off-site power system should be modified to fulfill Criterion 39 so that no single failure will prevent the operation of minimum electrically powered safety features necessary to protect the core.

(Crystal River Unit #3, Florida)

The applicant is performing a detailed analysis of the effects of sudden failure (e.g., by seizure) of a main coolant pump. . . . The Committee continues to believe that control and protection instrumentation should be separated to the fullest extent practical. There remain questions in this area on the Point Beach design.

(Point Beach Nuclear Plant, Unit #2, Wisconsin)

The Committee continues to believe that control and protection instrumentation should be separated to the fullest extent practical. There remain questions in this area on the Kewaunee design.

(Kewaunee Nuclear Plant, Wisconsin)

The emergency power system originally provided for Units 1 and 2 has been redesigned and expanded to serve all three units. . . . The design as proposed appears marginally acceptable. Questions arise regarding the capacity of the diesel-generators and regarding the necessity for paralleling of generators at some time after an accident. Consideration should be given to improvement of the system.

(Browns Ferry Nuclear Power Station,
Unit #3, Alabama)

The latter is doubly significant because it is the third unit of the stupendous TVA project which ACRS member Stephen H. Hanauer found so hazardous that he filed a public dissent, a precedent-shattering move. Not only was the AEC going ahead with the first two units, which the ACRS had found worrisome enough, but it was considering a third unit before the first two were even built, let alone proven.

The fifth of the five reports is particularly noteworthy for the reservations expressed by Committee members, two of whom saw fit to add separate statements to the main text of the document. These statements are, at the risk of trying the reader with material of a semitechnical nature, presented here in their entirety. The first was written by Dr. David Okrent, who in 1966 was chairman of the ACRS:

> The Fort St. Vrain Station [in Colorado] will have the first prestressed concrete reactor vessel designed and constructed in the United States, although such vessels have been built abroad. However, even abroad, only limited experience exists with these vessels. Not all of that experience has been favorable, and none of the existing experience covers more than a fraction of the operational life of the vessels. Only a limited amount of safety research work has been done in connection with various failure modes of these vessels, or on the effects of anomalies and errors of design, construction or operation. History teaches us that errors and misjudgments have been and will be made in the design and construction of vital components. The chance of such errors is increased when a long experience with design, construction, and operation is not available. At this time, it is not clear to me that significant faults in a prestressed concrete reactor vessel would necessarily be detected prior to the loss of integrity of the vessel. The inaccessibility of the vessel liner, cooling tubes, and thermal insulation compound this difficulty.
>
> From the standpoint of reactor safety, the Fort St. Vrain design is especially vulnerable to vessel failure because a single structure serves as both reactor vessel

and secondary containment. I believe it acceptable to construct the Fort St. Vrain station, in view of the remote character of the site, the moderate power of the reactor, the apparent great conservatism in the design of the reactor vessel, and the fact that only one unit is involved. However, I believe that it would not be prudent at this time to construct larger reactors of the Fort St. Vrain type at more populated sites without additional safety features to cope with major accidents involving various modes of failure of the reactor vessel.

The second statement was made by Dr. Joseph Hendrie:

I believe the Fort St. Vrain reactor should be contained in a building of such design pressure and leakage characteristics as to protect the public in the event of a major failure of the reactor vessel. I do not agree with the applicant's argument that the present design of the reactor vessel provides both primary and secondary containment of the reactor in an adequate manner. The great merit of the traditional secondary containment building is that it is a separate and independent barrier to protect the public from the effects of failures of the primary system. In the Fort St. Vrain design, this essential separation is lost, and the safety of the public depends upon the integrity of a single structure. The applicant concludes that a significant loss of integrity of the reactor vessel is impossible, due to the reinforced, prestressed concrete construction. This may be a correct conclusion, but in a matter as important as the public safety I believe it should be supported by a substantial amount of favorable experience in the construction and operation of high-temperature, gas-cooled reactors with concrete vessels. In the absence of such experience, I believe the Fort St. Vrain reactor, and any similar units that might be proposed in the near future, should have secondary containment buildings.

But despite the obvious hazardousness of these five nuclear plant proposals, and despite the undeveloped technology in many critical areas—in short, despite every good reason to withhold approval of a license until all crucial problems were solved, the Advisory Committee in every single case ended its report with the following words, or slight variations:

> *The Committee believes that the various items mentioned can be resolved during construction and that the proposed power plant can be constructed at the site with reasonable assurance that it can be operated without undue risk to the health and safety of the public.* [Emphasis ours.]

On July 26, 1968, the ACRS issued two more safeguard reports, these on the Maine Yankee Atomic Power Company's proposed plant in Wiscasset, Maine, and the Sacramento Municipal Utility District's proposed plant in Sacramento County, California. Again, descriptions of treacherous problems in the submitted design—and again, the same breezy reassurance that the problems could be ironed out during construction.

On July 31, 1968, another ACRS report, on two plants proposed by Commonwealth Edison: Zion Station Units 1 and 2, forty miles north of Chicago. Same story.

As if this procedure were not farcical enough, it came to light in 1966 that some utilities were seeking construction permits for plants of one power level, then raising the power level significantly a relatively short time later. An AEC Licensing Board, hearing the application of three utilities seeking a construction permit for a nuclear plant at Millstone, Connecticut, examined the safety features of a 550,000-kilowatt blueprint. After the evaluation, it was learned that the Millstone plant's power level would be stretched to an ultimate level of 675,000 kilowatts. Panel Chairman Arthur G. Murphy was quoted as declaring: "We are being asked to approve a reactor substantially different from the way it will be operated. Maybe you can take care of this at the operating stage, but then I don't know what purpose the construction permit serves at all." Another panel member asked why possible hazards from operation at 675,000 kilowatts had not been evaluated. General Electric spokesmen replied that safety is not dependent on power level and that by the time a permit for operation at the higher level is sought, experience would be available from actual operation of other plants of the same size.

The Atomic Energy Commission has made other moves to make sure its safety review process moves along at a vigorous clip without annoying delays. For instance, the AEC is currently considering proposing legislative changes that would relieve the ACRS of the mandatory case-by-case review requirement. The reasoning behind this change is that a number of proposed reactors are similar to types already approved. In some cases a utility will apply for a second or third unit identical to one already built or approved: Why make the ACRS go through review procedures in such cases?

The answers, of course, are obvious. First, research and development might have come up with safeguard improvements since the first reactor was built. Second, the addition of a second, third, or fourth reactor on the same site demands a new look at cooling water resources, emergency electrical systems, interconnection of safeguards, siting, availability and training of personnel, structure of control systems, and so forth. Third, the building of a reactor in, say, Wisconsin that is identical to one in New Jersey may still present a host of new siting considerations demanding modification of plans. Fourth, the *original* reactor may, upon going into operation, have proved faulty or hazardous, so that "copies" of it will duplicate the same unsafe features.

Most important of all, reactors are not assembly-line products about which it can be assumed that if one is good the rest are just as good. In the 1967 congressional hearings, Harold L. Price, AEC's Director of Regulation, stated: "We just haven't seen any standard—

what you would really call a standard—reactor yet."
Then in the next breath he said:

> The only duplicates we have seen are the twins where
> a few of these companies have applied for two identical
> plants to be built at practically the same time on the
> same location.
> If I may be a little facetious, we handle that second
> one real fast.

Perhaps it was remarks like these that Justices Hugo
Black and William Douglas anticipated when they
referred, in the Fermi case, to "a light-hearted approach
to the most awesome, the most deadly, the most dangerous process that man has ever conceived."

The Atomic Energy Commission has also managed
in great measure to neutralize the congressional committee charged with the stern duty of overseeing the
AEC's activities, the Joint Committee on Atomic Energy.

Admittedly the Joint Committee is not so much a
regulatory body as a review panel serving to keep Congress informed of atomic energy activities, to keep the
AEC informed of congressional moods and measures,
and to act as go-between on atomic energy legislation.
However, being an arm of the legislature, the Joint
Committee could if it chose wield powerful influence
over the AEC, for implicit in the legislative review
system is the threat of sanctions imposed by Congress if
it is not satisfied with what the Committee reports back
to it. Even if that were not the intention, the Joint
Committee is constantly in a position to assume such
powers at its discretion.

Early in nuclear power history, the Committee did
play this "watch-dog" role, its hearings being conducted
with a certain arm's-length formality with the AEC,
suggesting that a highly critical eye was being cast on
the AEC's activities. Still, many of the Committee
members were, by admission or deed, most sympathetic
to the cause of atomic power, and when the Great

Atomic Power Promotion got under way, these members were in the vanguard.

A crisis occurred in the Fermi case, when some Committee members, including the chairman, cried "Foul" over the handling of the ACRS's negative safety report, and encouraged legal action to stop the building of Fermi. The Supreme Court's decision severely undercut the congressional Committee's power, however.

Reading the transcripts of the 1967 Joint Committee hearings on atomic power, one is puzzled by the seeming lack of skepticism, anxiety, or dissatisfaction expressed by the legislators about the AEC's and the industry's activities. There are few conflicts or dramatic clashes. Sometimes the reader's pulse quickens as the questioning turns up an alleyway bristling with the makings of a good fight. But alas, the interrogators step away, declining to engage. Typical is the following exchange between a Committee member and AEC Chairman Seaborg:

REP. HOSMER: I have only one question. In years past we used to hear the argument that while the Commission had this licensing and safety responsibility, and at the same time it had a promotional responsibility in connection with the nuclear industry, that somehow there was a conflict between the two—that it might be detrimental to the full and complete discharge of the AEC's licensing and safety responsibilities.

You have recited the magnificent safety record we have. I don't hear this talk much anymore but do you have any feelings about whether there is a conflict or not?

DR. SEABORG: As I have watched it, and with the separation of the regulatory function as we have it now, a step that we took in 1961, the Commissioners are pretty careful and quite meticulous in their regulatory responsibility and have this possibility of conflict in mind. I think that it has worked, so far as my experience is concerned, quite well, with a minimum of that kind of interference in regulatory decisions.

This combination of the two responsibilities in one agency has the very much compensating advantage that you have the expertise that is required in your organization in order to discharge the regulatory responsibilities adequately and this is very important in a new and growing technology like this.

That is why we think that the time is not yet right for the separation of the responsibility, and that this advantage far outweighs any potential disadvantage from a possible bias that might be introduced due to the dual responsibility.

REP. HOSMER: I quite agree with your feelings and the facts as the record has displayed them over the years.

Sometimes there is levity:

REP. HOSMER: I think the Turkey Point reactors in Florida are about, what is it, 18 or 22 miles from Miami?

DR. BECK: It is 18 miles. No; I beg your pardon. The low population zone at Florida Power & Light is 5 miles but Miami, I believe, is 18 miles.

REP. HOSMER: I wonder if we could actually consider that a remote location? It depends on which way the wind is blowing, I guess?

DR. BECK: That is quite right.

From all indications, much of the forward propulsion for the nuclear power program seems to be provided by the Joint Committee itself. Joint Committee Chairman John O. Pastore, senator from Rhode Island, has actually proclaimed himself an "enthusiast" of atomic energy, and other members of the Committee have indicated impatience and concern with the rate of progress made in our reactor program. Hence:

REP. HOSMER: Dr. Okrent, you said something that rather disturbs me that you are kind of laying down these academic rules for people coming in for licenses, and you said they ought to be conservative in their design.

I am just wondering how fast we are going to progress if the Committee [the Advisory Committee on Reactor Safeguards] is insisting upon this retention of conservatism all the time.

And:

REP. HOLIFIELD: I share the concern of Mr. Hosmer in regard to the length of time required for licensing. It is important because all of these companies are faced with a phenomenal increase in the need for electricity. Naturally, they have to fit it into the schedule of customer need at the end of the 4- or 5-year construction period.

And:

REP. HOSMER: This problem of getting these things closer to big cities is really a tough one. Even if you could get an okay technically from the ACRS, you still have a problem of getting a piece of property somewhere and not making a whole bunch of people mad as they are at Malibu.

I am just wondering every time I go in and out of a big city airport and see all this flat land around there and pieces of property and perhaps the idea might be for the AEC to develop some kind of low profile installation that could take advantage of this already barren land around airports and already mad people, so you would not make anybody else mad, and maybe that might be the area to look.

T.E. Murray, the former AEC member whose remarks we have quoted in another context, had much to say on the subject of congressional control over the AEC.

But the Joint Committee's supervisory or "watchdog" powers vis-à-vis the AEC are vague. . . . From time to time, the Joint Committee is called upon to make important decisions, for instance in reporting out the proposed agreements to permit international nuclear cooperation. But when it makes these decisions, it usually has little choice but to make them within a policy framework which for the most part has been constructed by other agencies of the government. . . .

I am not, of course, suggesting that the Congress should be the sole authoritative body to give comprehensive, positive program directives to the AEC, spelling out in precise terms what types of construction projects the Commission should undertake. . . But it certainly seems to me that within a democratic society the representative legislature must retain the power to make broad policy determinations of a continuing effect and to see to it that they are generally adhered to in the long run.

Thus the internal structure of the Atomic Energy Commission, and the external regulatory function that could be imposed by Congress, have both succumbed to the inexorable thrust of the nuclear power program. The third area where such acquiescence is in evidence is in state jurisdiction.

Although traditionally the responsibility for citizen safety falls within state jurisdiction, as part of the state's general police powers, radiological protection of the citizen has in large measure been preempted by the Federal Government. Although state and local governments have some say in conventional safety problems in nuclear power plants, and may regulate some radiation problems under delegation of Federal authority in non-power plant situations, Uncle Sam is the sole boss in power plant radiation safety. The result is that a traditional, and traditionally powerful, defense against the unfair exertion of centralized political power is not operative in the atomic utility field. John Conway, executive director for the Joint Committee on Atomic Energy, tried to pin down two AEC members on this point in the 1967 hearings:

MR. CONWAY: The point has been made, at least the Commission's position has been, that the Federal Government has preempted this area and hence the states do not have the authority to pass laws or impose restrictions relating to radiation protection for nuclear reactors.

MR. PRICE: So far as radiation safety is concerned, that is right.

MR. RAMEY: We don't use the word "preempt" so much. I think we used a different word in the Joint Committee hearings.

Just as so many other key issues came to the fore in the Fermi dispute, the issue of state and local rights was raised at that time as well. Senator Clinton P. Anderson, one of the most active individuals in the campaign to control the atomic energy effort, said at a meeting of the Council of State Governments, May 10, 1957:

> Consider the Dresden reactor. It is to be built 45 miles southwest of Chicago. But is it of no concern to the Governor of Illinois or the Mayor of Chicago? It might explode, it might run away. What happens to the lives of hundreds of thousands, possibly several million, citizens who might be in the direct path of any radiation or fallout from such a catastrophe? Isn't that your problem?
>
> Now suppose that the runaway isn't going to be severe enough to affect the lives of people. There still remains several hundred million dollars worth of property within a 50-mile area of the reactor, and in the direct path of the fallout carried by the prevailing winds.
>
> What do you do to the Merchandise Mart if, through an accident, it becomes dangerously radioactive? . . .
>
> As a comparison of the public interest involved, let us consider this situation: Before the Mayor of Chicago was satisfied that the Prudential Life Insurance Co. would build its new building in Chicago safely and by good standards, he required his representatives to examine the plans before it was built to see if the foot-

ings were sufficient for a skyscraper of that size. He can't blindly trust the Prudential Life to build correctly, he must insist on the right of original examination of all the plans.

Likewise, the Governor of Illinois and the Mayor of Chicago ought to insist upon the right of original examination of reactor plans so that they may check them or have them checked by someone familiar with reactor processes to be sure that the reactor will be reasonably safe. Staffs are not yet available for States and cities to do this job completely, but if they continue to abandon this work to the Federal Government on the grounds that the staffs are not yet available, then no staff will ever be available, and as long as the Republic stands, all checking will be in the hands of the Federal Government only. . . .

Big government, given an opening, always takes over. But surely you want to hold on to the things that the State has always looked after, namely, the body—the physical welfare—of the citizens, and their ultimate health and safety.

The issue raised its head again in 1963, after the Atomic Energy Commission launched its big push to erect giant reactors around the country, causing Congressman John Saylor to ask the House of Representatives: "Was it actually the intent of Congress to empower the AEC to force a State and/or community to accept a plant, device, or contrivance to which that State and/or community vigorously object? I think not." A number of attempts to establish states' rights in this field, such as a bill introduced by Congressman Leonard Farbstein of New York on January 4, 1965, have been to no avail.

Unfortunately, Congressman Saylor's assertion that many states and communities "vigorously" object to the Federal Government's attempts to "force" plants upon them is not quite accurate. For although there have been some motions toward acquiring state and local jurisdiction over nuclear plant radiation problems, the states and communities have not always fought "vigorously." Tax inducements, public relations campaigns, and official reassurances have comforted opponents' anxieties. As a result, the issue to this day remains unresolved.

Early in 1965, for example, the New Jersey Board of Public Utility Commissioners ordered public hearings inquiring into the Oyster Creek nuclear plant proposed by Jersey Central Power and Light Company. Later in the same year, the Board asserted some jurisdiction in the matter, noting that while Federal law had pre-empted states from imposing regulations with regard to radiation hazards, states retained other protective rights. The Board also recognized that New Jersey state law required it to work for the public interest without regard to distinctions between radiation and non-radiation hazards, and that the constitutional implications of the Atomic Energy Act were not clear, and had not yet been resolved.

But the New Jersey Board of Public Utility Commissioners backed off from testing the rights question, explaining it was in "substantial accord" with the AEC on the radiation protection required. Senator Anderson's warning eight years earlier—to the effect that if the states didn't "do" for themselves in the area of radiological protection at atomic power plants, the Federal Government would—was fulfilled. The constitutionality of the Atomic Energy Act on these grounds has not been tested.

The fourth area in which the Atomic Energy Commission has managed to overcome serious opposition is the local community, specifically in the matter of public hearings and public efforts to prevent construction of dangerous reactors in the vicinity of population concentrations. Under Section 189 of the Atomic Energy Act of 1954 as amended, applications for construction permits of nuclear power plants must be given public hearings. We emphasize "as amended" because it was not until 1957, when the secrecy of the AEC's proceedings in the Fermi matter enraged so many congressional members, that public hearings and disclosure of information on safety aspects of reactors was made mandatory.

Since, to all appearances, the "public forum" arrangement is one of the best means, in our democratic system, of counteracting excesses in the behavior of the Atomic Energy Commission and proponents of nuclear-powered utilities, one would think that here, at last, the public had the upper hand. Sad to say, that is not the case. The rules under which they are conducted, the issues allowed for discussion, and the persons permitted to intervene or pursue viewpoints opposite from the atomic energy party line are managed by the Commission in such a way as to make the term "public hearing" quite appropriate, for it is the public that does most of the hearing, and the AEC most of the talking.

Although public enthusiasm, or even approval, is not necessary to the success of a nuclear plant construction application, it is obviously highly desirable. Resentment on the part of the public or its press can initiate a ground swell of apprehension and hostility which, if not quickly and effectively placated, can turn into a massive, professionally organized resistance leading to a court fight. The further the issues move away from the sanctuary of the controlled public hearing, the greater their exposure before the nation, and the greater the threat to the nuclear power establishment. Although, as we shall see in a later chapter, hard-sell public relations campaigns undertaken by the utilities are instrumental in softening up public resistance to nuclear reactors, it is on the public hearing that utilities pin their highest hopes of subduing opposition.

There is another important reason why it is crucial that opposition go no further than the hearing, and that is that contested applications play hob with utility construction schedules. When, in congressional hearings, Representative Craig Hosmer asked Commissioner James Ramey if realistic schedules were being set for the utility companies, he answered "Yes, but tight," and then added, "And they don't take into account intervention."

Tremendous pressure therefore exists to make sure the natives are kept firmly in their place.

The AEC's "Outline for the Conduct of Proceedings by an Atomic Safety and Licensing Board" lays down the ground rules on which the hearing is based, but the rules are unique in that the AEC's Atomic Safety and Licensing Board itself, and itself alone, is authorized to decide who shall participate and what the issues will be. ". . . A member of the public does not have the right to participate unless he has been granted the right to intervene as a party or the right of limited appearance for the purpose of making a statement," says the AEC rule book. "The board rules on each request to participate in the hearing on either basis. . . . The important question which may . have to be decided is whether a prospective intervenor has such a relation to the subject matter of the proceeding as to warrant granting him leave to intervene." As Harold P. Green pointed out in the aforementioned *Notre Dame Lawyer* article, ". . . despite the statutory provisions for licensing reactors 'in a goldfish bowl' with public hearings and public disclosure of safety analyses, in actual practice the regulatory procedures tend to stifle public awareness and discussion of the safety issues."

It will be recalled that in 1965 the AEC appointed a Regulatory Review Panel to examine various AEC functions and procedures. This is the panel "from outside the Government" that recommended that internecine quarrels between AEC safety review groups be suppressed and concealed from the public. This panel also had some interesting things to say about public hearings, namely, that their basic purposes were: to give the public a "firsthand impression of the applicant's character and competence"; to show the public that the AEC has been "diligent in protecting the public interest" and that the AEC and ACRS staffs "have only the public interest in mind"; to give the public a "convincing demonstration" that a "thorough and competent review" of the applicant's proposal has been undertaken; to develop a factual record in public; and, finally, to provide the public with a "forum for recording its views, both pro and con, on the applicant's proposal." Harold Green summarizes the Panel's findings nicely when he says, "Implicit in the Panel's conclusions was the proposition that public hearings are mere window dressing and that the actual decision to license a reactor is made (behind closed doors and beyond public scrutiny) by the ACRS and the AEC's regulatory staff, primarily the latter."

Many proponents of nuclear power, both within the AEC and on the Joint Congressional Committee on Atomic Energy, appear to regard the public hearing as a necessary nuisance, held in great measure to give the anti-nuclear "nuts" their day in court, tolerated largely because it is a good antidote against bad press or the threat of court fights. This attitude can be clearly seen in passages from the 1967 hearings.

For example, in response to a question by Representative Hosmer as to how much mandatory public hearings really accomplished, AEC Commissioner Ramey replied: "I think our experience has been at these hearings that on the first day you do get a sort of representation of the public and of a few individuals and you get other individuals who are sort of hipped on this question of atomic safety attending them." He went on to give an opinion that without mandatory hearings interventions were more likely, and it was agreed by all that once people "hipped on the question of atomic safety" witnessed the competence of the AEC and utility personnel, they would realize how groundless their fears were. Representative Hosmer summarized the sentiment of the hearing when he said: "I guess we can say that these mandatory hearings are at least a safeguard against these extremist antinuclear people holding a 'kook-out'." According to the record of testimony, this remark was followed by laughter.

The person or group seeking to intervene in the public interest finds the battlefield arrayed with the mightiest resources of the Federal Government and private atomic industry. The prospective intervenor, unless himself an expert or capable of acquiring the help of experts, is fatally handicapped by his own technical ignorance, and in any event the process of intervention can be prohibitively expensive.

We have seen how, in the case of the attempt by attorney Paul Siegel to intervene in the Turkey Point proceedings on the grounds that the AEC had not considered its responsibilities for reactor sabotage, a prospective intervenor was not even allowed to raise the issues at the public hearing. A similar incident occurred when a group called the Conservation Center attempted to intervene after Consolidated Edison of New York proposed to build "the largest reactor to be considered for licensing to date": Indian Point Unit #2.

The public hearings were held September 14-15, 1966, and there were certainly enough references in the AEC's Division of Reactor Licensing Safety Evaluation to merit serious public discussion. Among these were the facts that Indian Point #2 *was* the largest reactor ever considered thus far, and that it was sited about twenty-four miles from New York City. In addition, the proposed plant had some features that were in effect experimental. One was a penetration pressurization system which, the Safety Evaluation Division stated, "has not been previously proposed for use in other licensed facilities." Another passage declared that:

> The American Standards Association and the Institute of Electronic and Electrical Engineers are actively engaged in the development of standards governing the design, testing and installation of reactor protection systems. . . . Evaluation of the Indian Point Unit No. 2 reactor protection system will be based on such standards, as they are proposed or adopted.

The Evaluation did not explain what would happen if, after Indian Point #2 were completed, the ASA and the IEEE came up with standards which the reactor failed to meet.

With regard to another safety criterion, the Evaluation stated: "Further experimental information should be available from the San Onofre and Connecticut Yankee facilities by the time the Indian Point II facility is to operate." But the Evaluation did not explain what would happen if those two facilities reported serious inadequacies in that particular safeguard.

Despite these and other chilling deficiencies, the report concluded with what has since become an old, familiar tune: "We believe that these matters can be resolved during the construction of the facility."

But Larry Bogart, director of the Conservation Center, did not find this glossing over of the issues any too tranquilizing, and filed a petition to intervene, listing eighteen objections to the Safety Evaluation.

Unfortunately, Bogart filed a few days late because he had difficulty securing advisers on the Safety Report, but although the AEC's rule book allows latitude in the filing of petitions to intervene, the Commission chose instead to stand on ceremony, and the petition, which would have aired questions of desperate importance to the public, was denied. When Bogart appealed, the AEC told him, "Even if we were to hold that the petition was timely filed, its very general statement of organizational purpose does not set forth an interest of the petitioner in the proceeding which may be affected by Commission action, as required by our Rules." The AEC was referring to the Conservation Center's statement of purpose, which read:

Conservation Center was organized in an effort to help protect the health, welfare and safety of the public in the Hudson River Valley Basin as well as in other areas of the Eastern United States, where blight and pollution are present dangers.

The outcome of the present procedure, and any increase in levels of radioactivity by the operation of the type of plant proposed, manifestly affects the interest of the petitioner.

Obviously, that purpose wasn't good enough.

Nucleonics, the industry trade journal, could not disguise its delight with this triumph. In its October 1966 issue, it captioned its report "Con Ed Breezes Through Hearing," and noted "one encouraging fact": that utilities, reactor manufacturers, and the AEC regulatory division "have learned to anticipate the potential trouble spots and work together as a team to suppress them through good planning." *Nucleonics* admitted that the Indian Point #2 hearing had "probed only briefly into a few scattered areas for this biggest nuclear plant . . . ever to come up for licensing," then all but declared that that consideration was nowhere near as important as stifling opposition:

> This advance planning [Con Ed and the AEC had of course met on several occasions prior to the public hearing] . . . apparently paid off at the serene hearing. A potential source of trouble evaporated when the petition of the Conservation Center, New York City, represented by Larry Bogart, to intervene in the case in opposition to the project was firmly turned down by the board.

The AEC and the Joint Committee on Atomic Energy are currently considering legislation abolishing the mandatory hearing altogether.

An observation made by Frances T. Freeman Jalet about the Fermi hearings holds true of hearings held today, and indeed provides a fitting conclusion to this examination of the Atomic Energy Commission's unlimited power. The Commission's rules and regulations, she stated, "obviously were drawn with great care and with meticulous attention to preserve the unfettered freedom of action so uniquely an attribute of the Atomic Energy Commission since its birth. It is as though they constitute a protective shield surrounding the actions of the Commission, making them almost as impervious to attack as are the various containments that shield the reactor itself."

Mrs. Jalet's arrow struck just a little off the mark, however. For if the "various containments that shield the reactor itself" were indeed as impervious to attack as the rules and regulations with which the AEC is clad, this nation would have no cause to be alarmed about the menace of atomic power.

CHAPTER XIV

Of Practical Value?

"You will recall the oft repeated statement in those days that electrical power from atomic reactors would be so cheap that it would not even be worthwhile to meter it," Senator Thruston Morton reminded the Senate in his February 29, 1968 speech proposing a reevaluation of the atomic power program.

A variety of rationales has sustained the thrust of the atomic power industry since the end of World War II, but none has been more compelling than that of fabulously cheap energy. Who perpetrated it? No one, actually; like all others, it sprang out of this nation's initial infatuation with the peaceful atom's promise, and was nurtured collectively by government, business, and public. *Perpetuation* of the myth is something else entirely, however. For atomically produced electricity long ago proved to be an economic disappointment, and at the present moment may be shaping up to be an economic catastrophe. By quietly absorbing the losses and displaying a confident façade to the public, business and government have managed to keep the adjective "cheap" pretty firmly lodged in the public mind. How much longer the word will stay there, as consumers scrutinize rising electric bills and stockholders study discouraging statements, is a matter of conjecture.

As we pointed out in our discussion of the Atomic Energy Commission, the business community at large was a reluctant partner in atomic power from the outset, in the early 1950s, until the mid-1960s. During that period, the businessman cautiously observed developments in the various Government or Government-supported demonstration programs and was not overly impressed with what he saw. All sorts of unforeseen problems, many extremely serious, had caused breakdowns and delays, and these had proven quite costly. If the ledgers did not show appalling losses, it was because Uncle Sam, directly or indirectly, was entering grandiose sums in the accounts receivable columns. By mid-1963 the Government had sunk, into research and development of nuclear reactors, about $3.416 billion, of which $900 to $1200 million was estimated to be related to civilian applications. At the same time, private utility plant costs, research and development in reactor technology amounted to about $520 million, roughly half of the Government contribution.

Among the direct subsidies paid by the U. S. Government to private industry were: (1) direct contributions to reactor construction costs; (2) research and development support; (3) five-year waiver of lease charges on fuel. And among the indirect subsidies were: (1) low guaranteed charge for reprocessing irradiated fuel; (2) high guaranteed buy-back prices for by-product plutonium for weapons use; (3) undefined costs in waste disposal; (4) Government indemnity to cover third-party liability claims in the event of major reactor accidents.

Yet all the king's treasury could not make atomic power a genuine economic competitor, and that fact was becoming apparent to many thoughtful men like Adolph Ackerman, a distinguished consulting engineer. On April 28, 1965, Ackerman delivered a most enlightening paper before the American Power Conference in Chicago, Illinois, describing the unreliability, danger, and costliness of power reactors. The figures he produced on costs and performance of eight atomic plants must have caused great unease among the conferees, for those figures clearly indicated the illusory nature of all claims to nuclear competitiveness. First, he pointed out that of the eight plants, only one—the Dresden at Morris, Illinois—had been completed at the cost originally estimated. As for the others:

1. The Yankee plant, Rowe, Massachusetts, had originally been estimated at $40 million; it ended up costing $50 million, of which $9 million, or 18 per cent was directly contributed by the U. S. Government.
2. The Indian Point plant in Buchanan, New York, had originally been estimated to cost $55 million; it ended up costing $134 million, more than 2.4 times the original quotation.
3. The Big Rock Point plant, Big Rock Point, Michigan, had originally been estimated to cost $34 million; it ended up costing $37 million, of which $6 million was directly contributed by the U. S. Government.
4. The Hallam plant, Hallam, Nebraska, had originally been estimated at $67 million; it ended up costing $84 million, of which $63 million, or 75 per cent was directly contributed by the U. S. Government. After numerous difficulties, it was permanently shut down.
5. The Humboldt Bay plant, Humboldt Bay, California, had originally been estimated at $20 million; it ended up costing $26 million.
6. The Elk River plant, Elk River, Minnesota, had originally been estimated at $13 million; it ended up costing $18 million, of which $16 million, or 89 per cent was directly contributed by the U. S. Government.
7. The Enrico Fermi plant in Lagoona Beach, Michigan, had originally been estimated at $62 million ($45 million if turbine generating and associated equipment are excluded); it ended up costing $109 million, of which $8 million was contributed by the U. S. Government. And that was before the accident, which has kept the plant shut down for over two years.

Ackerman also produced data illustrating the capacity factor of each plant. The capacity factor measures the average amount of power produced annually by a plant, in terms of kilowatts, as against the plant's rated capacity. Thus if a plant is officially rated as capable of producing 100,000 kilowatts, and it only averages 50,-000 kilowatts for the year, its capacity factor is 50 per cent, which is obviously rather poor. Here are the figures on the eight plants surveyed by Ackerman:

	1960	1961	1962	1963	1964
1. Dresden	22%	33%	73%	54%	56%
2. Indian Point	—	—	28%	38%	26%
3. Yankee	25%	76%	55%	69%	78%
4. Big Rock Point	—	—	—	35%	36%
5. Hallam	—	—	—	20%	15%
6. Humboldt Bay	—	—	—	78%	77%
7. Elk River	—	—	—	1%	31%
8. Enrico Fermi	—	—	—	—	—

Ackerman then reviewed the operating histories of six of the eight plants. Two of these we have already described: the Fermi, which has been off the line for two years following its accident, and the Hallam, which was permanently decommissioned after a plague of difficulties. The others were almost as dismal; we reproduce here one of them:

Indian Point Atomic Power Plant—a 255,000 electrical kilowatt plant constructed thirty-five miles north of Times Square, New York, by the Consolidated Edison Co. About two thirds of the capacity is provided by the reactor, the balance by oil-fired superheaters.

Mar. 26, 1962	Provisional operating license granted by AEC.
Mar.–May	Fuel loading delayed for on-site mechanical modifications.
Aug. 2	Initial criticality.
Nov.–Dec.	Outage of 6 weeks to correct piping deficiencies limiting power output to 50% of design value.
April 1963	Plant on line, after 8 months of test operation.
June	Outage of 2 weeks for modifications.

August–Sept.	Outage of 6 weeks "for work inside the containment vessel to which access is not permitted while the reactor is critical."
October	Outage of 5 weeks for work inside containment vessel.
November	Outage of 2 weeks to repair steam line.
Jan. 30, 1964	Shutdown for inspection of fuel elements and installing new stainless steel liner in concrete canal.
June 25	Operation resumed after 5 months' shutdown.
Mid-Aug.	Resumed full-power (off full-power for total of 6½ months).
September 25	Shut-down to correct leaks in boiler tubes and in primary coolant pump....

As discouraging as these data were, the Government refused to bow to the growing increment of negative evidence and experience. Instead, it asserted that no conclusive assessment of the economic value of atomic energy could be made until the giant reactors then on the drawing boards—theoretically economical if situated close to population concentrations—had been given a chance to show their stuff.

The sticking point, of course, would come over the issue of safeguards: Would higher costs of engineering, necessary to protect the public against reactors built so close, wipe out savings gained by putting the plants up nearer to our cities? The issue was well stated by Paul E. Gisiger in the *Journal of Professional Practice,* "Proceedings of the American Society of Civil Engineers": "No weight should be given in this to the complaint that long transmission lines will increase the cost of atomic power," Gisiger argued. "If atomic power is to be truly competitive, it must be able to absorb the cost of making it safe, just as water power must absorb the cost of transmission lines as well as that of making dams strong enough to prevent failure and consequent disaster."

That the industry was failing to match its ambitions for large reactors with adequate safeguards was suggested in 1967 by Milton Shaw, director of the AEC's Division of Reactor Development and Technology, in a summary statement of the Commission's development of criteria, standards, and codes. "It is not known how much industry is spending currently on nuclear safety research," the statement said, "but it is not apparent that the effort is commensurate with the current level of business or with the extrapolations in design being made by the manufacturers on engineering and technology." Thus the argument, heard frequently in the mid-1960s, that nuclear power was "coming into its own" economically was valid only because the true cost of safety was not being taken into account.

But such discrepancies will out, either in the form of accidents or as costly shutdowns, construction delays, and other problems reflecting premature applications of technology. As a result of putting the cart before the horse, to mingle metaphors, the industry laid a lot of technological eggs, and the chickens hatched therefrom are now coming to roost in the form of serious economic problems.

Although capital costs for new plants and equipment have risen for fossil-fueled as well as atomically fueled utilities, the rise in the latter case has been far steeper. In July 1967 *Nuclear Industry* said that prices of nuclear steam supply systems had *increased 30 to 50 per cent during that past year,* and in February 1968 Milton Shaw told the JCAE that "over the last year or so some nuclear steam supply system costs have increased up to about 40 percent and the costs of the rest of the overall plant have increased maybe 10 percent."

The same JCAE hearings brought out a similar admission by AEC Chairman Glenn Seaborg. Equally important, the reasons for these sharp increases were discussed as well. While higher costs of construction, labor, and materials were acknowledged, one Committee member wondered how much the boost "reflects making up deficits which might have been incurred by industry prior to that time—when, because the market wasn't there, they were for a temporary period assuming these costs, and now perhaps are trying to recoup those costs." Seaborg said, "I don't know; I just don't have that information."

But if the chairman of the Atomic Energy Commission didn't have that information, someone else did. Resources for the Future, the organization that has served in an official advisory capacity to the Government in matters of energy management, suggested in its annual review for 1967 that many manufacturers were now trying to recover money lost during earlier developmental days. "For some time," the review stated, "the suspicion has been voiced that the major equipment manufacturers were quoting prices that did not fully cover their own costs of development and production and that the scales were thus temporarily tipped in favor of nuclear plants. This received a degree of confirmation in early 1967 when General Electric, in its 1966 *Annual Report,* acknowledged that ' ... earlier commitments made to win customer acceptance of this new technology continue to affect earnings.' "

The consistent failure of industry to anticipate costs is in evidence everywhere. In March 1968, for instance, Virginia Electric Power Co. said the cost of its two-unit Surrey nuclear station had increased, in only ten months, from $238 million to $255 million. That very same month, the Bolsa Island nuclear power desalting project was reported to be suffering from tremendous increases, from an original estimate of $324 million to $444 million, with the possibility voiced that it might end up costing $750 million before the spiral ended. The Federal Government's 1968 estimate of the cost of desalting sea water at Bolsa Island rose from its 1965 prediction of about 22¢ per thousand gallons to 35-37¢. Even these figures were challenged by Representative John P. Saylor, who was reported to predict that the Government's Saline Water Program, of which Bolsa Island was a part, would report to Congress in 1969 that the estimate had gone to 40-45¢ per thousand gallons, and that it might even go to 50-55¢ later. On August 1, 1968, a coal newsletter reported that Southern California Edison Company had withdrawn from the Bolsa Island project because of raised costs. Most significantly, *Water Desalination Report* stated that "teaming with nuclear on any project may be a luxury desalting can no longer abide."

In June 1968 the Long Island Lighting Co. reported that anticipated costs of a nuclear plant it planned to build near Brookhaven, New York, had escalated from $65-75 million to $127 million, principally reflecting rising costs of labor, material, equipment, and financing. The Government, too, was having trouble keeping costs down, and increases on one project, the Advanced Test Reactor, seemed to spring up year after year like perennial weeds, as this dialogue between John T. Conway, executive Director of the Joint Committee on Atomic Energy, and a number of AEC officials, shows:

MR. CONWAY: . . . When you first came before the committee and requested authorization for that project for fiscal year 1961, it was estimated it was going to cost you $24 million. The following year you had a supplemental authorization which raised it to $40 million. Now since then nearly every year you have been adding to that. Your estimate in 1963 was $47 million. Then in 1966, you were estimating the cost would be $51.9 million. Last year, you estimated it would be $55.3 million. Now the most recent estimate that we have received as of January this year is $58.1 million.

MR. SHAW: That is correct.

MR. CONWAY: Are these costs going up because of the valve problems and piping, or was it very poor estimations originally?

DR. KAVANAGH: Let me answer that. My fellow witnesses were not here at that time, but I was. The first problem was poor estimating. There is no question about it. That is what led to the rapid increase in the total authorized price in the first few years. I believe that the problem since then has been the other type of problem you have talked about. But there was an estimating problem in the early days.

The increased problems, delays, and costs connected with nuclear power generation have reached the point where a number of utilities have begun hedging their bets by ordering units fired by fossil fuel to go side by side with their reactors. Of great significance was an announcement made in June 1967 by the Tennessee Valley Authority that it had purchased a 1.3 million kilowatt coal-fired unit, the largest ever built, along with a nuclear plant. In its announcement TVA said its analysis of the new coal and nuclear units "indicates that power from the two units will cost approximately 2.75 mills per kilowatt hour. A year ago, when we contracted for our first nuclear units, they had an appreciable advantage in the calculated cost per Kwh generating compared to conventional units. Our calculations at that time showed a cost of 2.39 mills per Kwh from nuclear generation." In other words, nuclear costs had jumped about 15 per cent in one year.

The following winter, Wallace Behnke, assistant to Commonwealth Edison's president, told *Electrical World's* Third Energy Transportation Conference that because coal-fired and nuclear-fired electricity costs were approaching equality, his company would "continue to look at both alternatives," nuclear and fossil fuels. "It is readily apparent," he said, "that nuclear generating costs have risen more rapidly than those for fossil-fueled generation, and today, nuclear's margin appears to be relatively small. Moreover, these figures do not reflect the cost effects of the recent increase in nuclear lead times, from approximately four to nearly seven years, during a period when fossil unit lead times have increased only slightly. Time is money, and an increase in lead time necessarily means an increase in the interest and other overhead costs. . . ."

As if to hammer home its growing doubts, Behnke's

company, Commonwealth Edison, which according to one source "has gone in heavier for nuclear power plants than any other U.S. utility," announced in September 1968 that it was planning to build an 800,-000-kilowatt coal-fired generating plant. Chairman J. Harris Ward declared that the coal-fired unit would "serve as insurance against possible delays in service dates of some of the nuclear units now being built for us."

Official, if somewhat grudging, recognition of nuclear power's economic difficulties came in May 1968 when Representative Hosmer of California told an Oklahoma City conference about some "unpleasant facts of life":

> First: the trend of continually reduced economics in an environment of steadily rising costs may exceed the capacity of even modern technology to counteract. In short, nuclear power may not be a universal economic panacea. We may have to reconcile ourselves to some modest increases in power costs, at least until the breeder arrives in full force.
> Second: Construction delays, which are now so widespread in the utility business. While minor technical problems in conventional plants may have no effect on operating schedules, nuclear plants present special problems.

And yet, in the face of these rather imposing "unpleasant facts," Hosmer continued to be optimistic:

> I cannot fault the utilities for their enthusiasm for nuclear power. Basically, they are *betting* that the dynamism of the nuclear industry will continue to spawn technological and economic improvements and help alleviate environmental problems. Their hope is that five or six more years of experience will smooth out some of the wrinkles in the nuclear field, particularly on the regulatory side. I think it is a good bet—not a sure thing but a very good bet nevertheless. [His emphasis.]

More guarded optimism—optimism so qualified one wonders whether it can be called optimism at all—was voiced at a two-day nuclear power briefing in Washington sponsored by the Federal Bar Association. The speakers were both internationally recognized experts on power generation, Philip Sporn, retired president of the American Electric Power Co., and Murray Joslin, retired vice-president of Commonwealth Edison. Mr. Sporn, reminding his audience that proper evaluation of nuclear plants involves more than "simply comparing bid prices," stated: "It still remains to be proven whether the glitter that has attracted the phenomenal nuclear capacity orders of the past few years is just merely that, or whether it has a more substantive basis." Mr. Joslin, after citing some of the problems in nuclear plant construction involving cost increases and the unreliability of present cost estimates for future decisions, declared:

> ... I continue to be optimistic about the future of atomic power despite the current problems too often—I am afraid and I am guilty, too—laid entirely at the doorstep of the regulatory authority. This optimism is long-term, however, because the present picture is not as bright as I once hoped it would be. The darkest element is the delay in making schedule, which seems to threaten most of the large projects. This can be extremely serious and I feel sure that fossil projects of both baseload and peaking types will have to be rushed in to rescue the nation's capacity situation.

Thus, even if the nightmare of a nuclear power plant disaster does not focus attention on the inadequacies described in these pages, atomic power may still have an *economic* day of reckoning ahead when the industry is forced to confront the emptiness of its myth of cheap electricity. Such a confrontation will, it is very possible, take place over the issue known as "Practical Value."

What does "Practical Value" mean?

The Atomic Energy Act of 1946 stipulates that whenever, in the opinion of the Atomic Energy Commission, any industrial, commercial, or other non-military use of atomic energy has been sufficiently developed to be "of practical value," the Commission is obliged to report to that effect to the President, so that the political, economic, and social implications can be evaluated and acted on. On a number of occasions, the AEC has been petitioned to make a formal declaration of the practical value of atomic power plants, and on each occasion the Commission has declined to do so, reaffirming its policy of licensing all reactors under the section of the Atomic Energy Act pertaining to *developmental* reactors, not commercial ones.

The Commission's stated reason for this refusal is that only *now* has industry begun building reactors of a size viewed as commercially competitive with fossil-fueled power plants, so that "pending the completion of scaled-up plants, and the information to be obtained from their operation, there has not yet been sufficient demonstration of the cost of construction and operation of light water, nuclear electric plants to warrant making a statutory finding of practical value."

The significance of this statement cannot be overestimated. Let us consider it.

We have been stating that because power reactors of the size planned for the 1970s have never been built or tested in this country, they must be regarded as nothing more or less than gigantic experiments. Undoubtedly most readers will have interpreted this statement as a mere figure of speech. After all, the total non-Federal capital investment in atomic power is estimated to be between seven and ten billion dollars. That money will buy over a hundred reactors producing some 73,000,-000 kilowatts of electricity to light the towns and cities of the United States. AEC Chairman Seaborg has recently forecast a total nuclear capacity of 150,000,000 kilowatts by 1980, representing an investment of more than twenty-two billion dollars by private utility companies. This electricity will be paid for by you, the consumer.

It is only natural, then, to take for granted that atomic power is nothing if not a *commercial* operation.

However, as formally defined by the "Practical Value" clause of the Atomic Energy Act, atomically produced electricity is still in the research and development stage. In other words, *the nuclear power plant going up outside your community is officially an experiment.*

This "Practical Value" business appears to be a constant source of embarrassment to the Atomic Energy Commission, for it puts the Commission in a very difficult position. If it does not find atomic power to be of practical value, what are we doing building reactors of unprecedented size so close to population centers? On the other hand, if tomorrow the Commission did find nuclear power plants to be of practical value, much of the direct and indirect subsidization now given the utilities to assist their "research and development" would have to be curtailed, placing burdens on private operators which are now borne by Uncle Sam. Because these burdens would, it will be demonstrated, be intolerable, a finding of practical value for the nuclear power plants would reveal them for the impractical, uneconomical, and hazardous things they are.

The glaring contradictions in the AEC's approach to nuclear power are nowhere more apparent than in an attempted intervention in the licensing of a nuclear plant in South Carolina in 1967, when for the first time the question of practical value was actually raised in licensing proceedings. Duke Power Company had applied to build a three-unit 2.6 million kilowatt nuclear facility at Oconee, South Carolina. A group of eleven North (*sic*) Carolina municipalities organized as Piedmont Cities Power Supply, Inc., challenged the application on the grounds that the installation would create a monopoly situation. The AEC regulatory staff denied the intervention, claiming that anti-monopoly provisions were not applicable to research and development licenses—only to commercial ones. And since *all* reactors licensed by the AEC are for research and development by technical definition, the intervention was invalid. Duke Power's annual report, however, defined the Oconee nuclear plant as a "commercial nuclear station" and proposed financing the installation as a commercial unit. This inconsistency did not prevent the AEC's Atomic Safety and Licensing Board from issuing construction permits on all three units that fall. Such inconsistency did, however, provoke Senator George Aiken of Vermont, early in 1968 in discussing practical value, to declare, "While a utility is applying to the AEC for a license as a research project, the utility officials go down the street to the Securities and Exchange Commission and ask permission to issue stock as a profit-making corporation."

In June 1968 the Commission again was challenged on this point when the City of Dover, Delaware, filed exceptions to an application of Philadelphia Electric Co., Delmarva Power and Light, and Atlantic City Electric to build two reactors at the Peach Bottom station in York County, Pennsylvania. Were the Peach Bottom units experimental or commercial? Once again, the AEC ruled that such plants did not qualify for "practical value status."

Perhaps tiring of being displayed prominently on the horns of the "practical value" dilemma, the Commission, around the same time as it issued the Peach Bottom decision, sent a bill to Congress seeking repeal of the "Practical Value" provision of the Atomic Energy Act. This would, of course, have the effect of doing away once and for all with the distressing distinction between developmental and commercial facilities. At this writing the bill—introduced by Senator John O. Pastore, chairman of the Joint Committee on Atomic Energy—is being considered by Congress, as well as one resembling it prepared by the Joint Committee itself.

If passage of such legislation were disputed, could the atomic energy establishment make a case for the practical value of nuclear power plants? Perhaps—if no one raised the explosive issue of insurance.

In the following chapter the explosive issue of insurance will be raised.

CHAPTER XV

The Hazard Is New

Go to your strongbox. Open it and take out your home-owner's policy. Run your finger down the column headed PERILS INSURED AGAINST. Do you find anything covering your property for radioactive contamination resulting from accidental discharge of radioactivity from an atomic facility?

No? Perhaps it's elsewhere. Keep going. Ah, *there's* something: "Nuclear Clause." But wait. It says: "This policy does not cover loss or damage caused by nuclear reaction or nuclear radiation or radioactive contamination, all whether directly or indirectly resulting from an insured peril under this policy."

You may want to call your broker to ask whether this clause means that if the reactor going up outside your city has an accident and the fallout contaminates your property, you cannot recover. He will tell you that that's precisely what it means. He may even be aware that Lloyd's of London itself will not write such a policy. He may tell you not to worry, that such an event is highly improbable, but you will wonder why, if it is highly improbable, no one will insure against it. Couldn't an insurer make a fortune insuring against the highly improbable?

Your broker will inform you that although nobody will insure your property against radiation damage, reactor operators are "heavily" insured against claims. A $74 million indemnification put up by insurance pools is backed up with another $486 million guaranteed by the U. S. Government. Altogether, over half a billion dollars could be funded to compensate victims, an unprecedented sum.

Impressive though this figure will sound at first, it will be recalled that the Federal Government estimated —in 1957, when much smaller reactors were being built much farther from our cities than today—that a major atomic plant accident could cause property damage *alone* in the billions—as high as seven billion dollars. Even at this figure, supposing the worst, where would the other six billion plus come from? And what about life and health insurance? Your policies probably cover you for radiation injury or death, but if property claims alone can reach seven billion dollars, life and health claims would be equally staggering, would they not? Possibly large enough to wipe out even the biggest insurance companies.

These vexing questions might lead a curious insurance broker to wonder whether the public is being told *everything* about atomic power plants. And if he decided to follow up his curiosity about the anomalies in nuclear insurance, he would learn some very interesting things.

He would learn, first of all, that the atomic power program was in big trouble in the mid-1950s because neither the utilities nor the reactor manufacturers were able to calculate the astronomical damages that would result from a major accident to an atomic facility. Even if they *had* been able to do so, the insurance companies weren't prepared to put up indemnification even approaching the amounts necessary. In 1955 an advisory committee of representatives of the insurance company had been appointed by the AEC to study this problem, and two significant findings were made: The first was that in order to cope with the nuclear risks, a property and liability pool would have to be formed by the country's stock and mutual insurance companies. The second was that even with such a pool, the industry would not be able to offer satisfactory public liability insurance on atomic power installations.

The feelings of the insurance industry were well expressed in 1956 by Hubert W. Yount, vice-president of Liberty Mutual Insurance Company. After considering possible consequences of a major nuclear plant accident, Yount was forced to declare to the Joint Congressional Committee on Atomic Energy:

The hazard is new. It differs from anything which our industry has previously been called upon to insure. Its potential is still unknown and must therefore be calculated currently in terms of a body of knowledge which is expanding from day to day. . . .

Very few insurance companies have had any opportunity to develop first-hand knowledge of the problems involved because of the present limited scope of operation. By the same token, very few insurance companies have developed trained technical personnel to assist their underwriting personnel in insurance evaluation of the hazards involved. . . .

The catastrophe hazard is apparently many times as great as anything previously known in industry and therefore poses a major challenge to insurance companies. . . . We have heard estimates of catastrophe potential under the worst possible circumstances running not merely into millions or tens of millions but into hundreds of millions and billions of dollars. *It is a reasonable question of public policy as to whether a hazard of this magnitude should be permitted, if it actually exists.* Obviously there is no principle of insurance that can be applied to a single location where the potential loss approaches such astronomical proportions. Even if insurance could be found, *there is a serious question whether the amount of damage to persons and property would be worth the possible benefit accruing from atomic development.* [Emphasis ours.]

That Yount was not content to confine his remarks to the dubious insurability of atomic power plants but took it upon himself to question the wisdom of the entire program is an extraordinary indication of the depth of the insurance industry's reservations.

Their own anxieties now strongly reinforced by those

of insurers, private developers of atomic power had to tell their Government that unless *someone* was prepared to indemnify them, they could not proceed with an enterprise so fraught with unknowns and risks.

It was thus to head off a major rebellion of private industry that the Federal Government proposed legislation aimed at removing this chief obstacle to forward progress. That legislation, passed in 1957, was known as the Price-Anderson Act, named after its sponsors, Senator Clinton Anderson of New Mexico and Congressman Melvin Price of Illinois, members of the Joint Committee on Atomic Energy.

The Price-Anderson Act provided for Federal funds of $500 million to be made available for the settlement of damage claims resulting from a nuclear power plant accident if the insurance purchased by the plant operators proved insufficient. Since at that time the insurance pools were willing to put up $60 million altogether, the total amounted to $560 million. Beyond that ceiling, however, all obligation, both of the plant operator and the Government, ceased. A recent change in the Act has raised the insurance pool fund from $60 million to $74 million, and lowered the Government fund from $500 million to $486 million, but the important thing is that under present law no more than $560 million is provided to compensate victims of a nuclear plant disaster.

We have it on the testimony of Representative Price himself that his Act was pretty much responsible for averting economic disaster in the atomic power field at that time. In an interview over ABC Radio in August 1966, Price was asked if it had originally been impossible for private industry to get insurance against atomic power plant accidents. He answered: "That's correct. The power development program was bogged down; there was nothing but studies back in the early fifties, and it wasn't until passage of the Indemnification Act, known as the Price-Anderson Act, incidentally, that the program got off the ground and they started to build plants. The utilities, or the manufacturers of these vessels and reactors, wouldn't risk going into this uncharted area without some type of indemnification protection."

But if the atomic power industry received its biggest boost from the Price-Anderson Act, it was almost entirely at the expense of the American public, for it meant that We the People were assuming liability for someone else's risks.

Furthermore, we weren't even getting a very good policy. In the event of the maximum credible accident, which the Government had asserted could cause as much as $7 billion in property damage *alone,* the insurers would not be able to make good on more than $560 million, or 8 per cent of the total damage claims. The other 92 per cent would come out of our pockets to pay for uninsured damages. As for those of us who recovered less than the losses sustained, or recovered nothing whatsoever—well, that's life. Since you, through your billions of dollars of subsidy-supporting taxes, are responsible for the existence of the atomic power industry, it is only fair and proper that you should pick up the lion's share of the bill for damages, is it not? That would appear to be the implicit philosophy behind this insurance plan.

It is worth reminding the reader that seven billion dollars in property damages was an early estimate, and that developments since 1957, as we have demonstrated, could conceivably cause a catastrophe with a far higher price tag. Yet no matter how substantially all other industries and the public are exposed to potential bankruptcy, the nuclear industry is protected by virtue of the "no recourse" provision of the Price-Anderson Act.

In the commercial market place the imposition of liability has always served, among other purposes, to discourage management from proceeding with potentially hazardous enterprises by making it intensely aware of its financial obligation should that enterprise prove harmful to the public. As a result of the Price-Anderson Act, however, the nuclear industry was released to proceed with its hazardous enterprise secure in the knowledge that its annual insurance premium on sixty million dollars worth of indemnity per nuclear power plant constituted the limit of liability against damages that could amount to fifty or a hundred times sixty million dollars, or more. Accordingly, one of the traditional and fundamental balances to caution was removed from the scales. *Temptation to cut cost,* in an industry in which engineering safety is expensive, *was no longer counteracted by fiscal responsibility*. And since Price-Anderson coverage was extended to liability of third parties such as reactor manufacturers, they too were relieved of a good deal of legal compulsion to honor the yellow light of caution.

If the reader feels anything less than despair at the prospect of being compensated, it is undoubtedly because he clings to the hope of being awarded *some* of the $560 million that is supposed to be made available for that purpose. Unfortunately, survivors of an atomic plant calamity might discover their woes compounded by a Congress uncertain about its obligations—so that even that $560 million might not be totally freed, or freed at once, to aid the ailing and the destitute. Speaking before the House early in August 1965, Representative Robert T. Secrest voiced the opinion that serious questions of liability and constitutionality were inherent in the Price-Anderson Act, and that unless time-consuming litigation was avoided, it seemed "logical to assume that several years will pass after an atomic power plant accident before any funds can actually be paid to persons injured."

It is most significant, Secrest pointed out, that even the Atomic Energy Commission expressed serious reservations about the constitutionality of the Price-Anderson approach to indemnification. On page 43 of the 1956 Governmental Indemnity Hearings transcript can be found this statement made by the AEC before the Joint Committee on Atomic Energy: "We have carefully considered the approach of limitation of liability and do not recommend this method primarily on account of doubts as to constitutionality of this approach. Also limitation of liability does not offer the degree of protection to the public that is offered by the indemnity or reinsurance approach."

Despite the AEC's own misgivings, the Price-Anderson Act was carried. Supporters of the plan assembled a number of arguments for the Act's constitutionality should the matter come to a court test. But Congressman Secrest, reviewing those justifications in his House statement in 1965, cast doubts about their validity. For instance, it was assumed when the Act was passed that plutonium produced in power plants might be needed for military purposes. That need, Secrest pointed out, has been filled. Secondly, in 1957 the law provided that all atomic fuel must be the property of the U. S. Government, but under "private ownership" legislation enacted since Price-Anderson, that is no longer true. Thirdly, Secrest thought the bankruptcy power of Congress would not justify the constitutionality of the Price-Anderson Act's no-recourse provision. Bankruptcy power presumably applies only in the event of actual or threatened insolvency. "It hardly seems proper to assume that the bankruptcy power gives Congress the authority to completely eliminate financial responsibility for damages without even touching the assets of the utility involved."

Secrest's last point was telling:

It does appear that Congress has jurisdiction over the construction and operation of atomic power plants because of the commerce clause. Even so, the delegation of jurisdiction under the clause does not give us complete constitutional authority to act as we wish, without limitation. Whatever laws we pass under the commerce clause will not be constitutional unless they are reasonable and appropriate means to a lawful end. There is very serious question as to whether or not an act of

Congress giving complete immunity from responsibility for negligency constitutes a reasonable and appropriate means to a lawful end.

Intimately connected with questions of constitutionality are those surrounding the matter of liability. A substantial body of law maintains that the owner-operator of a dangerous enterprise must assume full financial responsibility for the destructive effects of that enterprise, and that, as one court decision puts it, "the person who for his own purposes brings on his land and collects and keeps there anything likely to do mischief if it escapes, must keep it at his peril and if he does not do so, is prima facie answerable for all of the damage which is the natural consequence of its escape." It might therefore be maintained that the absolute cutoff of liability now guaranteed private industry by the Price-Anderson Act was unlawfully granted, and liability should be pinned back on the concerns that shed it when the Act was passed. The *Insurance Counsel Journal,* in January 1963 predicted that as a result of this issue of "strict liability," in the event of an accident there would be "plenty of lawsuits."

Although members of the two houses of our Federal legislature would be horror-stricken if an atomic plant catastrophe occurred, they would still wish to be on certain ground before releasing damage awards, and opponents in those houses might resort to a number of legal defenses against full assumption of liability. For instance, suppose the reactor accident had resulted from an earthquake; might not Congress try to claim that damages resulting from such an Act of God were not insurable? Or suppose foreign sabotage could be proved; might not Congress try to claim that an Act of War invalidated damage claims? Consider another view: Acts performed in pursuance of a public duty or for national defense or security may exempt those performing those acts from liability for resulting damages. Since the atomic energy program is founded on the principles, as stated in the Atomic Energy Act of 1946, of "improving the public welfare, increasing the standard of living, strengthening free competition in private enterprise, and promoting world peace," might not our Government try to claim that the reactor accident occurred in pursuance of public duties?

Many other questions would be raised should tragedy strike, and even a brief outline of some of the issues that might be brought to court will make it readily apparent that much new legal ground may have to be broken before damages can be properly assessed and compensation disbursed.

Formulas would have to be established to determine priorities. Would an individual who suffered immediate illness from a high dose of radiation be entitled to compensation ahead of one whose exposure to a smaller dose might not produce harmful effects for years? How would it be determined that cancer and leukemia were directly attributable to radiation exposure experienced at the time of the accident? Since there does not seem to be a threshold below which radiation is harmless, would the courts be obliged to hear claims from people who believed their lives had been shortened appreciably by minute doses of radiation? Will the cost of evacuation and decontamination of an area be recoverable? If radiation causes damages to a parent's genes, might a deformed child be entitled to bring action? If the disaster carried damage claims beyond the $560 million limit, how would further claims be handled? Which would take precedence, and how would funds be apportioned?

The machinery for dealing with some of these questions exists in the original Price-Anderson Act and in subsequent amendments, but just how fast that machinery would move is open to debate. Our court system is already staggering from an unprecedented volume of claims; auto accident litigation alone is, in many areas of the country, years behind reasonable schedule. Recent revision of the Act has set up ways and means of expediting payment, but even if Federal aid were put on an emergency relief basis, would that aid be speedy? After the Alaskan earthquake of 1964, for instance, it was complained that Congress was slow to appropriate even fifty million dollars for damages estimated at some five hundred million dollars; and *that* tragedy was a fairly cut-and-dried instance of an Act of God, where no complex questions of human liability or constitutionality were involved.

So important has the Price-Anderson Act become to the nuclear industry that, at hearings held in June 1965 on the extension of this law, which was due to expire in 1967, representatives of several utilities testified that unless it was extended they would "probably not" build additional nuclear plants at present. Mr. Mel Frankel, on behalf of the Department of Water and Power, City of Los Angeles, stated for example that: "Without the protection which presently is provided by the Price-Anderson Act, it is doubtful that any utility would consider it prudent to build nuclear plants." Several utility representatives confirmed this, and the following year Philip Sporn, one of the most highly regarded authorities on electric power, declared in a revew of nuclear power economics that "Price-Anderson insurance is absolutely essential to the continued development of nuclear power. Its elimination would choke off the construction of nuclear power plants."

The Act was extended until 1977, but a basic question has never been answered. For if utilities are sufficiently convinced of the safety of nuclear plants to be willing to gamble with the lives, health, and property of the public, why are they not equally willing to assume financial responsibility for accidents at such plants? It was this line of reasoning that produced a move by Congressman Leonard Farbstein of New York to make utilities and manufacturers responsible for an additional hundred-million-dollar indemnification beyond the amount guaranteed by the insurance pools. It was never passed.

Harold Green, the attorney whose views have shed considerable light in this book on other legal aspects of atomic energy, illuminates the matter of insurance, too, noting that "although the licensing of nuclear reactors proceeds on the assumption that there are no undue risks to the public, the Price-Anderson Act is bottomed on the premise that operation of a nuclear reactor involves undue risk to industry. The public assumes the very same risk of a serious accident that the utilities and equipment manufacturers are unwilling to assume and against which they are indemnified by the Government. The only sop thrown to the public is some assurance that funds will be available to provide compensation for damages incurred if liability can be established." The paradox Green has formulated has been stated with eloquent simplicity by another critic, who phrased it: "If a thing isn't insurable, it isn't safe." And an even less temperate characterization of the Act was given by Rolla D. Campbell, a lawyer of Huntington, West Virginia, in a letter inserted into the Congressional Record for July 16, 1965:

The license which AEC is authorized to grant to the operators and manufacturers of an atomic plant can fairly be characterized as a license to them, for their own financial benefit, to create huge risks to others, involving death, sickness, and property damage, without any liability whatsoever for the harmful consequences, and to throw all such risks (over and above private insurance available) upon the U. S. Treasury and upon the persons suffering death, personal injury, or property damage. . . ."

These are some of the things your broker would learn when he decided to explore the prospects of compensation for radiation damage due to an atomic power plant accident. There would be other avenues he might care to explore if he were industrious enough: the largely unformulated policy on insurance coverage for transportation accidents involving nuclear materials, for instance. An amendment to the Price-Anderson Act embraces such accidents, but the insurance pools have yet to establish codes in that area, and many forms of transportation are uninsurable when atomic material is involved. Or there is the matter of accidental releases of small doses of radiation which merely add to the harmful "radiation budget" growing each year in our environment. The Price-Anderson Act gives the AEC the exclusive right to declare what is a nuclear accident and what is not; yet the gradual seeping of radiation into our air and water represents a long-term health threat which even the grossly inadequate insurance we have does not recognize.

"The hazard is new," said the insurance man, and it is dubious that this nation will be in any better a position to deal with the economic hardships than it will be to handle the appalling suffering and dislocation produced by a major accident.

Take another look at your homeowner's policy. Reread the Nuclear Clause.

Now what?

CHAPTER XVI

From Fissile to Fizzle

Proponents of atomic energy like to awe laymen with the fact that one ton of uranium fuel is equivalent, in electricity-producing energy, to roughly 17,380 tons of coal. Out of this fact has emerged a widely held belief in the existence of an incredible bounty of inexpensive atomic fuel, of resources so plentiful that the question of depletion will not arise for hundreds or even thousands of years. And if the atomic power industry isn't quite as optimistic as the public about our future nuclear fuel reserves, it is nevertheless investing billions upon billions of dollars in atomic power plants on the assumption that cheap fuel will be in supply for the indefinite future.

According to a number of experts, however, *around 1980 we will begin to feel a uranium pinch, and ten years afterward shortages will be critical.* Unless a fabulous lode is discovered—which even AEC officials believe dubious—and unless breeder reactors are perfected and built en masse by the early 1980s—even more dubious—the fuel of the future may be the fuel of the past before the twenty-first century gets under way.

AEC Chairman Glenn Seaborg, addressing an investment forum in October 1968 sponsored by the brokerage concern Hayden, Stone, Inc., told his audience that the sharp increase in nuclear power capacity projected for the next two decades "has caused some concern" in the AEC about future supplies of uranium. It will require about 250,000 tons of refined uranium ore to meet the utilities' needs for fuel between now and

1980, he explained, but by contrast—at the current official price of eight dollars a pound—economically recoverable uranium reserves total only 148,000 tons. The total economically recoverable reserves at ten dollars a pound would still come only to about 200,000 tons. However, if an eight-year reserve inventory, which is modest as utility reserves go, is figured in, then we will need 650,000 tons of refined uranium to supply atomic power plants through 1980. By 1980, annual demand will be 40,000 tons, and 35,000 tons of uranium will have to be discovered every year between now and 1980 to meet needs. On that score Seaborg's colleague, Commissioner Wilfred E. Johnson, has voiced serious doubts: "We can expect to have to search in deeper locations," he stated before the Atomic Industrial Forum, "in areas not presently known to be uranium-bearing, and eventually, in areas where present knowledge of uranium technology does not suggest much chance of success." It is estimated that half a billion dollars will have to be invested to discover and delineate reserves by 1980.

How, in view of our suppositions about a nearly limitless fund of nuclear fuel, has government and industry managed to come up so absurdly short? There are two reasons, both of them monuments to human misjudgment.

When the AEC reported on civilian nuclear power to the President in 1962, it foresaw a U.S. nuclear generating capacity of only 40,000,000 kilowatts by 1980. No serious fuel shortage was anticipated to meet the resultant demand, but the AEC felt that after 1980 a problem would arise unless the technology for operating breeder reactors, which create more fuel than they burn, was perfected. In its 1962 report the AEC stated that "should breeders be seriously delayed, for example by as much as a few decades, the high-grade uranium ore might be exhausted while large amounts of uranium-235 were still required."

One would think that the AEC would have reined in

sharply the industry's movement toward construction of conventional reactors until breeder technology could be perfected. Conventional reactors, the kind now being designed and built for generation of electricity in the coming decades, are extremely wasteful affairs, converting only about 1 per cent of the potential energy in their uranium fuel into actual energy. Breeders are not only supposed to be more efficient, but ideally will produce more than enough fuel to keep the atomic power program operating long into the future. So important did the AEC consider breeders that, in the 1962 Report, the Commission declared that unless a viable breeder program was developed, atomic energy's "contribution to our total energy reserves would scarcely be worth the developmental cost."

Without waiting to see whether breeders would work or not, however, the AEC intensified its program of promoting fuel-wasting conventional reactors. And so intensely did it concentrate on that program that the relatively modest goal of 40,000,000 nuclear-generated kilowatts by 1980 was vastly surpassed by orders in the mid-1960s, presaging a huge drain on uranium reserves. As we have seen, nuclear plants with a total capacity of 72,939,700 kilowatts are at present operable, under construction, or on the drawing boards— almost twice the capacity forecast in 1962—and in 1967 the AEC projected between 120,000,000 and 170,000,000 kilowatts as the U.S. atomic capacity by 1980—no less than three, and possibly a little more than four, times higher than originally estimated.

The disturbance which this pell-mell acceleration is causing in AEC and industry thinking is reflected in a number of comments drawn from recent papers and speeches. James A. Lane of Oak Ridge National Laboratory, in a presentation made in Vienna in September 1966, stated that if the number of reactors grew at the rate *then* forecast (the rate has increased since, incidentally) and no breeders developed, the fuel requirements for conventional reactors would necessitate "the mining of all our reserves costing less than thirty dollars per pound by shortly after the year 2000." The price generally accepted as competitive, remember, is eight to ten dollars a pound.

Even if breeders do go into operation by 1980, it has been asserted that it will be too late for them to prevent the drain on uranium resources now occurring as a result of soaring orders for conventional reactors. J. H. Wright of Westinghouse, in the May 29, 1967, issue of *Electrical World,* stated that an atomic power program operating at 150,000,000 kilowatts (which is roughly the capacity anticipated by government and industry by 1980) will require two million tons of uranium before breeders, even if introduced in 1980, produce enough fuel to bring fuel creation and consumption into equilibrium in the year 2020. Yet it has been estimated that the probable U.S. *maximum* reserve of uranium priced at thirty dollars a pound or less is *1.5 million* tons.

One alternative frequently suggested is to buy uranium from overseas suppliers. In order to protect domestic uranium producers, this course is prohibited by the AEC until June 30, 1973, but even when that date arrives it is utterly unrealistic to put any eggs in the foreign basket. *Petroleum Press Service,* an authoritative British publication examining the world energy picture at the end of 1967, stated that "From 1973 onwards the annual consumption of uranium throughout the non-Communist world will exceed production, and by 1980 there will be a foreseeable short fall of some 100,000 tons a year.... World consumption of uranium is expected to increase by almost 20 times by 1980, while the present rate of production from known reserves will not even double." If our Government and utilities really expect to secure Free World uranium after 1973, then they can't possibly hope to pay a low price for it, and it would be more realistic to believe they won't be able to get it for *any* amount of money. Fossil fuels are also in short supply overseas, and the

Free World can therefore afford to outbid us for uranium.

There are a few other alternatives open to the industry. Thorium, a "fertile" element convertible into fissionable uranium 233 by means of breeder reactors, is abundant in nature. But even if the breeding process can be perfected, which we shall soon see is far from the case, uranium 233 will not resolve the safety and pollution problems posed by other fissionable fuels.

In another branch of atomic physics, physicists have been examining atomic fusion as a possible alternative to atomic fission as an energy source. In fusion, which is the source of the hydrogen bomb's potency, small atomic nuclei such as those of hydrogen combine to form larger ones; whereas in the fission process used in today's reactors, heavy nuclei such as those of uranium are split and thus broken down. In both processes huge amounts of energy are released, but some scientists view fusion as safer, more efficient and economical. This view is disputed in some circles, and considerable research remains before fusion can be applied on a large-scale commercial basis. When that time comes, its developers may encounter strong resistance by a public that has been "burned" by its experience with the other atomic process, fission, worlds apart though the two techniques may be.

Whether we manage to satisfy short-term uranium needs or not, the future of atomic energy depends on the breeder. Yet the problems besetting the breeder program are truly prodigious, and a quick explanation of this technology may help us understand some of them. Uranium in nature comes in two forms, or isotopes, which are mingled together in the ore: uranium 235 and uranium 238. Uranium 235 is the only "fissile," or fissionable form, but it constitutes only seven tenths of 1 per cent of the total ore. The rest—99.3 per cent—is uranium 238. Uranium 238, however, is not fissile; it does not "burn," as uranium 235 does. Thus we have a tiny amount of uranium that does burn, and a large amount that does not.

Does this mean that non-burning U-238 is useless? Far from it. When the refined uranium, composed of both isotopes, is burned in a reactor, the U-238 is converted into plutonium, and plutonium is a most valuable "fissile" fuel. Indeed, it is this vast storehouse of "fertile" U-238 that is the hope of atomic power's future—*if* we can master the technology for converting it into plutonium in a big way. Conventional reactors aren't the answer. Most of the plutonium they generate is simultaneously burned during operation, and only relatively small amounts are recovered when the fuel is reprocessed.

By contrast, breeders are designed to convert a much higher percentage of the fertile U-238 into fissile plutonium—theoretically all of it, but realistically 50-60 per cent of it. Over a period of time, a breeder will produce more fuel than it requires, and the surplus can be used to operate other reactors. The time it takes for a breeder to create twice as much fuel as went into it is called its "doubling time." But don't get the impression that the conversion of uranium to plutonium takes place overnight. The most optimistic projections of doubling time in breeders run from eight to ten years— that is, it would take that long for a "fast" breeder to produce enough plutonium to replenish its own fuel supply and provide a surplus sufficient to fuel another reactor of the same size.

The trouble is that electricity consumption in the United States is growing at a rate of 100 per cent every ten years—doubling every decade, in other words. By the time breeders started in 1980 had doubled their fuel supply in 1990, that supply would be confronted with double the original demand. They could do nothing more than maintain equilibrium. But equilibrium is nowhere near good enough; massive surpluses must be produced to make up for the huge drain on our atomic fuel reserves created by the tremendous number of fuel-wasting conventional reactors planned for the coming decades. Even if breeders could be developed with doubling time of eight years, it would nevertheless take fifty years before surpluses were produced, much too late to do any good.

Another problem, or group of problems has to do with plutonium, the by-product of the fission process that goes on in the reactor's core.

There are three major uses for it: (1) as an explosive in atomic weapons; (2) as a fuel for conventional reactors; and (3) as a fuel for breeder reactors.

As to atomic weapons, until 1964 the Federal Government was prepared to guarantee purchase, at high prices, of all the plutonium produced in commercial reactors for the purpose of using it in nuclear bombs. But in 1964 President Johnson announced a full inventory of military plutonium, and the Government has begun phasing out its plutonium purchases. Which means that unless some other use is found for it, it will become a drug on the market.

Why can't it be employed to fuel conventional reactors? For the simple reason that the technology for economically "recycling" plutonium—substituting it for the uranium fuel now used—is still unperfected. The Government estimates that the state of the art will be perfected by 1974, but the only way to know for sure will be to experiment with it in the gigantic reactors now going up. Whether we want such experiments conducted outside our cities is one of the many questions the public must decide.

Can we employ plutonium as fuel in breeder reactors? As a matter of fact, it is beginning to appear that no other fuel will do for the fast breeders being developed for commercial use. Commissioner Gerald F. Tape of the AEC told the American Power Conference in 1968 that for a variety of reasons, "it may not be possible to operate fast breeders economically with U-235" as the fuel that converts fertile U-238 into plutonium. Plutonium will be needed instead, drawn from the inventory accumulated by conventional reactors. It is questionable, however, whether there will be enough of it to make the breeder program go. Dr. Tape, in the speech cited above, estimated that in the two-year period 1984-85, the conventional reactors then in operation will be producing enough plutonium to provide the total fuel requirements for about thirty-six breeders of 1,000,000 kilowatts each. It is hard to envision thirty-six breeders popping up in time to go on line by then, but even if the industry can pull that miracle out of the hat, it is doubtful—in fact, mathematically impossible, according to one line of reasoning—whether all those breeders will be able to provide sufficient fuel to meet the AEC's forecast that atomic power plants will generate half our electric power by the year 2000.

All this presupposes that we will have developed a safe, reliable, economic breeder that can double its fuel supply every eight to ten years. The state of breeder technology appears to be in such disrepair, however, that this prospect is quite dim. In 1967, Edward Teller stated in *Nuclear News* that "Altogether the fast breeder has resisted the head-on attack of our best technological people for 20 years. I doubt it will become a success very soon."

That same year the AEC issued a Supplement to its 1962 Report to the President in which it stated that while progress had been made in liquid-metal fast breeders (the kind given priority by the Government), a number of significant factors had yet to be considered in establishing the safety of those reactors. Some of those factors, it should be noted, were contributory to the Fermi debacle the year before. Others were causing problems in Experimental Breeder Reactor #2 at Idaho Falls, Idaho, which at this writing is the only liquid-metal fast breeder operating—*when* it is operating—in this country.

Not only is resolution of those problems a staggering challenge, but new ones keep turning up, and in 1967 and 1968 a couple of them arose which cast an ominous light on the fundamental principles by which breeders are designed. In the middle of 1967, for instance, evidence was discovered indicating that "high fast neutron fluences," the kind prevalent at the energy and heat levels operative in fast breeders, could cause serious damage to the stainless steel cladding that contains reactor fuel. They would swell to around 7 per cent greater than their original size, form "voids" (something like hot spots), and become highly brittle. The swelling of these fuel tubes interferes with the flow of coolant, which could lead to serious overheating and catastrophic melting of fuel. "The mechanism by which these voids form is not known," stated Floyd L. Culler, Jr., assistant director of Oak Ridge National Laboratory, in a letter to Dr. George M. Kavanagh, AEC's Assistant General Manager for Reactors. Culler predicted it would take at least four years to investigate fully the effects of these "fluences," then went on to offer a chilling thought: that since these inexplicable phenomena had turned up at only about 10 per cent of the exposure level of radioactivity anticipated for breeders, "is it not possible that there are new effects to be observed at high doses as yet unattained?"

Around the same time that Culler was describing these findings, three highly respected British scientists were dropping an even bigger bombshell at a meeting of the International Atomic Energy Agency in Germany. The subject was something called "alpha," which described a somewhat esoteric value vital to the efficiency of breeder reactors. The British scientists presented computations to the effect that everybody had been underestimating the value of "alpha," which meant that breeders would take twice as long to produce fuel as expected.

It was enough to send the assembled scientists scurrying into impromptu caucuses, for it would demand new design, new materials, new technologies, and new safety measures. New headaches, too, of course, and new expenses. In February 1968 a representative of the

AEC testified before the Joint Committee on Atomic Energy that it would take "several years" to conduct more definitive measurements of "alpha." The Englishmen might be wrong, of course, but the nuclear industry could not afford for them to be right.

"Fluences" and "alpha" are just samples of the many incredibly difficult problems harassing scientists and engineers today. The conquests of those problems would still leave a host of others whose solutions have been forecast by some experts at no less than fifteen years.

In its 1962 Report to the President, the AEC stated that "with luck and adequate effort, practical and economic full-scale breeder reactors might be achieved by the late 1970s or early 1980s." The 1967 Supplement, however, sang a more cautious tune: "It does not appear that a prudent commitment to build the first U.S. demonstration [breeder] plant can be made prior to 1969, nor can the number of demonstration plants be predetermined. It is foreseeable that over a period of perhaps 10 years, as many as 3 to 5 demonstration plants of different designs and sizes could be built and operated." With the discovery of vast "voids" in scientific understanding about breeder behavior, however, it might take even longer to design, construct, and debug large-scale breeders; and at least a few years beyond that must be allowed for observers from the utilities to convince themselves that breeders will fulfill their promise. David M. Williams, associate editor of *Electric Light and Power,* wrote in the April 1968 issue that 1985 looked like a more reasonable time for us to expect breeders to become available, rather than the 1980 deadline usually mentioned in the atomic power industry. Even that prediction leaves little time for delay, Williams said, and he suggested that unless fast breeder reactors are working within twenty years, *the first generation of nuclear power stations may be the last.*

Meanwhile, a lesser economic disaster will be developing in the 1970s, for unless the industry learns how to "recycle" plutonium economically for use as fuel in conventional reactors, it is going to be stuck with an awful lot of plutonium; and if breeders fail to materialize altogether, the industry will be glutted with the stuff. At the present time, and until January 1, 1971, the Federal Government is obliged to buy plutonium from utilities at premium prices—another important indirect subsidy that should be assessed in evaluating atomic energy's real economic value, incidentally. But when the Government's buy-back schedule expires, the industry will be faced with the burden of storing all that plutonium. Many utility men are very nervous about this possibility, for they chose to build nuclear plants mainly because they expected a good price for plutonium.

J. L. Everett, vice-president for Engineering and Research of Philadelphia Electric Co., told a nuclear fuel processing conference in 1967 in Augusta, Georgia: "If we do not sell the plutonium at $8 per gram or better, we pay a penalty of approximately 20%—on our fuel cycle costs, and that would have been enough of a difference to make the decision in many cases go the other way." And Representative Craig Hosmer of California, at a 1967 congressional hearing, advanced his conviction that if fast breeders are not developed, plutonium "is not going to be worth any $8 to $10 a gram." This could cause genuine hardship on electric utilities, he said, which had based their decision to go nuclear on the "rather firm assumption" that they would be recovering that amount for their plutonium.

One final factor should be mentioned here, and underlined, and that is that for breeder reactors to be most effective, as producers both of electricity and of fuel, they must each have a capacity in the 1,000,-000-kilowatt area. The trouble-plagued Fermi was designed for a capacity of about 130,000 electric kilowatts, but the operating license issued by the AEC restricted it to 60,900 kilowatts, and the accident occurred at a heat level sufficient to produce only about 11,000 kilowatts of electricity. Is it realistic to believe that businessmen, looking at the Fermi experience, will be eager to put huge amounts of capital into breeders that will be operating at nearly one hundred times the capacity at which the Lagoona Beach machine broke down?

The eminent Edward Teller has described the special dangers of the breeder in these terms:

> For the fast breeder to work in its steady-state breeding condition you probably need something like half a ton of plutonium. In order that it should work economically in a sufficiently big power-producing unit, it probably needs quite a bit more than one ton of plutonium. I do not like the hazard involved. I suggested that nuclear reactors are a blessing because they are clean. They *are* clean as long as they function as planned, but if they malfunction in a massive manner, which can happen in principle, they can release enough fission products to kill a tremendous number of people.
> ... if you put together two tons of plutonium in a breeder, one tenth of 1 per cent of this material could become critical. ... Although I believe it is possible to analyze the immediate consequences of an accident, I do not believe it is possible to analyze and foresee the secondary consequences. In an accident involving a plutonium reactor, a couple of tons of plutonium can melt. I don't think anybody can foresee whether 1 or 2 or 5 per cent of this plutonium will find itself and how it will get mixed with some other material. A small fraction of the original charge can become a great hazard.

To sum up, then, because our Government has encouraged the building of far too many fuel-wasting conventional reactors before solving the problems of fuel-breeding, we are well on the way to exhausting uranium reserves in the competitive price range. Unless we halt this profligate policy, the atomic power industry will price itself out of the market before the end of this century.

What will we do for fuel? A short look at this country's fuel reserves, and the economics of fuel energy, may provide some answers.

The capital costs of nuclear plants range from twenty-five to seventy-five dollars more per kilowatt than coal-fired plants, nuclear's major competitor; that is, a nuclear plant capable of generating 1,000,000 kilowatts of electric power will cost between twenty-five and seventy-five million dollars more to build than a 1,000,-000-kilowatt coal-fired one. The only way for nuclear plants to make up this initial disadvantage, then, is to be cheaper to *operate* than coal-fired plants. At present the two are roughly neck and neck, but a number of experts believe that nuclear cannot surpass coal in the short run, and certainly will not do so in the long run, with respect to operating costs. The reason is the rising cost of uranium.

The contest between nuclear and coal is scored in a number of ways. At present, coal delivered at about twenty-six cents per million British thermal units* is competitive with uranium costing slightly less than eight dollars per pound. However, a study issued by National Economics Research Associates, an economic consulting firm, points out that "a $3 increase in the price of uranium—say from $7.00 to $10.00 per pound—would represent an increase in equivalent coal costs of over 2 cents per million Btu. . . . Not only is this a significant cost effect, it comes at a time when inter-industry competition for energy markets has greatly intensified."

Now, a two-cent difference does not at first glance seem a lot to get excited about, but over an appreciable period it can total up to millions of dollars, and combined with the fact that it costs more to put nuclear plants up to begin with, that difference will most cer-

---

*A British thermal unit is the amount of heat it takes to raise the temperature of one pound of water 1 degree Fahrenheit starting at 60° F.

tainly make businessmen incline toward coal or some other energy alternative.

What reserves exist among those other fuels?

Undeniably, our nation has reason to look to the future with concern when it considers its fuel supplies. Energy consumption is soaring. The highly documented projections prepared by Resources for the Future, Inc., in 1963, relying on United Nations statistics, predict a threefold increase in United States energy use between 1960 and 2000. The U. S. Bureau of Mines puts it at fourfold.

The picture for natural gas, natural gas liquids, and oil indicates that by the end of the century, shortages will arise. The U. S. Bureau of Mines believes that by the year 2000 this nation will have used 1038.8 trillion cubic feet of natural gas, almost all of our minimum probable reserve. Resources for the Future, Inc., estimates that by 2000, 278.6 billion barrels of crude oil and natural gas liquids will have been consumed, again almost all of the probable minimum reserve.

The outlook for coal, however, is another matter entirely. The Bureau of Mines and the Department of the Interior's Geological Survey indicate that known coal reserves in this country are 1559 billion tons, of which 800 billion tons are recoverable, and 250 billion tons recoverable "at or near" present prices with present technology. How long will that 250 billion tons last? According to estimates made by the National Coal Association, based on energy consumption figures provided by the Federal Power Commission and the Atomic Energy Commission, coal consumption by the year 2000 for all uses will come to 1.12 billion tons annually—that is, if nuclear power captures half of the electricity market, as AEC forecasts suggest. At that rate, only 28.3 billion of the 250 billion tons of coal recoverable at present prices will have been used up.

It should thus be apparent why, in the race for control of the energy market, uranium must fall farther and farther behind. Compared to the 250 billion tons of known, recoverable, low-cost coal available in the United States, the known, recoverable, low-cost (eight dollars per pound or less) uranium reserves in this country—148,000 tons—have an energy equivalent of 2.572 billion tons of coal, or about 1 per cent of cheap, immediately recoverable coal reserves. Indeed, the 1.5 million tons of uranium we can hope to recover at *any* price up to thirty dollars a pound is equivalent, in energy-producing potential, to only 27 billion tons of coal, a little more than one tenth of the *cheap,* immediately recoverable supply of coal.

Such enormous surpluses give coal an incalculable advantage in the long run, because though coal prices may fluctuate upward occasionally, the threat of exhaustion will not begin to send them seriously upward until well into the twenty-first century. Whereas the threat of uranium shortages has already begun to reflect itself in sharply escalating prices. On November 9, 1967, the AEC had to admit that "Under the impetus of increasing demand, the domestic market price of [uranium concentrates] has risen significantly over the past two years."

Does our large reserve of coal indicate that we shouldn't worry about the future? Of course it does not. Quite the contrary, the lesson to which America is just awakening is that no natural resource is unlimited, and if we are to endure we must anticipate energy problems that will arise one hundred or more years from now. Today is not too soon to begin. At the same time there is a special lesson in the chronicle of atomic energy, for although that program was initiated precisely in the spirit of anticipating long-range energy problems, it was launched prematurely, well in advance of the accretion of scientific evidence demonstrating its technical feasibility, reliability, safety, or economic value.

What our great stockpile of coal *does* offer us, therefore, is an opportunity to evaluate and develop some viable alternatives to atomic energy *without* a loss of forward motion that would prove harmful to this nation's economy and the public's electricity needs. If we were on the verge of exhausting our fossil fuel reserves we might be forced to take our chances with atomic energy. But we are not by any means, and are blessed to be in such a position that if we halted the atomic power program tomorrow, fossil fuels could carry the ball well up to the time when this nation's great technology produced one or more means of generating electricity that genuinely possessed the virtues that atomic power was thought to have. Hopefully, however, we would utilize this opportunity to make absolutely certain, through intensive research, observation, and safe experimentation—unharried by attempts to press promising technologies into service before they had proved out—that we were not making the same mistake that we have made with the atom. We do have time, but not enough to afford going up another multi-billion dollar blind alley.

Before presenting some of the alternatives to atomic power, we should anticipate one possible criticism of our proposed approach. It might be asserted that by advocating continued use of fossil fuels to generate electricity in this interim period, we are also advocating continued pollution of our air with the noxious and poisonous effluents of those fuels.

The fouling of our environment with coal and oil effluvia is indeed a serious problem, and we in no way wish to relieve the fossil-fuel industries of their responsibility for controlling those hazards. It must be realized, however, that because the Federal Government spends only about one tenth as much money on fossil-fuel research as it does on atomic energy research, the fossil-fuel industry has been comparatively hobbled in its attempts to develop and promote the technology for pollution control.

Furthermore, it should be clearly understood that our Government has never pushed atomic energy as a complete substitute for fossil-fuel power. Indeed, the AEC's own projections of future fuel consumption not only show the two forms of energy sharing the electricity arena equally, but indicate that the burning of coal for electricity generation will actually increase in the next century because *all* forms of energy consumption will increase.

Therefore, whatever the future of atomic power, our legislators will still be obliged to give much greater support than hitherto to the solution of environmental pollution problems connected with burning of coal and oil. It might well turn out that as a result of such support, the means will be found to eradicate those problems, permitting us to burn coal and oil far into the future without hazard, and granting us even more time to develop other energy programs in a safe, orderly fashion against the day when fossil fuels begin to run out.

Recent developments indicate that such means may soon be on hand. Suppose we open the discussion of alternatives to atomic power, then, by examining how much more can be done with the conventional processes of burning oil, coal and gas.

One point that should be made clear at the outset is that the fossil-fuel reserves we have been discussing are the known *minimums* recoverable under present technology at more or less present prices. We know that there are larger reserves on hand, however. For instance, Resources for the Future, Inc., states that the known reserve of natural gas as of 1960 was 264 trillion cubic feet. But it also estimated that a probable reserve existed of between 1200 and 1700 trillion, and the 1965 U. S. Geological Survey finds that the reserve may be as much as 3600 trillion. Similarly, while the known reserve of oil and gas liquids in the United States was placed at 39 billion barrels as of 1960, the U. S. Geological Survey of 1965 stated the possible maximum may be as much as 1200-1300 billion barrels, about three or four times the known, immediately recoverable minimum. As for coal, while 250 billion tons are recoverable at or near present prices with present technology, the total estimated reserves have been placed at 3210 billion tons, or more than a dozen times the amount to which we have immediate access.

Obviously, recovery of a large portion of these staggering reserves will ensure a fuel supply for America throughout the coming century, perhaps even with a surplus to spare for exportation. The big problems, however, are extracting them from their sources and learning how to burn them efficiently and cleanly.

Much remains to be done with the technology for recovering coal, oil, and gas from natural deposits. To give just one example of this, the coal industry concedes that only about 50 per cent of any coal deposit is recoverable. Known coal reserves in this country, according to a 1968 Department of the Interior survey, are 1559 billion tons, but because of low recovery efficiency, only about 800 billion tons are recoverable, and of that only 250 billion are recoverable economically.

In a like manner, natural gas supplies are prematurely exhausted when the internal pressure in the pocket drops, although great quantities remain behind. And it is well known that at least twice as much oil exists in known deposits of oil shale and tar sands as the combined minimums of natural gas, natural gas liquids, and crude oil! If the technology for recovering these marginal coal, gas, and oil deposits were perfected, we would not have to undertake potentially hazardous "crash" programs in energy production such as the one which resulted in atomic power.

Hand in hand with development of more efficient means of recovering natural resources is refinement of our means of consuming them. The pollution problem derives from the inefficient way in which fuel is burned. Such inefficiency creates health hazards, produces less electricity per unit of fuel, and wastes opportunities for developing valuable by-products. Happily, our Government, in recognition of these facts, has recently loosened some purse strings to correct the gross imbalance between atomic energy research and research in fossil-fuel energy. In September 1968, for instance, a $255.6 million five-year plan for development and funding of research into control of sulfur oxides, promulgated by the National Air Pollution Control Administration, was made public. Some of the categories toward which funds will be applied are development of processes for removing sulfur oxides from flue gases, studies of dispersion of waste gases from chimneys and tall stacks, development of processes for removing sulfur from coal and fuel oil before burning, conversion of coal to liquid fuels or gases, new combustion processes, processes for controlling sulfur oxides from various industries, and development of pollution measurement equipment.

One can scarcely open an issue of a coal or oil industry trade newspaper or journal without finding mention of some promising process for attacking the pollution problem. Invariably such news items conclude with reference to funding problems; yet if our Government primed the pump it would stimulate the production of by-products which would soon pay their own way. At the present time, for example, coal possessing high sulfur content is undesirable for electricity-generating purposes because it pollutes the air. A number of techniques are available, however, for removing the sulfur during either processing or burning. Some of those techniques, such as the alkalized alumina process, catalytic oxidation, chemical scrubbing, and the molten salt process, can convert the sulfurous waste into pure sulfur, sulfuric acid, and other by-products of high value to industrial processes. Sale of those by-products will not only offset the cost of sulfur removal but may actually make high-sulfur coal a most valuable resource as the demand for sulfur increases in coming years. Similarly, advances in utilization of fly ash, another waste product of coal-burning, in building materials should encourage the Government to support means by which fly ash can be captured.

Possibly more promising than refinement of the conventional ways in which we burn fuel is the recent development of techniques for burning it in an entirely new way. At present, fossil fuels are burned to heat water, and the resultant steam turns power-generating turbines. The new processes, however, concentrate on more direct extraction of electricity from the burning fuel, and despite their jawbreaking names appear simpler in principle and operation than conventional modes —and possibly cheaper.

Magnetohydrodynamics, or MHD, has received so much attention lately that in October 1968 the Federal Government moved toward authorization of a demonstration plant utilizing it. MHD involves the acceleration of a very hot gas, such as one produced by burning coal, oil, or natural gas, through a strong magnetic field. The motion of the hot gas through the magnetic field generates electricity in a similar way to Michael Faraday's principle that an electrical conductor moved through such a field acquires an electric current. Industrial developers who have testified before Congress, such as Dr. Arthur R. Kantrowitz, director of Avco-Everett Research Laboratory and vice-president of Avco Corp., claim that with MHD up to 50 per cent less fuel is needed to produce a kilowatt-hour of electricity as compared to conventional fuel-burning processes. Just as significantly, MHD is said to be able to remove economically practically all of the noxious exhaust materials that contribute to air pollution, and can convert them into sulfuric and nitric acids. MHD can work with or without cooling water. If water is used, an MHD plant will nevertheless create between 25 and 40 per cent less thermal pollution than the best fossil- and nuclear-fired plants operating today. On the other hand, the ability of such a plant to operate without cooling water opens up important opportunities for development of areas where water is scarce and fuel abundant.

The promise held by MHD was described by Donald F. Hornig, Special Assistant to the President for Science and Technology and head of the Office of Science and Technology, to delegates of the 36th annual Edison Electric Institute meeting in Philadelphia. The power industry, he concluded, should learn that nuclear power was "not the only unconventional path available for more efficient and lower-cost central power generation."

Variations on MHD, such as magnetoplasmadynamics (MPD) and electrogasdynamics (EGD) have also shown high potential for electricity generation. In MPD, a gas plasma creates heat and, using cesium, the most electro-positive metal known, as a catalyst, produces electricity directly. In EGD, coal or oil is burned under high pressure, and the gas shot into a small tube attached to the furnace. At the entrance of the tube an electrode sprays a stream of charged ions into the gas flow, and the concentration of those ions within the pressurized flow creates a powerful electric current. In one experiment engineers sprayed charged ions into a gas stream using about a tenth of a watt of power, and the current picked up by electrodes at the end of the device registered about two watts of energy. Yet EGD's developers claim the process can produce electricity on a scale necessary to power heavily populated areas. Also, they say that since EGD doesn't need water, a power plant of that type could be located directly over the fuel source, such as a coal field.

Another application of fossil fuels to energy production is by means of fuel cells. Like batteries, fuel cells are designed with two electrodes separated by an electrolyte. But whereas in electrolysis electric current passed through an electrolyte solution breaks that solution into its component gases, fuel cells work on the reverse principle: Gases are piped in, producing electrical current and water.

Although fuel cells are as yet unfeasible for large-scale electricity generation, some recent breakthroughs may point the way to gigantic power plants operating by means of fuel cell dynamics. The September 23,

1968, issue of *Electronic News,* for instance, described a cell developed by Bolt, Beranek & Newman and the Arco Chemical Co., designed to convert the energy of natural gas, propane, kerosene, or gasoline directly into electrical energy. The special features of this particular device enable scientists to operate it for thousands of hours with no sign of energy loss. According to one spokesman for the developers, a 250-pound system could provide enough electric power to serve the needs of an average American home at a price competitive with utility rates.

Proceeding away from fossil fuels, we find a variety of energy sources which hold a greater or lesser degree of promise. Some of them, such as the sun, the sea, and the heat of the earth, are rather sublime, whereas others, such as ordinary garbage, are less so. Yet because mankind must begin thinking in terms of centuries and not merely decades in surveying its future prospects, no potentially useful source should be overlooked.

Hydroelectric plants, which generate electricity by means of water flow, no longer contribute as much to our energy budget as they once did. In 1922 they generated about 38 per cent of our total power, whereas by 1967 the figure had dropped to 18 per cent. The reasons, of course, are the growth of fossil-fuel generation and the decreasing number of waterways suitable for hydroelectric installations. While we should not count on this picture changing substantially in the future, there are in the north and northwestern half of this continent a number of mighty river systems now being developed or considered for development as power sources. American utilities are aware of the potential in those areas, and will undoubtedly explore it in due time. Late in 1966 it was announced that the Quebec Government had authorized construction of one of the world's largest hydro projects at Churchill Falls in the northern wilderness of Labrador, and that three possible American customers were still in the picture: New York's Consolidated Edison, Niagara Mohawk of

Buffalo, and Northeastern Power of Hartford, Connecticut.

Fresh water, however, is not the only source of hydroelectric power. Imaginative engineers have turned to the salt water of the seas as well. In November 1966 President de Gaulle dedicated a tidal power plant on the Rance River in France, hailing it as "the first large-scale use of the ocean in its ebb and flow." Built into a dam across the river's estuary are two dozen huge "bulbs," each containing generators operable on a water flow in either direction. The facility can therefore produce electricity both on the incoming and outgoing tides, or four times a day, and a reservoir system enables the installation to adapt those rhythms to normal power needs by holding water back or permitting it to pass through the bulbs.

In the 1930s the United States and Canada planned a similar project at Passamaquoddy to harness the sixty-foot tides of the Bay of Fundy, but abandoned the idea. The Rance plant has stirred new interest in that and other tidal power projects.

Solar energy is another form of power scarcely exploited by man. According to G. O. Jones, J. Rotblatt, and G. J. Whitrow, authors of *Atoms and the Universe,* the solar heat received by our planet in one year is approximately 700,000 times the energy at present derived from all fuels and water power. Solar light is another superabundant source of energy, and both heat and light from the sun are convertible to electricity. To date applications have been limited because of the low efficiency of conversion, and because many areas where electricity demand is great are too often covered with clouds. A number of authorities believe that both problems can be overcome. The low efficiency of converting solar energy into electricity, they suggest, is not a serious factor in view of the inexhaustible supply of that energy. As for clouds, a number of means are being developed for storage of collected solar energy, so that reserves can be built up, literally, for a rainy day.

While some men are looking to the sun, others are drawing electricity from the heat of the earth. In a valley eighty-five miles north of San Francisco known as The Geysers, engineers are utilizing natural steam, produced by the contact of underground water with molten magma close to the earth's surface, to produce electricity. The steam drives turbines which generate some 58,000 kilowatts of electricity at a cost 23 per cent below that of nearby conventional plants. Engineers estimate that by 1980, such "geothermal" energy could be generating as much as 10 per cent of the United States' total electrical output. As one report puts it, "No matter how much is used, the heat is not likely to be used up. Once scientists master the technology, they should be able to recirculate condensed steam back into the ground, giving virtually unlimited life to wells in states as dry as Nevada." If the idea sounds newfangled, consider that the Larderello geothermal plant near Siena, Italy, has been producing electricity for some sixty-five years.

Although the technology for harnessing geothermal power may prove a difficult challenge, another and possibly more feasible solution to our energy problems can be found right under our noses—in the garbage can. But while some cynics have been making light of the *idea* of garbage and refuse as an energy source, scientists have been—well, making light of the garbage and refuse itself, by means of electricity. In fact, because of its extremely low sulfur content, one expert went so far as to describe refuse as "the sweetest fuel this side of natural gas."

Refuse is an increasingly important source of European electricity. In Paris, for instance, the incinerator at Issy-les-Moulineaux derives 90,000,000 kilowatt-hours of electricity annually from 450,000 tons of household garbage. Munich, Frankfurt, Dusseldorf, Geneva, Rotterdam, and Milan are among the other large foreign metropolises producing electricity and steam heat from this homely resource. In Toronto, Canada, a plant treating sewage with bacteria produces heat by burning the resulting gas, suggesting possible application for generation of electricity.

Obviously, the use of garbage, refuse, and sewage as fuel is by no means a mere novelty. A recent *Fortune* article described the current "garbage explosion" as a genuinely dire threat, and this application of energy technology answers two serious needs of our society at a stroke: what to do with our mounting refuse, and where to obtain reasonably priced electricity. Since refuse can be burned with considerable efficiency, and by-products used in a variety of ways, a number of side issues are resolved at the same time.

All of the systems described here are definitely worth exploring if there is a genuine chance that they will prove safe, reliable, economic, and clean, and will serve for an appreciable length of time to alleviate our energy problems. Hopefully, some of these techniques will have been perfected by the end of the century. Indeed, if this nation persists in developing atomic power, it will be *imperative* that those alternatives be perfected by the end of the century, for by that time the electric industry, suffocating for want of uranium, will be grateful for any form of rescue available.

CHAPTER XVII

Where There's a Stack

A member of the National Coal Association, thumbing through the March 10, 1967, issue of *Time* magazine, came across a full-page ad by Westinghouse featuring a color photograph of the Connecticut Yankee Atomic Power Company's Haddam Neck plant, an atomic installation. He gazed at it for a long moment, frowning; something was wrong. Then he snapped his fingers. Of course! The plant in the picture had no stack!

He went through his files until he came across a pamphlet distributed by the utility. Just as he'd suspected—the artist's conception in the pamphlet showed the plant *with* a stack. Just to make sure, he sent a colleague to visit the plant site. There was the stack, clearly visible.

Where had the stack disappeared to in the Westinghouse ad?

"The public knows a stack means one of two things," Brice O'Brien, the Association's general counsel told the Joint Congressional Committee; "either something is being emitted during normal operation, or it is put there to handle extraordinary emissions in an emergency." Portrayal of a stack, in other words, would invoke in the public imagination an image of pollution or toxic release that contradicted the picture the utility industry was trying to promote—of nuclear fuel as clean, safe energy. "We are forced to conclude," O'Brien said, "that the artist's brush has been used to help sell atomic power to the public."

The Connecticut Yankee incident symbolizes the attempt of government and industry to sell nuclear power to the public "without the stacks"—that is, with the sense of hazard omitted. And the fact that an enormous segment of our population, including otherwise knowledgeable individuals in the scientific and engineering fields, in government, and even in the utility industry, is almost totally unaware of the dangers described in this book, constitutes a tribute to the effectiveness of the campaign to keep Americans in the dark about atomic power. "The man in the street hardly knows the problem exists," declared Walter Cronkite, narrating a television program on *The Mighty Atom,* in discussing the stupendous challenge of nuclear waste disposal. "They come up to me wanting to shake my hand, telling me they had no idea they'd been involved in anything so dangerous," reports an opponent of nuclear power who has lectured before utility executives. A few years ago, the *Journal of Professional Practice,* reporting on the results of a questionnaire sent to ninety-four deans of engineering and ninety-two heads of civil engineering departments, stated that 53 per cent and 70 per cent of the respondents respectively said they had not been aware that the insurance industry had refused to provide adequate liability insurance to the owners of atomic power plants in view of the great hazards involved. In addition, 16 per cent of the deans and 44 per cent of the department heads had not read AEC reports on the magnitude of potential damage to life, health, and property from a major accident.

A psychologist might be able to explain why so many Americans, including their information-gathering agents, the members of the press, have submitted so docilely to the campaign executed by the public relations arms of our Government and industry. Undoubtedly much of it has to do with the strong need, which we have described at the outset of this book, for people to believe that atoms for peace can be as benevolent to mankind as atoms for war are malevolent. But whatever the reasons for our credulousness, the atomic power establishment has lulled a good portion of our population into acceptance of, and even enthusiasm for, the idea of reactors in our back yards. Let's take a closer look at the ways in which nuclear power has been packaged, merchandised, and sold to an unwitting public.

The promotion starts at the top, of course, with the Atomic Energy Commission. The hearings held for public consideration of reactor applications are, as we have seen, one of the Commission's major vehicles for subduing criticism, pacifying anxiety, and furthering acceptance. Hearings are by no means the only ways in which these objectives are accomplished, however. The Commission also publishes and distributes a large number of pamphlets explaining the fundamentals of atomic physics and the principles of reactor technology in language the lay reader, including impressionable school children, can easily grasp. The message, sometimes explicit and sometimes covert, is always that the atom is your friend, and atomic reactors make good neighbors. The liabilities of our "friends" and "good neighbors" are glossed over or left out of the discussion entirely.

Nuclear Reactors, a booklet written by John F. Hogerton and distributed by the AEC's Division of Technical Information, is typical of the Commission's literature. Of its forty-five pages, only three are devoted to reactor safety, and these present the most highly idealized picture. For instance:

In normal operation, the fission products are locked in the fuel by the fuel cladding, which is thus the plant's first line of defense against release of radioactivity. [No mention is made of the fact that the technology of cladding metals and alloys is still rife with unknowns.] This material leaves the premises, so to speak, when "spent" (used) fuel elements are removed from the reactor and shipped to a fuel reprocessing plant. [No mention of the treacherous hazards of removing fuel elements from the core, of transporting them to the reprocessing facility through population centers, and of reprocessing them.] If any trace of the fission products escapes into the reactor coolant through defects in the fuel cladding, it is scavenged from the coolant by purification equipment, packaged and shipped to an AEC site for safe burial. [No mention of the fact that scientists have still not learned how to capture all of the fission products released during reactor operation; no mention again of the transportation hazards; no mention of the unsolved problems of burial and storage of hot atomic wastes.]

Another passage, reporting on the structure and policies of the AEC, fails to mention that construction of reactors is regularly authorized before safety problems are resolved:

> And before a nuclear power plant may be built in the United States, vigorous safety review procedures must be followed, including, among other steps, a specific safety review of the proposed project by an impartial board of reactor experts (Advisory Committee on Reactor Safeguards). This review takes into account not only the features of the proposed reactor installation but also the environmental characteristics of the proposed location—distance from population centers, terrain, meteorological conditions, and the like. A similar but even more detailed review is made before a license is granted to operate the plant. Once the plant is in service, an amendment to the license must be obtained before any significant change may be made in the operating pattern.

Other AEC pamphlets reflect the same pattern, and some present grossly oversimplified pictures, almost word-cartoons, that insult the adult mentality and possibly harm that of a child. Take, for instance, this quotation from page 22 of an AEC booklet entitled *The New Force of Atomic Energy—Its Development and Use:*

> The chances of your receiving an overexposure to radiation are slight. They depend upon how much you

know about radiation, the methods for protecting yourself against it, and upon whether you are a reasonable person. You can get quite a burn from a match, but you must be close to it. So it is with radiation. There is little danger if you know what you are doing.

It is hard to believe that the tens of millions of people who will be living in the vicinity of nuclear reactors in the 1970s, or the many millions more through whose towns radioactive waste-laden trucks will be passing, are unreasonable. Yet by virtue of the infantile logic that equates matches with reactors, the responsibility for getting burned in a serious radiological incident would rest with us, rather than with the utilities, transport companies, insurance firms, and the Government regulators.

Since the AEC position seems to be that protection against radiation depends on knowing what you are doing, one would think the Commission would have undertaken a vigorous campaign to inform the general public on "what to do" in the event of a reactor accident. But as we have seen, no publication outlining appropriate citizen action has been widely distributed, if one exists at all.

The Commission resorts to the spoken as well as written word in developing its picture of the safety of our atomic power program, and many Commission officials regularly deliver speeches painting rosy vistas of the atom's future. Early in 1968, for instance, AEC Chairman Glenn T. Seaborg addressed a convocation of students at Fairleigh Dickinson University. In a visionary speech entitled "Man and the Atom—by the Year 2000," Seaborg evoked for his young audience glorious visions of a utopian society energized by our friend the atom. "Nuclear power has surged forward remarkably in the past few years," he told the students, "because it is now realized that, in addition to being reliable, safe sources of power, large nuclear reactors can provide increasing amounts of electricity at economic costs and do so cleanly without adding to the burden of air pollution."

Safe, clean, reliable, economical—four of the most commonly used words used to describe the seductive wonders of nuclear power. More compelling phrases followed:

> Today it is essential that we encourage new directions and new dimensions to our thinking and our actions. We have to break down many of our ingrained prejudices, old habits and traditional attitudes and achieve a new degree of flexibility, imagination and innovation. There is no doubt that we will have to do this "on the run," so to speak. . . . Therefore we must learn to gain and maintain public understanding and support of positive programs. We must learn to overcome new obstacles that arise, because even in the best-made plans there are flaws, and we may often find ourselves having to make changes to take advantage of new innovations, to shift emphasis, to readjust timetables and goals. But not . . . to act now for fear of making the wrong moves could be far more disastrous.

What it all boiled down to was: There's an urgent need for expansion of our electric power program, but instead of hesitating to consider our alternatives and develop a truly safe source of power, we must plunge ahead with the atom, however flawed that technology may be. One wonders whether the students listening to this speech had done their homework in basic logic, or whether many of them, instead, were inspired to pursue careers in atomic energy by such phrases as "encourage new directions and new dimensions to our thinking" and "break down many of our ingrained prejudices, old habits and traditional attitudes" and "achieve a new degree of flexibility, imagination and innovation."

Television is another medium through which the AEC disseminates its soothing message. For example, in 1964 the National Educational Television Network aired a program entitled "Man and the Atom," produced by Harold Mayer in co-operation with the AEC. The show opened with a series of testimonials for nuclear power plants from residents of Buchanan, New York, location of Con Edison's Indian Point facility:

WM. BURKE: I'm William J. Burke. For the past 15 years I've been Mayor of the village of Buchanan. We're about 24 miles above New York City. I saw the plant from the very beginning . . . until it was fully completed. At first there was one group that was a little apprehensive, and we were kind to these people and talked to them and explained that the Federal government had spent almost a billion dollars developing these reactors. And I assume that we answered their questions satisfactorily because when we had a public hearing to rezone the property, there was no one at the meeting whatsoever against it.

After all, this isn't the first atomic energy plant in the country. Besides being the Mayor, I also happen to be the director of pupil personnel in the local high school . . . where there are over 1000 students. We have four grammar schools, elementary schools, and one parochial school. We have 2500 students housed in these buildings which are in close proximity—within a half-mile to a mile from the plant—so of course we want to be assured of the safety of these children. Today I don't think anybody realizes that the plant is over there; we know that it is there, it makes electricity and supplies us, but in this modern world, I know that for one, I'm very happy to have it here. And as I say, there's no fears, and if you stop the average person on the street, he'll tell you he doesn't even know the plant is over there.

LOCAL MAN: I can look out of my windows of my house and actually see the smoke-stacks. I can hear the excess steam coming off. . . . Nothing can really happen to it the way they have it set up and built over there. The structure itself, and the devices they have for any kind of . . . warning signals and all coming up; that there's no reason for worry. . . .

LOCAL WOMAN: I never hear anyone around here ever worry about the atomic plant. I think most people feel like I do. I think they think it's a wonderful thing. . . .
LOCAL MAN: It's very, very difficult to get a home here. The minute one is for sale, it sells almost within the next day.

This hallelujah chorus is almost too beautiful to believe until it is explained that Con Edison had enriched the townsfolk of Buchanan with a lot more than praise of the merits of atomic reactors—a *lot* more, as it shall be demonstrated at the end of this chapter. In any event, the rest of the television program was replete with the kinds of half-truths and misleading statements that have come to characterize the public face of atomic power.

But if propagandizing at the Federal level is one of the most depressing aspects of atomic power's drive for acceptance, it is by no means the most ordinary. Since, as might be expected, the private utilities have the most to gain from public approval, they carry most of the load of public misinformation. From the outset the industry has perceived that a comprehensive program of public and community relations is of exceeding importance to the acceptance of nuclear power on a national basis. Today, no utility company lacks a highly sophisticated public relations department armed with all the tools for instilling its persuasive messages.

The philosophy that guides the PR man has never been expressed as well as it was by Dr. W. E. Johnson, general manager of Westinghouse Electric Corporation's Atomic Power Division, during hearings before the Joint Committee on Atomic Energy in April 1963:

REP. WESTLAND: How much of a problem is it in overcoming civilian objections to the location of a nuclear power plant? . . .
DR. JOHNSON: I think there are some people who are frightened of it. I am not sure there are a lot of

such people, however, if you take them into the context of the total population. I don't know of any existing reactor site where the people are actively objecting. . . . I think a lot of this comes about by a few people being worried and making a lot of noise compared to the total population.

REP. WESTLAND: You don't think it is a big factor.

DR. JOHNSON: I do not think it is a big factor. *I think that if you do a reasonable job of public relations you can place a reactor anyplace it is needed.*

REP. WESTLAND: I quite agree. I think your public relations work is important in this area. The people of Los Angeles or New York City can be persuaded that the location of these plants in that area can be safe. [Emphasis ours.]

Former General Electric public relations man Harold A. Beaudoin phrased it a little differently, but in terms that would have gratified Pavlov: "It is far easier to borrow money from a friend if he knows from past experience that you won't play the horses with it. Likewise, if the mind is strongly conditioned on a continuing basis, then the public problem of a particular moment— locating a reactor in a populated area, for example— can be superimposed with a far better chance of understanding."

The task of the PR man, then, is to impregnate the minds of potential antagonists with the seeds of acceptance, directing the operation to the areas of their strongest interests. Then the idea must be embellished continually until attitudes have been conditioned— brainwashed, as the expression goes.

The methods employed toward this end are numerous and various. Some of the more prominently featured are (1) formally announced presentations for representatives of city, county, and state government, civic groups, and other local organizations; (2) a speakers' bureau for giving talks at group meetings and schools; (3) press conferences for news media; (4) publication of monthly progress reports; (5) preparation and showing of slides and movies; (6) publication of technical press packets describing the plant and nuclear power; (7) arrangement of panel discussions for television; (8) preparation of articles for industrial magazines; and (9) guided tours of the facility. In addition, some utilities construct information centers at the site, and even small auditoriums, which include plant models and pictures, nuclear power exhibits, full-time tour guides, and audio-visual equipment.

With a program like that, how can a utility lose? Well, in all but a couple of cases, it hasn't.

In 1966 the AEC published Volume I of a study entitled *Small Nuclear Power Plants,* which surveyed a number of aspects of design, construction, and operation of ten power reactors. Interestingly, considerable attention was paid to the role played by the public relations program in each case. Because of the success of these programs, the sections of each chapter devoted to public relations made rather dull reading. Note, for instance, how smoothly things went at the Hallam, Nebraska, facility:

> As a possible indication of the success of the Consumers Public Power District public relations program, no residents of the area opposed the reactor installation either publicly in local news media or at the public hearings convened by the AEC. The key to the success of the program was apparently the philosophy that the Hallam Nuclear Power Facility belongs to the people in the area; that the Hallam Nuclear Power Facility is an area project rather than an effort solely of the AEC or the operating utility. As a result, the residents of the community became a part of the program and took the initiative in establishing supporting facilities such as roads, housing areas, and general area improvements.

Once the reactor was built, however, things scarcely went smoothly, and the AEC survey of the Hallam facility describes a woeful series of mishaps, break-

downs, and shutdowns, which must have caused the
public relations liaison to tear his hair. In the first
month, several "scrams," or emergency thrusts of control rods into the core to prevent runaway chain reaction, occurred due to malfunctions of control and protective system components, and on August 3, 1963,
after six days of uninterrupted operation, the reactor
was shut down to investigate excessive leakage of heli-
um from control rod thimbles. The shutdown lasted
almost three months. The plant's nuclear reactor (the
utility had wisely constructed a conventionally fueled
steam boiler to keep the turbines running in case the
reactor failed) resumed operation in October 1963 and
carried on for four months—with "only" twelve un-
scheduled scrams, of which five were spurious, four
were due to operator error, and three were due to
control system malfunction. Moderator trouble developed—the moderator being the material used to control the reaction of the fuel—and between February 20
and April 24, 1964, there were five more scrams and
a four-day shutdown for control rod drop tests. On
May 6, the reactor was started up again, and ran for
all of twelve days before another moderator element
failed. For two and a half months, the reactor was
shut down. Twenty-two of the fuel elements stuck in
the core and could not be removed in the normal
manner. Subsequent investigation revealed no fewer
than twelve areas where serious and time-consuming
failures and malfunctions existed. On September 27,
the reactor was shut down for good. On August 9,
1965, the AEC announced termination of its operation contract with the utility, and in June 1966 the
Commission announced intentions to decommission the
facility.

"The Consumers Public Power District was com-
mended by the AEC for its fine work in demonstrating
that all phases of liquid metal-cooled reactor plant operation could be performed effectively and safely by

utility company personnel," the AEC report stated.
And the PR men, after waiting five years for something
positive to say about Hallam, must have shouted
"Hear, hear!" when they read that.

The fundamental tool for implanting the notion of
safety in the public mind is the word, of course, and the
respect shown by nuclear power proponents for the
power of words, in matters of atomic power, is well in
evidence in an address given by Hal Stroube, representing the Pacific Gas & Electric Company, at a recent
nuclear power industry forum. His speech also evinces
the condescension many PR men feel for the average
man's ability to understand facts when they are squarely presented:

> I would suggest that our problem . . . might better be
> defined as one of public misunderstanding rather than
> public understanding. . . . If we *confuse* them with tech-
> nical jargon, *belabor* them with scientific information,
> *bewilder* them with probabilities and maximum credi-
> bilities, and *frighten* them with the glossolalia [*sic*] of the
> laboratory and the testing ground, we are doing them
> and ourselves a terrible disservice. . . .
>
> [Earlier] some discussion by AEC officials at this
> meeting touched on the need for replacing the word
> "*hazards*" in the title of the so-called "Preliminary Haz-
> ards Summary Report." I suggest that these gentlemen
> have the *responsibility* as well as the *ability to make that
> change within a week of returning to Washington.* And
> while they are at it, I would add that the time has come
> for some semantic soul-searching about the need for
> eliminating some other objectionable words from the
> atomic lexicon. Words such as "critically"—"*poison*
> curtains"—"nuclear excursion"—"scram"—"maximum
> credible accident"—spring immediately to my mind, and
> I could list a dozen others if given time. . . . *Some*one
> has to start *some*where, and I would suggest that the
> best starting place is in the official language of the AEC.
> Surely the agency's Public Information Section has the
> talent and the manpower to make a study of this sugges-

tion and hopefully recommend some palatable synonyms for the "scare words" which make our job of public understanding more difficult. [Italics all his.]

It should be pointed out that Stroube and his utility company were licking their wounds from a confrontation with the citizens of the Bodega Bay area over the San Andreas Fault business. Stroube attributed the defeat in a large measure to bad images and scare words and, like some primitive shaman, proposed to exorcise their spell by banishing them:

One last suggestion [to the AEC] along these lines would be to do us a *great* big favor by *canceling* the now-in-progress updating of the Brookhaven Report. I've eaten a steady diet of [the Report] in the past three years as it became the Bible of the anti-Bodega crowd, and no amount of pointing to the disclaimers . . . could overcome those chilling words: "3400 people killed, 43,000 injuries, $7 billion in property damage." . . .

Stroube's thinking prevailed, and the Atomic Energy Commission never issued its revised estimate of the possibilities and consequences of major accidents at the newer, larger plants. And little wonder—for as astronomical as the figures in the original Brookhaven Report are, they would undoubtedly have been dwarfed by the new estimates.

The image brokers are constantly on the lookout for euphemisms to make nuclear power more palatable to the public. A good example of this was the wholesome phrase "sunshine unit" contrived to describe exposure levels of deadly strontium 90 around the time when A-bomb test fallout was raising the radiation in our environment to an alarming degree. Another, dreamed up when nuclear power interests were trying to set up an atomic waste processing facility in lower Cape Cod, Massachusetts, was "industrial park" for such a nuclear installation. Even normally responsible men of medicine have fallen prey to the temptations of coining happier phrases to make the dangers of radioactivity go away or diminish in size. In a 1963 Symposium on Radiation Accidents and Emergencies in Medicine, Research, and Industry held in Chicago, one conferee stated:

> One of our prime tasks, therefore, is to provide a more concrete, tangible, realistic, familiar "image" of radiation and of its effects. . . . A second approach might be to consider radiation as being like a more powerful form of sunlight. While sunlight is not really a tangible phenomenon (and it is far from simple or fully understood), it is very familiar and benign. With this approach, biological radiation effects can be seen as something like sunburn (which is not too far off): a phenomenon which is familiar, is tangible, and is viewed as basically good, though dangerous when overdone. . . .
>
> I do not wish to belabor either suggestion. Both are presented as examples only. The point is that we must develop a model of radiation which can be made into a reified, tangible, comprehensible thing, with primarily *good* qualities, which is reasonably consistent with our scientific concepts. We must communicate this effectively and often enough to the public and to personnel, so that the idea not only gets through, but that radiation becomes a familiar everyday matter, thus losing its mystery. . . .

A similar plea for plain—that is, positive—language was issued at a nuclear plant siting symposium in 1966 by George G. Biro, chairman of the American Nuclear Society's metropolitan New York section. If scientists conducted a plain-language information campaign, he said, they could prove that it is in the public interest to have "a friendly neighbor like a nuclear power plant."

Public relations men for the nuclear industry by no means confine their activities to suppressing the offensive words and phrases that arouse public fear and indignation; they also engage most actively in accentuating the positive. In a wide variety of publications similar to the

AEC pamphlets, the glories and miracles of the atom are sung to the heavens. Again, many of these are aimed at youth, such as General Electric's "Inside the Atom," a comic-book-style publication of which some eight million copies were reportedly distributed gratis among high school and college students. But it is in the realm of advertising that the wordsmiths really shine.

The most important weapon of the adman is repetition, of course, and the hammering home of certain key words like "cleanliness," "safety," "reliability," and "economy" are designed to condition the mind of the man and woman in the street to associate reactors with pleasurable responses. The *Catholic News* of December 15, 1966, ran an ad that stated in part: "Con Edison works constantly to hold down the cost of electricity ... by moving as quickly as possible into more *economical* and *totally, clean* nuclear power." General Electric took a two-page ad in the September 25, 1965, *Saturday Evening Post* to announce that "America's electric utilities find that *clean* nuclear power plants play an increasingly important role in their efforts to supply *reliable, low-cost* electricity and that people everywhere welcome them as truly '*good neighbors*' in their communities." The same ad continued with a string of testimonials for and by several other plants: "Consumers Power Company says of its Big Rock Point Station: 'We are operating a plant that is *safe* for anybody—next to the plant or ten miles away.' Pacific Gas & Electric Company reports that its Humboldt Bay Nuclear Power Unit at Eureka, California, is '*safe, clean,* and a *good neighbor* by any standard of comparison.' " [Emphasis ours throughout.]

New Yorkers were recently treated to the conversion of Con Edison's truck color from orange to blue, symbolizing the purity of the air in the sky over a city that will one day no longer use coal and oil to generate electricity. Con Ed's new motto is "Clean Energy," and the message of Good Neighbor Atom was beamed to New York Mets baseball fans, of whom tens of thousands are children, during television of the 1968 games, of which Con Ed was a sponsor.

Along with the Federal Government and industry propagandists, the press has been responsible for a great deal of ignorance and misunderstanding about nuclear power. Perhaps our newspapers and magazines are the least guilty, for they appear to be victims of the same public relations barrage as the general public. It is not hard to see that even a science-oriented newsman, confronted with the beguiling "facts" by smooth PR men, deluged with specially designed press packets, and treated to all manner of visual "aids" to his understanding, would be convinced of the safety of nuclear reactors, especially in the absence of an articulate and well-organized opposition. Still, an unquestioning acceptance of nuclear power propaganda is not in the tradition of vital, dynamic, truth-seeking American journalism. The news brownout is especially puzzling because disclosures of potentially catastrophic conditions make for lively reading, to say the least. The breakdown of the fourth estate's function—indeed, of its honorable duty—is one of the most pathetic aspects of the public's meek surrender to the forces of nuclear power.

Frequently the newspapers have taken, or transmitted, the benign view that any public work being undertaken by the Federal Government or the great utilities must be inherently good and safe. An editorial in the New York *World-Telegram & Sun* on June 17, 1963, belittled opposition to in-city nuclear plants by attributing it to "fear of the unknown, an unnecessary fear of the unknown." As cogent proof of the safety of such installations, the editor offered this argument: "The utility would never dream of installing such a plant in the heart of New York City if there were any danger."

Influential magazines, too, tend to disparage opposition to nuclear "progress" by identifying it with irrational fear. This point was made in an editorial in *The*

Nation's August 10, 1963, issue, which then went on to argue glibly that "the peril to human beings from any well-built reactor is small indeed compared with the risks of nuclear war." This is a perfectly monstrous argument, for, considering the fact that a nuclear war would kill upward of twenty million Americans, one should certainly *hope* that the peril from nuclear reactors is comparatively small. This is like arguing that the chance of your contracting smallpox is remote compared with that of contracting cancer, so why bother with inoculations? Obviously, the appropriate question is not which risk is smaller, but whether it is sane to take any unnecessary risk at all.

This comparison of potential reactor accidents with potential nuclear war destruction, like the analogy between radioactivity and matches, is an instance of the fallacious logic advanced by proponents of nuclear power, and there are many more than come to mind. In an article in *The Nation* of March 23, 1964, author Carl Dreher pointed out that the public had up to that date spent about three billion dollars through taxes and electric rates to develop the nuclear power industry. For this reason, he concluded, "we might as well get something out of it." Indeed, what we may get out of it is a catastrophe that would make three billion dollars look Lilliputian. Dreher then puts forward the standard "social progress" argument, namely that society must pay a price for its technological advances—"our accepted morality sanctions such a bargain whenever, on balance, a social gain can be shown." He goes on to note that many children are electrocuted by toasters each year, yet we do not cry out against electricity. Then he drags out the old auto accident argument—"The children who die annually in automobile accidents are numbered in the thousands. They die now and they will die in future generations."

The auto accident argument is a perennial favorite of nuclear power proponents, and even the Brookhaven

Report, published by the Atomic Energy Commission, compared the (supposedly) low odds—one in 50 million—against a person's dying in a reactor accident in any year with the one-in-5000 odds that that person will die in a car accident.

Arguments of this ilk overlook two vital points: first, that nuclear power represents not a quantitative but a qualitative change in our power industry, involving forces and consequences that we have only begun to understand; and, second, that when the public makes a bargain, it should have the privilege of deciding *freely* by itself, after all facts are objectively presented, whether a calculated risk is worthwhile. As we have abundantly demonstrated, the bargain involving our health, welfare, and safety has been made between a Federal Government dedicated to establishing a nuclear power program at any cost and a private industry committed to making the biggest profit while taking the smallest risk. It would take the combined ratiocinations of Euclid, Pythagoras, and Socrates to satisfy a reasonable man that he has the same freedom to choose the location of a nuclear reactor that he has to hold his hand over a lighted match.

Another favorite device of nuclear power promoters is the diversion of public attention from major worries to minor ones. We have seen how, in the case of thermal pollution, community interest is focused on the "fish issue," so that when concessions are made to satisfy wildlife conservationists, the wind is taken out of the sails of other potential opponents. The same dodge has been used to take advantage of current public agitation over air pollution and desecration of our country's natural beauties.

Trade magazines play their role too. An editorial in *Nucleonics Week* of February 25, 1965, fanned the fires of competition between nuclear- and fossil-fueled power companies by suggesting the nuclear industry use the following strategy:

The one issue on which nuclear power can make an invincible case is the air pollution issue. It is clear that nuclear power plants, as "clean air plants," have a claim to earn the public's positive preference as long as 19,000 persons are killed each year from the effects of smoke from fossil fuels, not counting such occasional catastrophes as the 5,000 killed at Donora, Pa., in 1948.

The problems faced by nuclear plants are not primarily technical or economic, the editorial went on to say, but rather those of siting. Arguments about safety and economy are not persuasive to a public concerned about location of reactors in heavily populated areas, concluded the editorial, and the only issue which can overcome those fears is "clean air."

The editor found it prudent, however, to publish a correction in a later issue stating that "further checking of our figures reveals that the figure of nineteen thousand deaths refers to an estimate of annual death from all sources of air polution, not just those from the smoke from fossil-fired power stations." In addition, the correction brought out that the death toll at Donora, Pennsylvania, during the five-day smog had not been five thousand—it had been twenty. The editorial was only 4980 people off. The editor, in all fairness, was thinking of a London smog in 1952 which did take a fearful toll. On the other hand, the same weather conditions that prevailed during that disaster would have produced immeasurably more deaths had the poison in the air been radioactive gas seeping from an exploded reactor. In any event, the clear implication of this episode is that the nuclear power industry continues to play upon the public's fear of pollution (ignoring radioactive contamination) in order to overcome any and all objections to siting nuclear plants in populous areas.

The best public relations gimmick of all, however, we have saved for last. It is the oldest but still the most effective, but rather than give it a name we will simply describe some instances of it and let the reader decide for himself what word most accurately describes it.

It will be recalled that the citizens of Buchanan, New York, did all but stand on their heads to find praise enough for the Indian Point reactor that Con Ed had built nearby. Perhaps their ardor can be better understood in the light of the fact that Con Edison's taxes to Buchanan total about $359,000 a year, which is more than five times the entire village budget in 1960 and more than half the budget in 1967. An article in the New York *Times* by Ralph Blumenthal reported that with all its new revenue, the town was able to build— with *cash*, not bonds—projects it had put off for years. "Con Ed," the article reported Village Trustee F. Webster Pierce as saying, "has been very good to us." "Everybody's getting a little of it," said Vernon Cole, Buchanan's police justice and hardware merchant. Indeed, the town was able to lower taxes from $20.20 for each $1000 of assessed valuation in 1960 to $17 in 1967. With two more units scheduled for Indian Point, the increment to Buchanan stands to be tripled.

It is not surprising, therefore, that when Con Ed announced it had come to agreement with the community of New Rochelle, population 73,500, on plans to build the stupendous reactor complex on Fort Slocum a half mile away and practically on top of the Bronx County line, New Rochelle Mayor Alvin R. Ruskin jubilantly declared, "This is the most historic day in the life of the city." "New Rochelle," he said, "has a golden opportunity to be one of the most prosperous communities in the nation." The little city was to get $2,943,-400 for sale of the island, and the prospects of a tax drop looked very good indeed.

Stories of joy and delight can be heard in many communities across the nation where nuclear plants are going up. A survey of the Waterford, Haddam, Northfield, and Rowe areas of New England in 1965 indicated that the tax windfall benefits that come with power plants seem to override most objections by conservationists and others. A news article published around that time may infect the reader with some of the breathless excitement of townspeople as they welcome their atomic good neighbors to their communities:

Perhaps the happiest board of selectmen in all of New England gathered at sundown the other day for a weekly meeting in this Mohawk Valley community. [Rowe, Massachusetts]

The happiness was built on affluence following the construction of an atomic-powered generating plant which has spilled new tax receipts into the community. A visitor to the meeting, former Selectman John H. Williams, a local real estate and insurance broker, summed up the cause for the happiness this way:

"Where else can you have an $18,000 new home and have annual real estate taxes of only $35? Why, you can pay them out of pocket money."

The selectmen nodded in agreement, and Mr. Williams continued:

"Those people down in Connecticut should count their blessings."

He was referring to objections raised to a program of public utilities to build atomic-powered generating plants, one already under construction on Haddam Neck on the scenic Connecticut River. . . .

Let us all count our blessings.

CHAPTER XVIII

Be It Therefore Resolved

The villain of this book is a process as old as human history. It is the process by which men lured by a compelling vision lose their sense of balance and self-restraint in pursuing it. The great American Dream of a virgin land of unlimited opportunity produced some of the noblest thoughts and deeds ever recorded, yet the process by which that dream was fulfilled has left Americans with a legacy of despoiled land, plundered forests, befouled lakes and rivers, ransacked oil and mineral fields, desiccated prairies.

The splitting of the atom has inspired mankind with a vision of equal grandeur, a vision of a world whose peaceful needs are served by a deadly force rendered tame by men of wisdom and good will. Unfortunately, the means by which we are attempting to achieve that vision bear a disquieting resemblance to the old process. The style is modern, the essence unaltered.

There is, however, a difference, and it is so crucial that one is justified in calling it literally a world of difference. For if man of today is no more responsible than man of yesterday, he is, however, more directly confronted with the fruits of his irresponsibility. The shrinking of our world is forcing us to recognize terrestrial life as a delicate closed system whose components are subject to irreparable attrition, and whose resources, to irreversible dissipation. At the same time, the violent blossoming of science and technology in our century has placed in man's hands more effective means than ever before for creating grave imbalances in his surroundings.

Thus while men of yesterday were able to "move on" after destroying or exhausting their local environment, we are today conscious that our local environment is nothing less than Earth itself, and there is no moving on. Because the relationship between nature and technology has become too finely balanced for us to take the same old liberties, it is incumbent on us to reflect more seriously upon the significance of all our enterprises, to assess possible ways in which temporary advantages are secured only at the intolerable cost of long-range liabilities. Nothing better illustrates this truth than the contrast between the potentially catastrophic consequences of atomic power and its ephemeral, even illusory, benefits.

Although the Atomic Energy Commission and the atomic power industry deserve praise for maintaining a low accident rate, the facts marshalled in this book suggest forcefully that that record, as atomic power rises from its current 1 per cent of this country's electricity-producing capacity to about 25 per cent by 1980, will not be maintainable. More importantly, the fact that one accident alone can create havoc equivalent to innumerable conventional disasters, plus the fact that even if no major accident occurs, the cumulative problems and hazards will burden future generations with a cross of staggering weight—these facts point to the conclusion that *continued effort to develop a safe atomic power program is not worth the risk to humanity*.

Over the period of time during which this book was being written, the authors asked themselves what recommendations they could make toward rectifying the many problems they were documenting. Scores of solutions were considered, then rejected when it became clear that they promised only partial or temporary alleviation, and that in due time the old iniquities would flourish again.

Gradually, therefore, a profound realization emerged:

that because we were dealing with ultimates, nothing less than ultimate action was essential. By allowing the nuclear power industry to expand to its present size at the cost and risk of every other industry in the country and of all private citizens, this country has made a mistake which may surpass any made in its history; yet we dare not allow the enormity of our error to intimidate us into denying its existence or foregoing whatever measures are required to correct it—*however drastic*.

The proposal that follows will thus, we know, seem on the surface extreme, presumptuous, and impracticable. Yet we believe the reader will, upon reflection, see that the most difficult part will be for this nation to recognize collectively that in the matter of peacetime atomic power we have made a mistake. That recognition, plus another—that we have actually stepped only a few paces down the road, if we compare the size and number of plants now in operation compared to those projected for the next decade—will enable us to proceed with *the complete abandonment of the nuclear power plant program*.

As we have said, we are the first to realize that this suggested termination of a program in which billions of dollars have been invested by government and industry will appear extreme, and some critics will probably call it mad. Yet we can't help but believe that the reader who has seriously weighed the facts and possibilities must be asking himself *whether anything could be madder than to continue erecting this threat to the human race of incredible magnitude*.

As a matter of fact, far from being mad, the cancellation of a stupendous and costly technological enterprise is in no way unprecedented in recent American experience; nor is cancellation of *this* one by any means beyond present capabilities.

As these pages are being written, for instance, President-elect Nixon has expressed serious doubts about continuing production of the F-111 all-purpose military airplane, which has not only failed to satisfy a great many requisites for which it was designed, but has sent a number of pilots to their deaths in both test and combat flights. The program seems to have suffered from many of the same problems plaguing the atomic industry, including soaring costs. While the 1963 estimate of the F-111's costs, based on 1708 planes, was $7.809 billion, a revised estimate issued in 1967, based on 548 *fewer* planes, came to $11.187 billion. Here is a white elephant potentially more costly even than atomic power, yet our Government may well have to swallow its pride and admit that the plane just doesn't work. On a smaller but still impressive scale, Boeing Company, after spending tens of millions of its own, of the Government's, and of the airline industry's dollars to research and develop a swing-wing supersonic plane, has had to confess it just can't swing the swing-wing, and is therefore reverting to more conventional fixed-wing design.

For that matter, abandonment of huge projects is nothing new to the atomic power establishment. When, for example, AEC Chairman Glenn Seaborg notified the Joint Committee on Atomic Energy, early in 1967, that the Government was closing down its Heavy Water-Organic-Cooled Reactor project after spending some $22 million, it brought to a total of $358.4 million the sums spent on civilian power projects "passed out," as one report put it, "without achieving their announced objectives."

While admitting failure will not come easily to the atomic industry, it will presumably come easier than taking the sizable losses connected with ending the reactor power program. Despite the industry's contribution to the dangers of atomic power, we do not believe it should be required to bear the full brunt of losses entailed in ending the program, and a well-structured program would encompass ways in which those losses could be minimized. Subsidies, tax inducements, or other Federal relief could be made available to assist manufacturers and utilities affected.

The Government and its constituent taxpayers will have grounds for complaint that such aid to the industry is throwing good money after bad. Yet to the extent that our Government has promoted atomic power, and to the extent that the taxpayer, however unwittingly, has sanctioned that promotion, it is only realistic to assume that both government and citizen will have to accept some of the responsibility for compensating the industry. When we consider what we would pay for damages sustained in a major accident, or what we will undoubtedly pay for atomically produced electricity as its price increases radically toward the end of the century, or what our children will have to pay to maintain mammoth storehouses of atomic wastes for centuries— then the good money we will have to throw after bad now should not seem inordinate.

It must also be borne in mind that we will have to pay for decommissioning nuclear power plants some day whether we abandon the program or not. The effective life of such plants is generally thought of as thirty years. Our Government and industry have clearly failed to reckon on the problems and costs involved in closing down and decontaminating those plants when their term of usefulness has ended. In a letter and supplement by Glenn Seaborg to the JCAE, entered into the record of hearings on 1968 authorizing legislation for the AEC, the letter disclaimed responsibility for the costs of decommissioning plants, and even suggested it had little idea of how such matters would be handled. "The financing of the decommissioning of a power plant may come under the cognizance of the utility regulatory authorities, but not AEC," we read, and "We understand that the regulatory commissions do not anticipate and include in utility rates any provision for the cost of premature abandonment or sudden obsolescence of the plant."

If such an event occurs, Seaborg's document went on

to say, the regulatory commissions would be faced with the question of "whether such extraordinary costs are to be borne by the customers, by the stockholders, or by a combination of the two." The only thing that seemed fairly certain was that "Within prescribed safety requirements, the cost to a utility of decommissioning its nuclear plant is dependent upon the extent of decommissioning that the utility decides is most to its economic advantage."

Seaborg expressed the conviction that the costs of decommissioning would not be substantial—he suggested $5 million for a 1,000,000-kilowatt plant. It is difficult to understand how he arrived at that figure. In the same group of documents is a letter from AEC General Manager R. E. Hollingsworth stating that the estimated costs of making the recently shut-down Hallam plant "radiation-safe" is $2.2 *million,* not including the offsite storage or reprocessing or disposal of the fuel and sodium! And Hallam was just a mere slip of a thing compared to the 1,000,000 kilowatters planned for tomorrow.

In short, we, as taxpayers, ratepayers, or stockholders, will have to absorb the costs of closing down atomic power plants no matter what happens. The price paid now, however, will be far lower in every sense of the term than the one paid tomorrow.

The vacuum left by the abandonment of the atomic power program will of course have to be filled by new energy sources and techniques of electricity generation such as those sketched earlier. Here again is a way in which industries affected by the halt can recoup, for the Government might award them a variety of incentives to develop alternate technologies. If that support doesn't compensate them entirely, they must consider that they may be getting away cheaply compared to losses they would probably sustain in the future either from a plant catastrophe or the catastrophe of astronomic costs.

The seminal lesson to be learned from the saga of the

atomic power program is that reasonable reservations, even when expressed by scientific, technical, and governmental experts pre-eminent in their fields, do not always prevail once a project of this scale begins to pick up impetus. Thus it cannot be hoped that a mere appeal to reason, even when supported by a body of facts and arguments as impressive as we believe we have assembled here, will overcome the resistance of vested interests. Reason, therefore, may have to be reinforced by most vigorous action on the part of the entire national community.

It is hard to say whether our nation is beset by more problems today than in the past, but it can probably be asserted safely that the constant barrage of pleas by organizations seeking support for their causes has had the unintended effect of paralyzing the sense of concern Americans have traditionally felt for their country's problems. While practically all of those causes deserve our attention, their collective clamor has caused many to seek refuge in apathy. The result is that when a genuine challenge to survival confronts us, our numbed sense of values may have difficulty identifying it as a crisis of the highest priority.

Not long ago a columnist half-humorously suggested that this form of paralysis could be overcome by a program of "selective apathy," of ordering our public concerns so that some issues took a back seat to others. "Selective apathy," of course, is just another way of saying that we must place first things first, and without suggesting that such problems as poverty, education, racial discrimination, transportation, communication, balance of payments, urban blight, and mental health are deserving of apathy, we do not feel unreasonable in asserting that they are of secondary importance to the question of simple survival. For only after survival has been accomplished can men seek other social goals.

It must thus be urged that the American public review its priorities and grant the menace of atomic power the primary consideration it requires. Neither scientist nor private citizen can afford to be on the fence in this issue, but must take a definite stand against the unprecedented risks to which nuclear power plants are increasingly exposing us. "Great public problems," said Robert Rienow in *American Problems Today,* "cannot be ignored; they clamor for solution. And the citizen who sleeps is helping to decide whether he wills it or not. The large associations, the groups, are lined up for and against an issue. They will force it to a verdict. To refuse to cast your influence one way or the other is to stand for the stronger group. As the Bible says, 'He that is not with me is against me.' "

Whether America endures or not may well depend on whether enough Americans, Americans of every interest and persuasion, can cease struggling against one another in order to recognize a mutual hazard and join this larger battle: the battle for sanity, safety, and survival.

CHAPTER XIX

Closing the Responsibility Gap

"The only thing necessary for the triumph of evil," said Edmund Burke, "is for good men to do nothing." Because vital information about the atomic power program has been obscured from public consciousness, good men have been unable to combat its evils effectively. But though the menace has reached substantial dimensions, it has not yet arrived at the point where we are helpless to reverse it. A void exists, but there are a great many things that can be done to fill it, and because our personal and national futures may ultimately depend on timely, concerted action, a forceful program must be launched at once.

At the conclusion of this chapter we will indicate a number of ways in which you, the individual citizen, may take action, and how other members of the national community can participate. Before taking up those roles, however, the spotlight must be focused on one group whose voice is indispensable in averting the perils facing us in nuclear power: the scientists.

For better or worse our supertechnology has forced us into dependency on our scientific leaders, not merely for technical guidance but in large measure for moral guidance as well. Unless the wisest leadership, courage, and responsibility are exercised by this powerful segment of society when we turn to it for counsel and support in the nuclear power issue, we may be led by others up a path from which there is no returning.

A number of critics within and outside the scientific disciplines have recently made us aware of the subtle

311

ways in which the scientist's vested interests frequently subvert his resistance to projects not always in the best interests of the social community. The scientist, being only human, is no more eager than anyone else to put himself out of business; and certainly there are more than enough rewards from the private and public concerns that employ him to make sacrifices of leadership easy for his conscience to bear. Yet every such sacrifice casts far more than conscience into the shadows; it casts public security into them as well. Such conduct may have been more acceptable in an earlier day when scientific decisions did not touch on the totality of life on this planet. But today, when that totality is directly threatened by every erosion of scientific conscientiousness, the scientist is morally bound to assert the most positive leadership.

This lesson should have been learned when the fruits of the Manhattan Project were harvested in the skies over Hiroshima. Yet to read some published accounts, the scientist's struggle with his conscience ended with the atomic bomb, and the issues are now largely history. A passage from "The Integrity of Science," prepared by the American Association for the Advancement of Science, reminds us that the issue still burns as brightly as the fireball that razed Hiroshima:

> The growing interaction between science and public policy requires considerable attention to the problem of distinguishing scientific problems from those issues which ought to be decided by social processes. An example of the tendency to confuse scientific evaluation with social judgment is the matter of radiation standards. Here, a scientific body, the Federal Radiation Council, is engaged in setting standards of acceptability which are basically social judgments regarding the balance between the hazards and benefits of nuclear operations. These judgments are, or ought to be, wholly vulnerable to political debate, but their appearances in the guise of a scientific decision may shield them from such scrutiny.

As we have seen, many scientists have spoken out against the rapid expansion of the commercial atomic power program. Unfortunately, these individuals have been unable to convey their anxieties adequately due to lack of effective organizations through which such opposition may be communicated to the public. At the same time, Congress, including the all-important Joint Committee on Atomic Energy, has been guided by an army of scientists employed by the Atomic Energy Commission and the nuclear industry. Our governmental leaders have thus been given every positive hope for nuclear power, while scientists of pessimistic persuasion are either unrepresented or outnumbered.

The most promising groups for presenting the scientist's reservations about environmental threats to the Government are scientific-information or scientist-citizen organizations. But, most regrettably, as valuable as these organizations are, conditions have frequently constrained them from taking aggressive actions.

Consider the position of these groups. A conference on "Crisis in the Environment" sponsored by the Scientists' Institute for Public Information in May 1967 made it clear that the Institute felt there were many valid reasons for confining its role to supplying information only. The point was repeatedly made in various speeches that: (a) the press respects the scientists' objectivity in a way which would not be possible if they made specific recommendations and thus became in effect a "pressure group"; and (b) to assume a directive role would deprive other citizens who are not scientists of their rightful role in a democracy.

Furthermore, in private conversations with some of the members of the Committee for Environmental Information, one of the authors was given additional reasons for pursuing a policy of "information only," namely: (1) that while such groups can present scientific data without disagreement or internal conflict, the scientists who compile these data differ widely on political issues and may tend to disagree on solutions to health and safety problems; and (2) should such groups take more definite stands they would be subjected to pressure from industry and Government agencies affected by any adverse recommendations they might make—and hence might not be able to continue to operate at all.

An article on the Committee for Environmental Information, published in *Science* on August 25, 1967, pointed out that originally the goal of this group was much broader:

> One of the three announced purposes mentioned at the time of the committee's founding was the eventual expression of citizen opinion on policies relating to nuclear energy. However, after the first year of operations, the Board of Directors decided that the committee would never attain the kind of community support it needed as long as there was a possibility that it might become an organization for expressing opinions. Consequently, the Board adopted by-laws which denied the committee the possibility of ever taking a stand on issues.

> To this day, the CEI continues to assert that it takes no position on the problems it discusses. One of the CEI directors pointed out that this policy of refraining from advocacy has at least two benefits: first, it helps insure that contributions to the organization will be tax-deductible; second, it secures wider press publicity for CEI statements. In the committee there is a widespread feeling that CEI would be less noticed if it allowed itself to be viewed as yet another "pressure group."

Sensible as these reasons may be, they do not close the responsibility gap between scientific information and the public need for leadership. Nor can we agree with what appears to be the consensus of opinion of these groups: that the evidence and information they provide speaks loudly for itself, and that non-scientists can assume responsibility and take action without specific leadership from scientific information groups.

The facts do not bear out this view. Private citizens outside of the scientific field have not taken actions which would seem justified on the basis of the scientific information provided to them. Instead, they have remained passive, and the nuclear power program has been erected on that passivity. But is the public to blame? Citizens, understandably hesitate to judge scientific issues without scientific counsel, tend to feel that if the hazards related to nuclear science and technology were sufficiently grave, scientific information groups would speak out more aggressively against them and assume more decisive leadership.

There are two tragic by-products of this failure. First, it leaves the public with the impression that those who do urge greater caution are exaggerating the hazards. The citizen, observing the failure of scientists as a group to take a more definite stand against the proliferation of nuclear power plants, may conclude that things aren't that bad after all.

Second, even if he concludes that things really *are* that bad, how much support can he expect from experts compelled, by the charters of their organizations, to restrict their activities to supplying information? The layman's instincts, in matters of self-preservation, have often proved accurate. Yet, because modern society is so constituted that the layman is virtually helpless in the public forum without expert counsel, the scientist who limits his responsibility fatally undercuts attempts by laymen to combat threats to the welfare and health of the community.

Thus, while we recognize the important contribution of scientific information groups, and fervently hope to see them continue their efforts to enlighten laymen on technological hazards, there is nevertheless desperate need for scientists prepared to involve themselves more deeply in scientific policy-making. It appears, therefore, that a new kind of organization will have to be created in which independent scientists are freed to express views and promote policies they deem to be in the best interests of public health and safety.

As we have seen, a number of scientist-citizen committees now in existence, such as the Scientists' Institute for Public Information and the Committee for Environmental Information, restrict their activities to public presentation of information about the problems and hazards of modern technologies such as atomic power. A committee such as we envision would move beyond those areas.

It would for instance undertake direct-mail campaigns to newspaper editors and columnists, radio and television producers, religious leaders, writers, educators, conservation groups, and other organizations. It would arrange for lectures, prepare and place advertisements in the various media, and perhaps develop a reference library documenting radiological and other hazards relating to atomic energy. One of the most important functions of the committee would be to advise the Government on the determination of a realistic environmental "radiation budget" such as we will be describing presently, and to assist the Government in the assessment and publicizing of growing environmental radiation.

The formation of such a committee would, we believe, fill an urgent need, both during the time when atomic power was under study and beyond, when phasing-out of that program would hopefully be in progress. For even if a halt to construction of new civilian reactors were called tomorrow, an organization would be necessary to alert the public to, and promote control of, radiation releases from reactors now in operation, from wastes already accumulated, and from current tests and other sources. Another important task it could perform at once is publication and distribution of a booklet informing the public of what to do in the event of a major nuclear plant accident, or other accident involving release of radiation. Still other functions would be to promote training for all police and fire department personnel in handling transportation, power plant, and other accidents involving radiation; promote extensive training for hospital personnel throughout the nation in radiation emergencies; and publicize advances in other forms of energy technology and electricity generation.

Will scientists step forward? It is difficult to see how scientists who feel strongly that greater caution is needed in this area—and the number who have declared themselves publicly and privately is great indeed—can fail to unite to take action. While they may differ in details, it is unlikely they will take issue with a statement made in a report of the Congressional Subcommittee on Science, Research, and Development made in October 1966:

Time was when man could afford to look upon the innovations of technology with some complacency. For the innovations came slowly, they were put to use in a relatively slow and modest fashion, and their side-effects developed at a sufficiently relaxed pace to permit man to adjust to them—or to alter his course if the threat were great enough.

Surely it is obvious that this day is gone. The tempo of our times can almost be described as a gait of "running away."

The sum of scientific knowledge is doubling every decade or so—and our galloping technology is doing its best to stay on even terms. Human ingenuity has never had at its command a wider choice of tools with which to stimulate the economy, or defend the country, or provide for the general welfare, or just to make money.

All this is being done with dynamic efficiency, but so rapidly that there is scarcely time to look around and assess the side-effects of the new technology put into action. Yet these effects apparently are so strong—and quite possibly so dangerous—as to pose a genuine threat to man and to his physical, mental, and spiritual environment.

The subcommittee believes that we can no longer blindly adapt technology to our needs with the traditional assumption that there will be ample time to iron out any bugs on a leisurely shakedown cruise. A bigger effort must be made not only to foresee the bugs but to forestall their development in the first place. The alternative could be disastrous and indeed might turn our physical and social world into something almost uninhabitable.

Let us now turn to the role of the private citizen.

As a taxpayer you are entitled to protest, to your representative in Congress, the use of your tax dollars to subsidize an industry which threatens your life, health, and property. You should therefore urge him to support legislation calling for reassessment of the nuclear power program, including suspension of plants under construction and a moratorium on new ones, until a thorough evaluation of the objections raised by scientists, medical experts, conservationists, and other critics has been made. You can also urge him to back other legislative moves such as those we will outline presently.

Citizens may also organize community groups geared for a variety of important activities.

a. One of these is public information, for the nuclear power program's hazards must above all be brought to the attention of citizens in every walk of American life, and the false impression given by government and industry that nuclear plants are clean or pollution-free rectified. Wider press coverage of radioactive hazards should be sought by citizens' committees, who can insist that newspapers, magazines, radio, and television stations present the views of those who urge caution in nuclear power, rather than devoting as much attention as they have in the past to the so-called "miracles" of the atom.

b. You can join, or your citizens' committee can explore the possibility of affiliating with, conservation groups dedicated to all phases of environmental protection; or arrangements might be made for noted conservationists and others dedicated to the cause of a sane energy policy to lecture on the dangers of atomic power before clubs, churches, and other organizations capable of effecting community action. You can subscribe, and persuade your library to subscribe, to a variety of conservationist and scientific information bulletins designed to inform laymen in non-technical language of atomic hazards and other threats to the environment; and citizens' committees can arrange for community distribution of reprints of important articles on the subject or of related literature.

We particularly recommend *Environment* (formerly *Scientist and Citizen*), published by the Committee for Environmental Information, 438 N. Skinker Blvd., St. Louis, Missouri 63130, for its clear and concise presentation of environmental and technical problems.

c. It should be noted here that conservation groups themselves, for all their splendid work, have permitted the responsibility vacuum to expand. Not realizing the full scope of atomic power's perils, they have concentrated their attentions on more conventional forms of pollution, or limited description of atomic plant pollution to thermal and radioactive effects on local marine life. But those effects are merely one link in an ecological chain reaction of unimaginable dimensions, as we have seen, and so it is incumbent on conservation groups to awaken to the menace of, or broaden the base of their opposition to, atomic power.

d. We believe that religious leaders of every denomination must take a particularly active role in opposing nuclear folly. Can they, in good conscience, neglect to urge a new concern, a new sense of humility and responsibility, on the part of science, industry, and government toward human and all other forms of life which may soon be irreparably damaged by the deadly process of nuclear power? Are they not obliged to ask penetrating questions about the justification for building large nuclear plants around the country before safety problems are fully understood, or before those related to storage or disposal of radioactive wastes have been solved, and before assessment of radiation's threat to future generations can be made? Are they not aware that if proponents of nuclear power continue to prevail, it is altogether possible that tomorrow's, or even to-day's, children may inherit a world in which the air they breathe, the food they eat, and the water they drink has been irreversibly polluted with man-made radioactivity? And in view of the movement among today's clergy toward activism in matters of civil rights and racial injustice, might it not be appropriate for religious leaders to speak out against this threat to men of all colors and conditions? Who knows but that by uniting to combat it the races and faiths will be brought into closer harmony? Consider the possible alternative of a brotherhood of sorrow and suffering through nuclear calamity.

Organized citizens have many courses of action available for local combat against atomic power and its dangers: monitoring of air and water for excessive radiation, and pressure on public officials for strict enforcement of local and national radiation "budgets"; distribution of information on radiation threats and on measures to take in the event of a nuclear plant or transportation accident; a campaign for adequate training of police, fire, and other emergency services; a blueprint for evacuation of endangered areas; increased stress on training and equipment in hospitals for handling of radioactivity disasters.

There are also several legal or quasi-legal modes of action for citizen groups to take. One is intervention in AEC licensing hearings. Another is lawsuits aimed at barring construction and operation of nuclear plants. The reader has only to cast back through the pages of this book to find many grounds on which such actions may validly be based. Citizens' groups might also strive

to have independent surveys made of the potential consequences of a major nuclear plant accident at each of
the facilities now operating or under construction. Such
studies are essential, for realistic action can be taken
only by examining specific reactors at specific sites and
assessing both the probabilities of a serious accident
and the possible effects upon the surrounding land and
population centers.

While the individual citizen, alone or in concert with
other citizens, can exercise significant influence on the
atomic power program, an even more telling thrust can
be made by the business community, whose financial
resources and organizational structure can be mobilized
for action on the scale required. The twin rationales for
such action should be apparent:

First, *the safety of every other industry in the country is now hanging precariously on that of the nuclear
industry.*

Second, *commercial atomic power is an unpromising
investment.*

The prospect of devastation resulting from a single
major nuclear plant accident, or even of a smaller one
such as a transportation accident releasing radioactive
cargo into an important watershed, should be sufficient
reason for the most extreme opposition on the part of
leaders of every commercial enterprise. Evacuation of
all or part of a city would cause calamitous losses and
disruptions. Financial losses due to damage or suspension of businesses would radiate throughout our nationwide network of interdependent firms, and eventually
affect foreign trade. Business records and vital information systems might be inaccessible for long periods of
time; deposits and assets irretrievable indefinitely.

The effect of an "incident" on agricultural production and real estate values is impossible to estimate, but
it is perfectly conceivable that hardships would be
suffered from which there was no economic recovery.
Small businesses, shops, and stores stand to be ruined,

not only by radioactive contamination of premises and products, but possibly by the looting which almost invariably follows in the wake of disaster. Consider too that relief for property or personal damage might well be held up in a ghastly tangle of litigation, or that available insurance funds might be exhausted in the accommodation of the most desperate and immediate cases.

Even if no such event occurs, it should be borne in mind that if the assertions made in this book are valid, then the wise businessman will conclude that *atomic power is, simply, an unprofitable proposition.* In due time the business world will be adversely affected by the atomic industry's serious misjudgment of costs, which will lead to increased prices of goods and services within that industry (as has already happened), leading in turn to inflation and mounting charges for industrial electricity. Eventually the economic disaste predicted by some observers for the nuclear power field would touch every other area of business endeavor. Consider another problem in a nuclear oriented future: If, either because of a plant accident or some other reason, our Government required suspension of atomic plant operations throughout the country pending investigation, critical electricity shortages would result.

The indifference toward nuclear power's risks and hazards demonstrated by the rest of the business community can only be laid to unfamiliarity with the scope and depth of the menace. If this book has dispelled some of that ignorance, then several courses of action will be open to the business community.

Every industry with a Washington lobby can apply pressure on Congress to effect legislative changes. Farmers' co-operatives and labor unions can do the same. Stockholders in various industries can exercise their influence on directors to oppose the construction of nuclear plants which threaten not only their investments but their very lives and the safety and security of their country.

The life and health insurance industries, which unlike the property insurance industry do not exempt radiation harm, have good reason to press for change, for a single nuclear accident could threaten bankruptcy for scores of insurance companies burdened by hundreds of thousands, and possibly millions, of claims. Indeed, the nuclear and utility industries, by virtue of the uncertain constitutional position of the Price-Anderson Act, are not entirely secure from liability beyond the present nominal insurance limit.

There are other courses too. Direct appeals by threatened industries to the public, such as the recent full-page ad taken by Macy's Department Store in the New York *Times* urging stricter gun control laws, would widen public awareness. The advertising industry, which has been increasing public service endeavors in such fields as air pollution and cancer, could turn its collective genius to the hazards of atomic power.

The business world must bear much of the cost of combating the menace of atomic power; while there is much for the citizen to do, it would be naïve to think that conclusive results will be achieved without the financial muscle that only commercial and industrial forces can provide.

Of course, the businessman can consider not only the negative aspects of the atomic power problem—its potential harm to his financial interest—but the positive side as well, namely the opportunity it represents for exploring new and potentially profitable avenues of energy development now closed due to lack of public support and funding. By merely being businessmen and pursuing the scent of profit—or avoiding the bad odor of profitlessness, such as has begun emanating from the atomic power program—businessmen can make a valuable contribution to averting the present peril.

Thus, working together toward a common goal, business and labor, agricultural interests and conservationists, scientists and other individuals in widely differing fields of endeavor, can present a united face to those in

Washington who are in a position to reverse the dangerous trend. Let us consider, then, the responsibilities of Congress and other branches of our Government.

As we have pointed out, there are currently significant indications that Congress is at last awakening to the critical implications of our rapidly growing nuclear power program, and a number of resolutions are on the floors of both houses. Among other things, these stress the need for assessment of the program in terms of its high cost, its unfair advantage over other energy sources, its incursion on funding of other vital programs such as health research, its threat to the health and safety of the public, its thermal and radioactive pollution threat, the location of plants near urban areas and other population concentrations, waste disposal problems, and possible accidents. Measures urging re-evaluation of nuclear power programs and policies and creation of a review body, such as Representative John Saylor's proposed Federal Committee on Nuclear Development, are receiving wide support. In endorsing a Senate resolution, West Virginia Senator Jennings Randolph wondered "whether we in this Congress—or in past Congresses that enacted nuclear power development legislation, or in Congresses yet to come—possess the right to gamble with the nation's and the world's future and safety by continuing a program in which such dangers seem inherent."

Not surprisingly, the AEC has opposed all such resolutions, claiming that since the Joint Committee conducts a continuing review of the nuclear program, an independent study of its hazards is not necessary. It is of paramount significance, however, that despite the fact that several of the Joint Committee's members have described themselves as ardent advocates of atomic energy for electricity generation, the Committee itself saw fit, in recommending congressional authorization of the 1969 budget for the AEC's civilian reactor power program, to issue the following statement:

The Committee feels compelled to repeat a word of caution concerning this sudden reliance on nuclear energy for the generation of electrical power. This dependence, which becomes a reality starting in 1971, when about 50 percent of the new additions scheduled for that year will be nuclear, involves many new and major technological developments in the fields of design, fabrication, construction, and operation. Encountering difficulties in any of these areas cannot be discounted—indeed, as with any new technology, they must be anticipated. Particular vigilance must be exercised by all concerned to anticipate and minimize such problems to the greatest degree possible. The Committee again urges designers, manufacturers and utilities to devote the closest attention to all of these factors.

Problems, some unforeseen, have already come to the attention of the Committee. For the most part, they have been controllable and have not resulted in serious interference with the Nation's energy supply. It has been reassuring to note that cautious surveillance has brought these problem areas to light at a stage early enough to permit competent authority to solve them fairly expeditiously. However, our concern is accented because of the major dependence being placed on this revolutionary new technology during the next few years. Contrary to attitudes that appear to exist in certain parts of the utility industry, nuclear power does involve significant changes in nearly all aspects of power generation, running the gamut from plant design to operation. While the major responsibility for making this new energy source a success resides with the plant and equipment designers and manufacturers, the Committee feels that the role which the electric utilities must perform has not been sufficiently emphasized. . . .

The electric utility industry's reputation for acting responsibly is not undeserved. However, there appears to be a portion of the industry which lacks a full appreciation of the job confronting the utilities at this time, particularly with regard to in-house technical competence. It is to the latter that this cautionary note is addressed.

Thus, with even the Joint Committee on Atomic Energy expressing anxiety about the problems of atomic power, the stage is set for a drastic new examination of policy in this area. Let us now quickly review some of the aspects that deserve scrutiny:

One of the most important is the Price-Anderson Act, with its no-recourse provision legally preventing citizens from recovering damages in excess of $560 million for property contamination as against the AEC's projection of damages as high as $7 billion. Repeal of this Act would place financial responsibility back on the manufacturer and utility, and thus increase pressure on the companies that insure them. If this responsibility proves so heavy that private industry is forced to withdraw from atomic power, it will only demonstrate what critics have been saying for over a decade: that safety and economy in nuclear power plants are compatible only if the public pays the difference. The public must refuse to pay that difference any longer.

Another move aimed at bringing issues to a head would be to explore many of the legal contradictions, inherent in atomic power policy. For instance, what about the AEC's acknowledgment that power reactors are not as yet of practical value? If they are not, then should utilities be operating them for profit? The Securities and Exchange Commission should investigate the paradox whereby utilities float stock and bond issues as if nuclear reactors were commercial facilities, when in fact they are licensed under the developmental provision of the Atomic Energy Act. Again, what about the "provisional construction permit," allowing reactors to be constructed in advance of resolution of technical problems? Can reactors be permitted on our doorsteps when scientific theory and practices are still wide open to question? What about the constitutional issue of states' rights in the siting and operation of atomic power plants?

Clearly, then, there are many fields in which legislative action would prove fruitful, and where test cases tried in Federal courts would bring to light many of the unreasonable, improper, and possibly unconstitutional practices which have until now gone unquestioned.

Whatever the outcome of such legislative actions, our Government should be pressed in every possible way to establish a realistic radiation "budget" for the American environment. What, exactly, does this concept entail?

At a colloquium held in December 1960 at the University of Chicago, Dr. Paul C. Tompkins of the U. S. Public Health Service pointed out that:

(a) the quantity of radioactivity which our environment can tolerate is limited and cannot be used twice; and

(b) that we therefore require a "budget" for environmental radiation: one that will allow not only for normal operations, but for accidents and engineering failures.

Dr. Tompkins further stated that current radiation protection standards reflect only emissions from *particular* sources, not the accumulated radiation from *many* sources; and that a public health program to deal with atomic age problems requires a "lead time" of from ten to twenty years.

On the basis of the facts presented by Dr. Tompkins and other experts, the American people are entitled to a careful, comprehensive study to determine how much radioactivity has already been introduced into our environment. Account should be taken in this study of all atomic reactors now in operation; the radioactive wastes they produce; deliberately induced reactor accidents aimed at determining effectiveness of safety devices; and various experiments such as Plowshare. All other nuclear accidents to date, the disposal of radioactive wastes in rivers and oceans, and radioactivity resulting from weapons-tests should also be included. Furthermore, current concentrations of radioactivity in flora and fauna along various ecological chains should be measured, so that changes could be monitored.

Only in this way can the American people know exactly how our radiation budget stands at the present moment.

After these determinations have been made, additional studies should be launched to ascertain:

(a) how much radiation is being added to our budget daily through nuclear reactors already operating, including nuclear ships; through other industrial uses of radiation; and through nuclear research and experimentation;

(b) how much additional radiation will be introduced into our environment if new nuclear plants are erected.

Such studies should take into account the probabilities of accidents, large and small, which, as Dr. Tompkins pointed out, must realistically be included in such a budget. The activities of other countries in reactor, weapon, and other nuclear technology must also be weighted, since the human environment does not recognize international boundaries.

The measurement of our radiation budget should be a function of the U. S. Public Health Service or a specially established, disinterested, and independent Government agency. Whatever agency undertakes it should be given wide latitude for utilization of Federal funds, information, and other resources in assessing the hazards of atomic energy. As we have said, even if the nuclear power program were terminated at once, such assessments would prove valuable; since it won't be, legislators can reasonably argue that a freeze on further activity in the field should go into effect while the radiation budget is being compiled. That period would also give the Public Health Service some of the lead time Dr. Tompkins suggested is needed to develop a public health program to cope with nuclear-age problems, and would give industry a chance to develop some viable energy alternatives in the event—an event we believe likely—that publication of conclusive radiation statistics persuaded the nation's leaders to drop atomic power for good.

To accomplish all of the legislative tasks we have enumerated, pressure must be brought to bear on the men who wield the governmental tools. Perhaps, in addition to the conventional lobbies used by businesses and industries to promote their interests, a consumer-taxpayer "lobby" could be formed to represent electricity consumers who do not want to subsidize nuclear power. As is well known, governmental avenues have been established by which consumer interests can be expressed to the President and other high officials who are in a position to influence legislation. The consumer of electricity should be no worse represented than the consumer of supermarket products, especially where life-and-death conditions are involved.

Opposition to atomic power might also be rallied among other lobbies and special interest groups, for valuable tax dollars are being diverted from vital programs in order to serve the interests of the atomic power industry. Health research, aid to education, law enforcement, urban redevelopment—these needs are not only receiving less attention because of the hundreds of millions of dollars being poured by our Government into atomic power technology, but *are all actually jeopardized by the hazards that technology possesses*. Of what value, for instance, is Federally supported health research when the ever increasing fund of radioactivity in our environment as a result of atomic power operation and waste disposal poses a health threat of inestimable size? Well might other interest groups argue, as David Lilienthal did in 1963:

The time has come for us to cease thinking of the atom as a thing apart from all other segments of science. Until the atom is brought back fully into the mainstream of the scientific thought of this country, and becomes one element of that mainstream, Congress will continue to remain vulnerable to special pleadings for funds for atomic research, with too little opportunity to weigh that field, soberly and realistically, against our other needs and opportunities.

Lilienthal's plea extended to human as well as financial resources:

> Of all our national resources, minds are the most precious. Two-thirds of our trained minds available for exploring scientific and technical frontiers, we are told by the President, are absorbed by the space, defense, and atomic energy activities of our country. The rest of America's needs are relatively impoverished, neglected and starved.

We have presented here a program for the orderly cessation of the atomic power program and its gradual replacement by less hazardous and more economical energy sources. We have also suggested some avenues for the formation of new philsophies and policies in the area of power generation, as well as for a workable system through which they could be promoted. And we have outlined ways in which every sector of American life can produce these changes, without fatal economic disruptions, merely by shifting the focus of self-interest away from a perilous endeavor to a safer one. Human nature need not change to accomplish this shift; only some practical human goals.

Yet the cosmic questions that these issues raise, questions about the relations between man and his planet, about his thoughtless ventures into realms bristling with hazards and uncertainties, about his persistent disregard of warnings issued by the wise and by the groans of tortured nature itself, about the prospects of his survival for even the next century, let alone for the aeons in which he could prevail by husbanding his resources prudently—these questions lead one, forgivably, to wonder whether human nature itself is not at last confronted with an imperative to change.

And to those who believe in the existence of a Supreme Being, there is an added dimension to this question. For then it becomes not just a matter of scientists and engineers bucking the odds against turbulent nature and inexorable time; it becomes one of puny mortals pursuing power and profit through "the most deadly, the most dangerous process that man has ever conceived" in proud defiance of human limitations.

Such defiance is the stuff of which tragedies are wrought, tragedies from which man may emerge for a time as hero but never, when the last trumpet is sounded, as victor. "The fear of the Lord," it is written, "is the beginning of wisdom."

Knowing this truth, do we dare continue gambling against Fate?

Principal Sources

Abbreviations:

1. AEC or USAEC: United States Atomic Energy Commission.
2. Auth Leg 1968: AEC Authorizing Legislation, Fiscal Year 1968, Hearings Before the Joint Committee on Atomic Energy, Congress of the United States, Part 2, March 14 and 15, 1967.
3. Auth Leg 1969: AEC Authorizing Legislation, Fiscal Year 1969, Hearings Before the Joint Committee on Atomic Energy, Congress of the United States, Part 1, January 30, 31, and February 5 and 6, 1968.
4. Brookhaven Report: familiar title for *Theoretical Possibilities and Consequences of Major Accidents in Large Nuclear Power Plants, Wash-740,* Publ. by USAEC, March 1957.
5. JCAE: Joint Committee on Atomic Energy, Congress of the United States.
6. L&R: Licensing and Regulation of Nuclear Reactors, Hearings Before the Joint Committee on Atomic Energy, Congress of the United States, Part 1 (April 4, 5, 6, 20, and May 3, 1967), or Part 2 (September 12, 13, and 14, 1967).
7. NCPC: National Coal Policy Conference, Inc.
8. NYT: New York *Times.*
9. S&C: *Scientist and Citizen* magazine.

Note: *The following list omits those references whose sources have already been cited in full in the text of this book.*

CHAPTER I

pp. 2 ff. The account of the Fermi accident is based on AEC Docket No. 50-16, "Preliminary Report on Fuel Damage in Fermi Reactor," October 11, 1966; "Investigation of the Fuel Melting Accident at the Enrico Fermi Atomic Power Plant," J. G. Duffy, W. H. Jens, J. G. Feldes, K. P. Johnson, and W. J. McCarthy, Jr., National Topical Meeting, American

Nuclear Society, San Francisco, April 1967; and on additional remarks made by W. J. McCarthy, Jr., while delivering the latter paper. See also "'Breeding' Nuclear Power" by Sheldon Novick, S&C June-July 1967, pp. 97-105.

p. 4. "Some may have been thinking . . ." Account of SL-1 accident from "Radiation Control" by Robert E. Beardsley in *The Natural Philosopher*, V. I, Blaisdell Publishing House, 1963.

pp. 7 ff. Fermi plant history from Novick, op. cit., and "The Enrico Fermi Power Plant" by Saul Friedman, *Detroit Free Press*, July 17, 1966, Feature Section, pp 1-7.

p. 10. ". . . From a practical standpoint . . ." This and subsequent references to Fermi legal action taken from Brief for Petitioners, United States Court of Appeals, No. 15271; decisions on No. 15271 rendered June 10, 1960; Brief for Respondents, No. 315 and No. 454, Supreme Court of the United States, October Term, 1960; and Brief of Adolph J. Ackerman, Amicus Curiae, No. 315 and No. 454, Supreme Court of the United States, October Term, 1960.

p. 10. ". . . most hazardous . . ." Testimony before House Appropriations Subcommittee, June 29, 1956.

p. 13. "The builders of Fermi, PRDC . . ." "A Report on the Possible Effects on the Surrounding Population of an Assumed Release of Fission Products into the Atmosphere from a 300 Megawatt Nuclear Reactor Located at Lagoona Beach, Michigan. The Engineering Research Institute, University of Michigan, July 1957, foreword.

p. 14. ". . . considerably more radioactivity . . ." *Manchester Guardian*, March 19, 1958.

p. 14. "Many of the containment . . ." NAVORD Report 5747, Oct. 7, 1957, pp. i-ii.

p. 14. "To locate this experimental . . ." *The National Observer*, Nov. 6, 1967.

p. 18. ". . . one of six identical . . ." "Continuing the Fermi Story" by Sheldon Novick, S&C, November-December 1967, pp. 224-25.

p. 18. ". . . too small, too slow . . ." *Nucleonics*, December 1966.

p. 18. "Plans have just been announced . . ." *NCPC Newsletter*, October 3, 1968, p. 4.

CHAPTER II

Historical and factual background—though not necessarily the interpretations thereof—is taken, except where noted, from "The Arrival of Nuclear Power" by John F. Hogerton, *Scientific American*, February 1968, pp. 21-31.

p. 20. ". . . as Dr. James McDonald . . ." Statement before the New York City Council, June 14, 1963.

p. 20. "Barry Commoner . . ." "Fallout and Water Pollution—Parallel Cases" by Dr. Barry Commoner, S&C, December, 1964.

p. 21. References to Atomic Energy Act and amendments from *Atomic Energy Act of 1946 and Amendments,* compiled by Gilman G. Udell, U. S. Gov't Printing Office, Washington, 1966, pp. 71-246 o.

p. 23. ". . . regulatory bodies 'drift along' . . ." *War and Peace* by T. E. Murray, World Publishing Co., Cleveland, 1960.

p. 25. "It is unfortunate . . ." "When the Atom Moves Next Door" by David E. Lilienthal, *McCall's,* October 1963.

p. 27. "Saul Friedman . . ." Friedman, op. cit., p. 4.

p. 27. "It is also possible . . ." *Scientific and Managerial Manpower in Nuclear Industry* by James W. Kuhn, Columbia University Press, New York, 1966, p. 114.

p. 29. "It was not too many years . . ." Congressional Record, July 16, 1963.

p. 31. "There is little question . . ." Hogerton, *Scientific American,* February 1968.

p. 32. "Under the threat . . ." Kuhn, op. cit., p. 115.

p. 34. See references for Chapter 15 for Price-Anderson Act sources.

p. 34. "The chairman of the AEC . . ." Kuhn, op. cit., p. 115.

p. 35. "Nuclear electric power has been shown . . ." *Civilian Nuclear Power: A Report to the President,* USAEC, November 20, 1962, p. 4.

p. 36. "To have second thoughts . . ." and "The initial goal . . ." *Change, Hope and the Bomb* by David E. Lilienthal, Princeton University Press, 1963, p. 96.

p. 38. Data on subsidies from "Washington Merry-Go-Round" column by Drew Pearson, Washington *Post,* July 9, 1963.

p. 38. "By the same token . . ." Congressional Record, July 16, 1963.

CHAPTER III

Basic information for this chapter, except where noted, has been drawn from *Radiation* by Jack Schubert, Ph.D., and Ralph E. Lapp, Ph.D., Viking Press, 1957, Compass Books edition issued in 1958.

p. 43. "The first effect . . ." "The Hazards to Man of Nuclear and Allied Radiations," Medical Research Council, London, 1956.

p. 44. "There is a case . . ." "Radiation Accidents" by Gould

A. Andrews, in *Fallout*, ed. by John M. Fowler, Basic Books, Inc., New York, 1960, p. 112.

p. 49. "Although Hermann J. Muller . . ." "Radiation and Future Generations" by James F. Crow, in Fowler, op. cit., pp. 74, 98.

p. 50. "The sum total . . ." W. C. Hueper, "Recent Developments in Environmental Cancer" *A.M.A. Arch. Path.*, 58475-523, 1954.

p. 51. "Today we find our world . . ." *Silent Spring* by Rachel Carson, Houghton Mifflin Co., 1962. Fawcett Crest paperback edition, fourth printing, May 1966, pp. 214-15.

p. 52. ". . . It has been shown with certainty . . ." "Maximum Permissible Exposure Standards" by Robert S. Stone, Paper 89 in *Safety Aspects of Nuclear Reactors*, ed. by C. R. McCullough, V. 13, D. Van Nostrand Co., Inc., 1957.

p. 53. "There seems to be no dose . . ." "Biological Effects of Radiation" by Walter R. Guild, in Fowler, op. cit., p. 84.

p. 53. "Geneticists are convinced . . ." Crow article in Fowler, op. cit., p. 103.

p. 54. ". . . after a number of generations . . ." Ibid.

CHAPTER IV

pp. 61 ff. "In fact, reactor designers . . ." *The Technology of Nuclear Reactor Safety*, V. 1, ed. by T. J. Thompson and J. G. Beckerley, Cambridge, M.I.T. Press, 1964, introduction, p. 5.

p. 62. "A typical nuclear runaway . . ." Paper 853. "The Safety of Nuclear Reactors," in McCullough, op. cit., p. 140.

p. 62. "A description of some . . ." *Small Nuclear Power Plants, COO-284*, AEC Division of Technical Information, V. 1, pp. 24-26.

p. 63. ". . . on January 3, 1961 . . ." Beardsley, op. cit., p. 35.

pp. 63-64. ". . . numerous causes had been at work . . ." Thompson and Beckerley, op. cit., p. 35.

p. 64. "In the SL-1 accident . . ." "Engineering Out the Distance Factor" by Clifford K. Beck, *Atomic Energy Law Journal*, V. 5, No. 4, Winter 1963.

p. 65. ". . . everything but the kitchen sink . . ." Auth Leg 1968, p. 771.

p. 65. ". . . carrying engineered safeguards . . ." *Nucleonics Week*, V. 8, No. 15, April 13, 1967.

p. 67. ". . . New York *Times* recently . . ." NYT, July 2, 1968, editorial page.

p. 68. ". . . nothing within a tenth . . ." NYT, April 25, 1965.

p. 68. "We do have on record . . ." L&R, p. 121.

p. 68. "Though usually thought of . . ." *Tornado Statistics,* U. S. Dept. of Commerce, ESSA/PI 6600 29.

p. 68. "Around the same time . . ." NYT, April 25, 1965.

p. 69. "I mentioned earlier to you . . ." "Newsmakers" program, Nov. 21, 1965, Columbia Broadcasting System.

pp. 69 ff. Bodega episode taken from "A Quake at Bodega" by Lindsay Mattison and Richard Daly, *Nuclear Information,* April 1964, pp. 1-12.

p. 73. "This view was strongly . . ." NYT, December 31, 1968.

p. 77. "Every reactor that has been operated . . ." JCAE hearings on Indemnity and Reactor Safety, April 1962, p. 67.

CHAPTER V

pp. 81 ff. All testimony in this chapter from Auth Leg 1968, pp. 741-68, except where noted.

p. 85. ". . . although these actions . . ." Auth Leg 1968, p. 744.

p. 85. "To illustrate the magnitude . . ." Auth Leg 1968, p. 748.

p. 86. Auth Leg 1968, p. 883, Appendix 13, pp. 1296, 1298.

p. 86. ". . . any organization, private or public . . ." Lilienthal, "When the Atom Moves Next Door," cited above.

p. 87. "The backlog of unprocessed . . ." See Annual Reports to Congress of the AEC.

p. 87. "The Commission finally . . ." L&R, pp. 35, 45.

p. 89. ". . . downgrading of a great . . ." Lilienthal, "When the Atom Moves Next Door."

p. 89. "In the push . . ." Bill HR 9762, introduced July 12, 1965.

p. 90. ". . . we must reemphasize . . ." L&R, p. 18.

p. 91. "The ACRS believes . . ." Ibid., p. 90.

p. 91. "When we come right down . . ." Murray, op. cit., p. 202.

p. 91. "Unless you can point . . ." "Radiation Safety and Regulation" hearings before JCAE, June 15, 1961, p. 366.

p. 92. "Too often management . . ." "Loss of the USS 'Thresher,'" hearings before the JCAE, Appendix 3, pp. 136-44.

p. 94. "This has been the greatest complaint . . ." Auth Leg 1968, p. 763.

p. 95. ". . . while nuclear power was . . ." *Thresher* hearings, foreword, p. viii.

CHAPTER VI

p. 99. "Unless there is a drastic . . ." Ibid., foreword, p. ix.

p. 100. "Admiral Rickover, I understand . . ." Ibid., p. 128.

p. 100. "The importance of operator . . ." Draft of "Water-

Reactor Safety Program: Summary Description," prepared by Water-Reactor Safety Program Office, Phillips Petroleum Company, cited in Auth Leg 1968, p. 1369.

p. 101. "There are ample data . . ." "Mental Preparedness of Emergency Personnel" by Donald Oken, M.D., in *Radiation Accidents and Emergencies*, ed. by Lanzl, Pingel, and Rust, publ. by Charles C. Thomas, 1965.

p. 103. "A surprisingly large fraction . . ." Thompson and Beckerley, op. cit., pp. 700-1.

p. 104. "Although designers can provide . . ." Ibid., introduction, p. 7.

p. 104. "In reactor facilities one of the chief . . ." Ibid., p. 5.

p. 105. "The start-up procedure was . . ." Reports CRR-836 by W. B. Lewis and GPI-14 by D. G. Hurst, in *Reactor Safeguards* by Charles R. Russell, Pegamon Press, Inc., 1962.

p. 106. "Some 10,000 curies . . ." "Radiation Hazard in Industry" by Leo Goodman, speech presented to 32nd All-Ohio Safety Congress, Columbus, Ohio, April 17, 1962.

pp. 106-07. Case histories from *A Summary of Industrial Accidents in USAEC Facilities, 1961-1962*, TID-5360, Suppl. 4, December 1963.

p. 108. "On July 24, 1964 . . ." "Radiation Hazard in Modern Industry" by Leo Goodman, speech presented to John Fogarty Memorial Luncheon, Washington, D.C., April 26, 1967.

p. 108. "The AEC's Annual Reports . . ." Annual Reports to Congress of the AEC, 1966, p. 35, and 1967, p. 159.

p. 109. "The AEC's labor relations . . ." Annual Report to Congress of the AEC, 1967, p. 284.

p. 110. "The dispute might take a similar . . ." NYT, August 30, 1966, and Nov. 11, 1966.

p. 111. Gannon article. *Popular Science Monthly*, Feb. 1964. See also *Death of the "Thresher"* by Norman Polmar, Chilton Books, 1964, pp. 116-17.

p. 111. "The ramifications of civil disobedience . . ." *Nuclear Safety*, AEC Division of Technical Information, January-February 1968, p. 89.

pp. 112 ff. Siegel legal action taken from Brief for Petitioner and Joint Appendix in the United States Court of Appeals for the District of Columbia Circuit, No. 21, p. 342.

p. 115. "A single major mishap . . ." "How Shall Nuclear Technology Be Applied?" in *Modern Nuclear Technology*, ed. by Mills, Biehl, and Mainhardt, McGraw-Hill, 1960, p. 306.

CHAPTER VII

p. 118. ". . . since all the cost analyses . . ." Brookhaven Report, p. 25.

p. 118. "On July 10, 1968, the AEC . . ." AEC release No. L-162, July 10, 1968.

p. 120. "Increases in power density . . ." L&R, p. 95.

p. 120. "Pressures to increase . . ." Thompson and Beckerley, op. cit., introduction, p. 6.

p. 120. "Just how critical . . ." NCPC Newsletter, March 24, 1967.

p. 122. "At Con Edison's Indian Point . . ." NYT, November 6, 1967.

p. 122. "Technologists have thus managed . . ." "Reactor Siting and Practice in the U.S." by Clifford K. Beck, speech presented at American Nuclear Society, Los Angeles Section, February 16-18, 1965.

p. 122. "Until the atomic power program . . ." Beck, "Engineering Out the Distance Factor," cited above.

p. 123. "One authority stated . . ." Thompson and Beckerley, op. cit., introduction, p. 6.

p. 123. "competitive prices for electricity . . ." Beck, "Engineering Out the Distance Factor."

p. 124. ". . . a very great change . . ." Ibid.

p. 126. "would not dream of living . . ." Daily Argus, Mount Vernon, N.Y., July 18, 1963.

p. 126. "One newspaper ran . . ." Ibid.

p. 126. "We are confident . . ." Statement of December 10, 1962.

p. 127. "Connecticut Yankee, . . ." L&R, pp. 72-73.

p. 127. ". . . officially defined by the AEC . . ." Reactor Site Criteria Guides, Title 10, Part 100, from Atomic Energy Law Journal, Winter 1962, AEC Regulations.

p. 128. "A May 15, 1968, U. S. Public . . ." "Public Health Factors in Reactor Site Selection" by J. G. Terrill, Jr., C. L. Weaver, E. D. Harward, and J. M. Smith, presented at National Meeting of American Society of Civil Engineers, Chattanooga, Tennessee, May 15, 1968.

p. 128. "One siting case is of interest . . ." Nucleonics Week, April 13, 1967.

p. 129. "Significantly, on December 10 . . ." NYT, December 11, 1968.

p. 130. "The actual experience . . ." L&R, p. 70.

p. 130. ". . . the ACRS believes that placing . . ." Ibid., p. 94.

CHAPTER VIII

pp. 133-34. "In one experiment . . ." Living with The Atom by Ritchie Calder, University of Chicago Press, 1962, pp. 189-90.

p. 134. "An ill-considered . . ." NYT, May 23, 1964.

p. 135. "The special functions . . ." Russell, op. cit., pp. 275-76.

p. 136. "In May 1968, for instance . . ." NYT, May 15, 1968.

pp. 136-37. "Manpower shortages in the Navy . . ." NYT, March 14, 1965.

p. 137. "By a weird irony . . ." *Atlantic City Press,* May 16, 1968.

p. 138. "With respect to the merchant . . ." NYT, Feb. 23, 1965.

p. 138. "What is the status . . ." NYT, January 25, 1967.

p. 139. "On June 13, 1967 . . ." NYT, June 13, 1967.

p. 139. "In the autumn of 1967 . . ." NYT, November 10, 1967.

p. 139. "This very argument . . ." NYT, Nov. 18, 1967.

p. 140. "The most interesting . . ." NYT, Nov. 25, 1967.

p. 141. "As of mid-1967 . . ." AEC Annual Report for 1967, p. 17.

p. 141. "In February 1966 . . ." AEC Annual Report for 1966, p. 274.

p. 141. "In 1967 legislation . . ." AEC Annual Report for 1967, p. 211.

p. 141. "Forty-four major . . ." *The Nuclear Industry 1966,* prepared by AEC's Division of Industrial Participation, p. 161.

p. 141. "Some of it will go in planes . . ." Ibid., p. 164.

p. 142. "One official in ICC . . ." Goodman, Fogarty Memorial Luncheon speech cited above.

p. 142. "The relatively minor cost . . ." AEC release No. S-8-68, February 27, 1968.

p. 143. ". . . transportation of high-level . . ." Calder, p. 230.

p. 144. "The refusal of the eastern . . ." *The Nuclear Industry 1966,* AEC's Div. of Industrial Participation.

p. 144. "Air transportation of radioactive . . ." Ibid., p. 162.

p. 144. "It is estimated that the annual . . ." Ibid., p. 161, and AEC Annual Report for 1967, p. 4.

p. 145. "A typical harvest . . ." *A Summary of Industrial Accidents in USAEC Facilities 1963-1964,* TID-5360, Suppl. 5, December 1965, pp. 15 ff.

p. 146. "On top of these . . ." Ibid., pp. 1-7.

p. 146. "In April 1968, for example . . ." NYT, April 11, 1968.

p. 147. ". . . eighty-eight capsules of radioactive fuel . . ." Goodman, Fogarty Memorial speech.

p. 147. "An instance of loss . . ." NYT, August 19, 1966, and August 20, 1966.

p. 148. "Six weeks later . . ." NYT, September 9, 1966.

p. 148. ". . . a little boy named Henry . . ." Goodman, Fogarty Memorial speech.

CHAPTER IX

p. 152. ". . . quite diversified." Lanzl, Pingel and Rust, op. cit., p. 290.

p. 153. "At a 1963 symposium . . ." *Science,* March 20, 1964.

p. 153. "Take a transportation accident . . ." Lanzl, Pingel, and Rust, op. cit., p. 131.

p. 153. "The emergencies that can and do . . ." Ibid., p. 302.

p. 154. "I would guess that major . . ." Ibid., p. 134.

p. 155. "Just how prophetically . . ." Goodman, Fogarty Memorial speech.

p. 156. "We concluded . . ." Lanzl, Pingel and Rust, op. cit., p. 135.

p. 158. "It should be stated here . . ." Lanzl, Pingel, and Rust, op. cit., p. 123.

p. 159. "If the room . . ." Ibid., p. 126.

p. 160. "Contamination of bodies of water . . ." "Environmental Effects of a Major Reactor Disaster," Paper 482 in McCullough, op. cit., p. 157.

p. 160. "Water supplies may also . . ." *Nuclear Disaster* by Tom Stonier, World Publishing Co., 1964, pp. 75-76.

CHAPTER X

p. 165. "How fortunate . . ." Schubert and Lapp, op. cit., p. 269.

p. 166. "Ritchie Calder, in his book . . ." Calder, op. cit., pp. 74 ff.

p. 171. "But it is predicted . . ." *Nucleonics,* December 1966, p. 48.

p. 172. Buttermilk Creek data from Rochester Committee for Scientific Information, Bulletin No. 2, February 24, 1968, and No. 3, February 28, 1968.

p. 173. "The U. S. Congressional Joint Committee . . ." *Nucleonics,* December 1966.

p. 174. "Between 1945 and 1960 . . ." "The Atom's Poisonous Garbage" by Walter Schneir, *The Reporter,* March 17, 1960.

p. 174. "In 1959 Herbert Parker . . ." "The Atom . . . Friend or Foe?", first of three articles prepared by Research and Marketing Dept. of the United Mine Workers of America, *UMW Journal,* p. 21.

p. 175. "Dr. Donald R. Chadwick, chief . . ." Lilienthal, "When the Atom Moves Next Door," cited above.

p. 175. "These huge quantities . . ." Ibid.

p. 175. "We are talking about . . ." Remarks by Wilfred E. Johnson, AEC Commissioner, before the Health Physics Society, January 24, 1968, Augusta, Georgia.

p. 176. "A total of 149 tanks . . ." Auth Leg 1968, p. 935.

p. 177. "In 1959 the Joint Committee . . ." Calder, op. cit., pp. 203-4.

p. 177. "The Commission is now looking . . ." Johnson, op. cit.

p. 178. "Joel A. Snow, writing . . ." "Radioactive Waste from Reactors" by Joel A. Snow, S&C, May 1967.

p. 179. ". . . If we were to go on . . ." "The Atom . . . Friend or Foe?", p. 25.

p. 179. "We all live under . . ." Cited in Carson, op. cit., pp. 168-69.

CHAPTER XI

p. 180. "Early in 1963 . . ." "A Stink of Dead Stripers" by Robert H. Boyle, *Sports Illustrated,* April 26, 1965, p. 81.

p. 181. ". . . the hairsplitting explanation . . ." Remarks by Consolidated Edison vice-president W. Donham Crawford before White Plains Rally, October 19, 1968.

p. 182. Description of thermal effects on fish from *Sport Fishing Institute Bulletin,* January-February 1968, No. 191.

p. 183. ". . . virtually every large . . ." Report on the International Biological Program, published by House Committee on Science and Astronautics, March 1968.

p. 183. "There is no basis . . ." Remarks by Dr. Gerald F. Tape, USAEC Commissioner, at Annual Meeting of the Southern Interstate Nuclear Board, Hot Springs, Arkansas, April 1, 1968. AEC release No. S-12-68, April 1, 1968.

p. 183. "fossil fuel plants . . ." Terrill et al., op. cit.

p. 184. "Scientists estimate that by 1980 . . ." *Sport Fishing . . . Bulletin,* cited above.

p. 185. "One point of view . . ." L&R, p. 27.

p. 185. "For a while it looked . . ." NCPC Newsletter, May 19, 1966.

p. 185. "In February 1968 . . ." NCPC Newsletter, February 8, 1968.

p. 186. "Early in 1968 the Department . . ." NCPC Newsletter, February 29, 1968.

p. 187. "Two Rutgers University experts . . ." *Esquire,* January 1969, p. 24.

CHAPTER XII

p. 190. "A perfect example . . ." Nuclear Power and Environment: An Inquiry. Stratton Mountain, Vermont, September 11 and 12, 1968.

p. 192. ". . . removal of krypton 85 . . ." "Krypton-85, Nuclear Air Pollutant" by Malcolm Peterson, S&C, March 1967.

p. 193. "Norman Lansdell, in his book . . ." *The Atom and the Energy Revolution* by Norman Lansdell, Philosophical Library, 1958, p. 173.

p. 194. Discussion of zinc 65 from "Environmental Contamination from Nuclear Reactors" by Malcolm Peterson, S&C, November 1965.

p. 195. ". . . at Oak Ridge . . ." "We the People—and Nuclear Power" by Elise Jerard, Independent Phi Beta Kappa Environmental Study Group.

p. 196. ". . . radiation adds up to a sum . . ." Calder, op. cit., p. 268.

p. 197. "A case in point . . ." Schneir, op. cit.

p. 197. "And Dr. Theodore Rice . . ." Conversation reported by Ann Carl, member of Marine Resources Council, Nassau-Suffolk Regional Planning Board, March 25, 1968, in her report on Health Physics Society Symposium, January 24-26, 1968, in Augusta, Georgia.

p. 198. ". . . justify an adjustment . . ." "If Fallout Levels Rise—Should Standards Follow?" S&C, April 1967.

p. 200. "A recent article in *The Nation* . . ." "Nuclear Power on Salmon Rivers" by Anthony Netboy, *The Nation*, October 9, 1967.

p. 201. "One man who has considered . . ." "Can the World Be Saved?" by Dr. Lamont C. Cole, NYT *Magazine,* March 31, 1968.

CHAPTER XIII

p. 206. "In January, 1965, the AEC appointed . . ." " 'Reasonable Assurance' of 'No Undue Risk' " by Harold P. Green, *Notre Dame Lawyer,* June 1968, as reprinted in S&C, June-July, 1968.

p. 206. "The report characteristically . . ." Ibid.

p. 207. "We believe the public interest . . ." Friedman, op. cit., p. 5.

p. 208. ". . . neither a public hearing nor a review . . ." L&R, p. 41.

p. 209. "The important economic and safety . . ." Thompson and Beckerley, op. cit., p. 4.

p. 209. "In answer to a question posed . . ." L&R, p. 81.

p. 210. "On Tuesday, May 28, 1968 . . ." USAEC release No. L-109, May 28, 1968.

p. 213. "On July 26, 1968, the ACRS . . ." USAEC release No. L-172, July 26, 1968.

p. 213. "On July 31, 1968, . . ." USAEC release No. L-178, July 31, 1968.

p. 213. "As if this procedure . . ." NCPC Newsletter, April 28, 1966.

p. 214. "For instance, the AEC is currently . . ." L&R, p. 11.

p. 215. "The only duplicates we have seen . . ." Ibid., p. 36.

p. 216. "Typical is the following exchange . . ." Ibid., pp. 7-8.

p. 217. "Sometimes there is levity . . ." Ibid., pp. 72-73.

p. 217. ". . . has actually proclaimed himself . . ." Ibid., p. 129.

p. 218. "Dr. Okrent, you said something . . ." Ibid., p. 113.

p. 218. "I share the concern of Mr. Hosmer . . ." Ibid., p. 37.

p. 218. "This problem of getting these things . . ." Ibid., p. 133.

p. 218. "But the Joint Committee's supervisory . . ." Murray, op. cit., pp. 200-2.

p. 219. "Although state and local governments . . ." Report on "Nuclear Safety" made by the Assembly Interim Committee on Industrial Relations, the State of California, published as part of Report 10, Volume 2, Assembly Interim Committee Reports 1965-1967, published by Assembly of the State of California.

p. 220. "The point has been made . . ." L&R, p. 27.

p. 221. "Was it actually the intent . . ." Congressional Record, July 16, 1963.

p. 222. "Early in 1965, for example . . ." NCPC Newsletter, December 16, 1965. Also, Nos. 22603-22607 of Commerce Clearing House, Atomic Energy Law Reports, November 15, 1965, order of New Jersey Board of Public Utility Commissioners, and Summary of April 22, 1966, Interim Order.

p. 223. "When, in congressional hearings . . ." L&R, p. 37.

p. 224. "This panel also had some interesting . . ." Green, Notre Dame Lawyer article cited above.

p. 225. "I think our experience has been . . ." L&R, pp. 30-31.

p. 226. "A similar incident occurred . . ." USAEC, In the Matter of Consolidated Edison Company of New York, Inc., Petition to Intervene by the Conservation Center, Inc., Docket No. 50-247.

p. 227. "Even if we were to hold . . ." Memorandum and Order, AEC Docket No. 50-247, issued by W. B. McCool, Secy., on December 20, 1966.

p. 228. "An observation made by Frances T. Freeman Jalet . . ." Jalet, op. cit.

CHAPTER XIV

p. 230. "You will recall . . ." Speech of February 29, 1968, before Senate.

p. 231. "By mid-1963 the Government had sunk . . ." "Atomic

Power Plants—What's Wrong with Them?" by Adolph J. Ackerman, paper for the Hydroelectric Power Session, American Power Conference, April 28, 1965, Chicago, Illinois.

p. 231. "Among the direct subsidies . . ." Ibid.

p. 234. "No weight should be given . . ." *Journal of Professional Practice,* Proceedings of the American Society of Civil Engineers, V. 89, No. PP 1, January 1963.

p. 235. "It is not known . . ." Auth Leg 1968, p. 755.

p. 235. ". . . over the last year or so . . ." Auth Leg 1969, p. 194.

p. 236. "In March 1968, for instance . . ." NCPC Newsletter, March 21, 1968.

p. 236. "That very same month . . ." Ibid., and NCPC Newsletter of March 14, 1968.

p. 237. "On August 1, 1968 . . ." NCPC Newsletter, August 1, 1968.

p. 237. "In June 1968 . . ." NCPC Newsletter, June 13. 1968.

p. 237. ". . . When you first came before . . ." Auth Leg 1968, p. 787.

p. 238. "Of great significance was . . ." NCPC Newsletter, June 29, 1967.

p. 238. "The following winter . . ." NCPC Newsletter, December 14, 1967.

p. 239. "As if to hammer home . . ." NCPC Newsletter, Sept. 19, 1968.

p. 239. "Official, if somewhat grudging . . ." NCPC Newsletter, May 29, 1968.

p. 240. ". . . a two-day . . . briefing in Washington . . ." NCPC Newsletter, October 3, 1968.

p. 241. ". . . pending the completion of scaled-up . . ." NCPC Newsletter, June 6, 1968.

p. 242. "The glaring contradictions . . ." NCPC Newsletter, August 17, 1967.

p. 243. "Such inconsistency did, however . . ." NCPC Newsletter, January 18, 1968.

p. 243. "In June 1968 the Commission . . ." NCPC Newsletter, June 6, 1968.

p. 243. "Perhaps tiring of being displayed . . ." NCPC Newsletter, August 8, 1968.

CHAPTER XV

p. 246. "In 1955 an advisory committee . . ." Hearings on governmental indemnity before the Joint Committee on Atomic Energy, 84th Congress, second session, pp. 248-50.

p. 247. "The hazard is new. . . ." Ibid.

p. 250. "Speaking before the House early . . ." Congressional Record, August 4, 1965.

p. 254. "Mr. Mel Frankel . . ." "Proposed Extension of AEC Indemnity Legislation," hearings before the Subcommittee on Legislation of the JCAE, June 1965, p. 46.

p. 254. ". . . and the following year Philip Sporn . . ." "Nuclear Power Economics," a talk by Philip Sporn sponsored by Kuhn, Loeb, Inc., March 17, 1966, p. 29.

p. 255. "Harold Green, the attorney . . ." Green, *Notre Dame Lawyer* article cited above.

CHAPTER XVI

p. 258. "On that score Seaborg's colleague . . ." NCPC Newsletter, Nov. 9, 1967.

p. 258. "In its 1962 report . . ." *Report to the President,* p. 45.

p. 259. ". . . unless a viable breeder program . . ." Ibid., p. 22.

p. 259. Estimates of fossil fuel and uranium reserves, except where noted, from statement by James R. Garvey, President and Director of Research for Bituminous Coal Research, Inc., before the U. S. House of Representatives, Committee on Appropriations, Subcommittee on the Dept. of the Interior and Related Agencies, March 26, 1968.

p. 260. *"Petroleum Press Service . . ."* NCPC Newsletter, January 18, 1968.

p. 263. ". . . it may not be possible . . ." Introductory remarks by Gerald F. Tape, Commissioner, before the American Power Conference Symposium on "The Increasing Importance of the Breeder Program," Chicago, Illinois, April 23, 1968. USAEC release No. S-17-68, April 23, 1968.

p. 264. ". . . mathematically impossible . . ." "Special Report" by Brice O'Brien, National Coal Association, April 3, 1968.

p. 264. "Altogether the fast breeder . . ." NYT, September 12, 1967.

p. 265. ". . . high fast neutron fluences . . ." O'Brien, op. cit.

p. 265. ". . . something called 'alpha' . . ." Ibid.

p. 267. "If we do not sell . . ." NCPC Newsletter, May 18, 1967.

p. 267. ". . . is not going to be worth any . . ." NCPC Newsletter, March 30, 1967.

p. 267. ". . . a capacity in the 1,000,000-kilowatt area . . ." Tape remarks, speech of April 23, 1968, cited above.

p. 268. "For the fast breeder to work . . ." Paper by Edward Teller presented to northeast New York section of the American Nuclear Society, published in *Nuclear News,* August 1967.

p. 269. Comparison between coal and nuclear from O'Brien, op. cit., and remarks by Wallace Behnke, assistant to president of Commonwealth Edison Co. of Chicago, before Electrical World's Third Energy Transportation Conference, winter 1967.

p. 271. ". . . the AEC had to admit . . ." Federal Register, V. 32, No. 218, Nov. 9, 1967.

p. 272. "Indeed, the AEC's own projections . . ." See 1962 Report to President.

p. 275. "In September 1968, for instance . . ." Special Report by Joseph E. Moody, President, to NCPC Inc.

p. 276. "Industrial developers who have . . ." Congressional Record, April 25, 1968.

p. 277. "Variations on MHD, . . ." Wall Street Journal, March 2, 1966.

p. 278. "Late in 1966 . . ." NYT, October 6, 1966.

p. 279. "In November 1966 . . ." NYT, Nov. 27, 1966.

p. 280. "In a valley eighty-five miles . . ." Time, July 26, 1968, p. 60.

p. 280. "the sweetest fuel . . ." NYT, February 13, 1967.

p. 280. "Refuse is an increasingly . . ." Ibid.

CHAPTER XVII

p. 282. "A member of the National . . ." L&R, p. 22.

p. 283. "The man in the street . . ." "Twenty-First Century: The Mighty Atom," CBS News, May 14, 1967.

p. 283. "A few years ago, the Journal . . ." Journal of Professional Practice, Proceedings of the American Society of Civil Engineers, January 1963.

p. 286. "In a visionary speech . . ." Remarks by Dr. Glenn T. Seaborg at the Edward T. T. Williams Memorial Convocation, Fairleigh Dickinson University, Teaneck, New Jersey, March 7, 1968. AEC release S-10-68, March 7, 1968.

pp. 287-88. "For example, in 1964 . . ." Man and the Atom, National Educational Television Network, December 28, 1964, produced by Harold Mayer in co-operation with the AEC.

p. 290. "How much of a problem is it . . ." "Development, Growth and State of the Atomic Energy Industry," hearings before the JCAE, 1963, Part 2, pp. 493-94.

p. 290. "It is far easier to borrow . . ." Nucleonics, October 1960, p. 23.

p. 291. "As a possible indication . . ." Small Nuclear Power Plants, p. 143.

p. 292. ". . . a woeful series . . ." Ibid., p. 151.

p. 293. "I would suggest . . ." "Public Acceptance of Nuclear Power," presented before February 1965 Meeting of American Nuclear Society, reprinted in Nuclear Power Reactor Siting, AEC Conf. 65201.

p. 295. "One of our prime tasks, therefore . . ." Lanzl, Pingel, and Rust, op. cit., pp. 38-39.

p. 295. ". . . a friendly neighbor . . ." *World-Telegram,* March 22, 1966.

p. 300. ". . . a correction in a later issue . . ." *Nucleonics Week,* March 11, 1965, p. 2.

p. 301. "An article in the New York *Times* . . ." NYT, October 2, 1967.

p. 301. "This is the most historic . . ." NYT, July 25, 1968.

p. 302. "Perhaps the happiest . . ." NYT, May 9, 1965.

CHAPTER XVIII

p. 306. "While the 1963 estimate of the F-111's . . ." *Fortune,* June 1, 1967, p. 186.

p. 306. "When, for example, AEC Chairman . . ." NCPC Newsletter, March 16, 1967.

p. 307. "In a letter and supplement . . ." Auth Leg 1968, p. 888.

p. 308. ". . . a letter from AEC General Manager . . ." Ibid., p. 889.

CHAPTER XIX

p. 325. "The Committee feels compelled . . ." Auth Leg 1969, p. 17.

p. 327. "At a colloquium . . ." Calder, op. cit., pp. 261-62, 264-65.

p. 329. "The time has come for us . . ." "Whatever Happened to the Peaceful Atom?" by David E. Lilienthal, *Harper's,* October, 1963, p. 46.

p. 330. "Of all our national resources . . ." Ibid.

Index

Accidents
contingency programs, 151-164
and decontamination, 158-161
and human error, 97-109, 115-116, 136-137
insurance against, 245-256
liability for, 34, 245-256 *passim*
loss, 134
marine, 130, 137-138, 140
and mass panic, 161
medical preparations for, 153-158
in nuclear fuel reprocessing, 171-173
probability and damage estimates, 12-14, 59-77, 117, 124-125, 129
reactor, *see* Reactor accidents
and theft, 147-150
training for, 153-154, 156-158
in transportation of nuclear fuel, 144-149, 153-154
in waste storage, 175-176
Ackerman, Adolph, 231-234
Advanced Test Reactor, 83, 237
Advisory Committee on Reactor Safeguards (ACRS), 8-11, 34, 91, 130, 205-214
AEC, *see* Atomic Energy Commission
Aiken, George, 243
Aircraft, nuclear, 132-134, 167
Alpha, 265-266
Anderson, Clinton, 10-11, 207-208, 220-221, 248
Atomic Energy Act of 1946, 21-25
Atomic Energy Act of 1954, 28
Atomic Energy Commission

and accident contingency programs, 151-164 *passim*
accident reports of, 106-107, 108-109
and accidents, major, probability and damage estimates, 12-13, 56-63, 65, 69-77
and Advisory Committee on Reactor Safeguards, 8-11
and advisory groups, role of, 203-215
as a bureaucracy, 86-91
and enemy attacks, 111-115
and Enrico Fermi Power Plant, 9-18
history of, 19-39
and labor relations, 109-111
licensing policies, 204-215, 241-244
and local communities, 221-228
1962 Report to the President on Civilian Nuclear Power, 35-37
organizational flaws, 86-92
policies of, 86-92
and Power Reactor Development Co., 7-18 *passim*
powers of, 21-25
and Price-Anderson Act, 250-251
and private industry, 26-39
as promoter of nuclear power, 283-289, 291-294
and public hearings, 222-229
and reactor accidents, projections for, 12-13, 56-63, 65, 69-77

351